LEGACY OF LEADERSHIP

A HISTORY OF THE GEMOLOGICAL INSTITUTE OF AMERICA

LEGACY OF LEADERSHIP
A HISTORY OF THE GEMOLOGICAL INSTITUTE OF AMERICA

By William George Shuster

Copyright ©2003
The Gemological Institute of America
Carlsbad, California 92008
www.gia.edu

Printed in the United States of America

Library of Congress Cataloging-in-Publication Data
Shuster, William George.
Legacy of leadership : a history of the Gemological
Institute of America / by William George Shuster
—1st ed.
p.   cm.

Includes index.
ISBN 0-87311-040-4
1. Gemological Institute of America—History. I. Title.
TS720.S58 2003
736.2'0607—dc21
2003012828

Printed by Worzalla Publishing Company
Stevens Point, Wisconsin
(715) 344-9600
www.worzalla.com

contents

dedication

To the late Richard T. Liddicoat, the "Father of Modern Gemology"

foreword

It began innocently enough, with a speech at the Robert M. Shipley Luncheon during the 1997 American Gem Society Conclave in Chicago. I spoke about the beginnings of GIA and AGS—a story of the grand vision of one man, but a man whose persistence would give him the strength of legions.

Robert M. Shipley started GIA in 1931, in the depths of the Great Depression, and created the American Gem Society three years later. These organizations would ultimately emerge as two of the most important in the gem and jewelry industry. To my surprise, the seasoned audience of AGS jewelers I addressed that day were captivated by the story of how Robert Shipley, against almost insurmountable odds, created GIA and AGS during one of the most difficult periods in American history. And how, through good scholarship and good salesmanship, he laid the foundation for the gemology movement that we take for granted today.

I became convinced that GIA's history—and with it much of the history of gemological training and standard setting—must be told. Ironically, when I was made president of GIA a decade earlier, longtime board member and former AGS leader Robert Spratford had encouraged me to document the story of GIA, taking full advantage of those who were eyewitnesses to the creation of the Institute in the 1930s. Frankly, GIA simply was not prepared to handle the project at that time. But the comments I received on April 19, 1997, from an audience in awe of their founder, sparked my commitment to tell Shipley's story and the Legacy of Leadership that he and others have built into the multinational operation that is today's Gemological Institute of America.

We asked Bill Shuster, senior editor of *Jewelers' Circular Keystone*, to write the book. In his more than two decades with the magazine, Bill had written extensively about the Institute's history. A consummate researcher, Shuster reviewed hundreds of publications and archival documents in the Liddicoat Library, and spoke with dozens of staff members and supporters from GIA's infancy to the present. The original manuscript was some 1,200 pages, filled with exhaustive detail and extensive documentation that we are fortunate to have on record. Our challenge in editing was to stay true to Shuster's original work while we tightened the text for readability and interest. The result—this book—is an accurate and, we hope, thoroughly enjoyable read on the history of GIA and, with it, the history of gemological education in America.

GIA's story is as much about people as it is about gemstone facts and figures. The Institute, a nonprofit public benefit corporation throughout most of its existence, has attracted a unique mix of personalities who helped shape the modern gemological world. You will be introduced to many of them in the pages that follow. But the two most dominant figures were Robert M. Shipley Sr., our founder, and Richard T. Liddicoat, our longtime president and later chairman. It was Robert Shipley who created GIA and, thus, the gemological movement in America. But it was Richard Liddicoat who truly built GIA and, with it, modern gemology as we know it. Of GIA's seven-plus decades of existence at this writing, Richard Liddicoat was a dominant influence during six of them.

The story of GIA—its creation, growth, and expansion—is a testament to the impact that two committed leaders, like Shipley and Liddicoat, can make. Together, and with the support of hundreds of equally dedicated staff members, they enabled the Institute to accomplish on a global scale Shipley's original objective, and our long-standing mission: to ensure the public trust in gems and jewelry. I hope you will enjoy this work as much as we have enjoyed bringing it to you.

William E. Boyajian
President, Gemological Institute of America

author's note

"No man is an island, entire of itself," wrote the great English poet and clergyman John Donne. "Every man is a piece of the continent, a part of the main." What is true of humanity also applies to writers of the histories that chart its complex story. None works alone. Each is indebted to many other people, living and dead, for information, insights, oral and written accounts, details, and recollections, as well as others' assistance in researching and preparing the work.

That is certainly true of this history of the Gemological Institute of America, the first comprehensive, book-length account of the Institute from its modest start in 1931 out of a night-school class to its position in the 21st century as an internationally acclaimed leader in gemological education, research, laboratory services, instruments, and publications.

While I'm responsible for the research, organization, content, writing, and most revisions of this book, I am deeply indebted to hundreds of people, past and present, who contributed so much to it. They include scores of writers—academics, experts in gemology and related fields, Institute staffers and officials, and journalists like myself—who in the past 10 decades wrote the books, documents, and articles in newspapers, magazines, and GIA publications that I used in my research.

Space limitations prevented inclusion in the book of the original manuscript's hundreds of footnotes, which give these people their proper recognition. However, many of the references are listed in the book's bibliography, and my sources are footnoted in the original manuscript, which is on file at the Richard T. Liddicoat Gemological Library and Information Center at GIA headquarters in Carlsbad, California. Indeed, I hope other writers and historians will widen the path I started with this book. I personally call this "a" history of GIA, not "the" history, because there is still so much to be studied and told about the Institute and its influence on the world's gem and jewelry industries, their customers, and the public.

I also want to acknowledge some of the sources and people who contributed to the creation of this authorized history of the Gemological Institute of America.

The seeds for the book were planted in 1981 in several articles I wrote about GIA's early years for *Jewelers' Circular Keystone* magazine in an issue commemorating the Institute's 50th anniversary.

Some information from those articles was used, in much-expanded form, in this book, with acknowledgment and the permission of *JCK*.

The book itself is the brainchild of William E. Boyajian, current president of GIA, who had read my 1981 articles. It was his idea to produce a readable, well-researched account of the Institute's history, while some who played important early roles in it could still provide their personal accounts. Peggy Jo Donahue, an award-winning writer and editor of jewelry and medical trade publications, knew of my articles and Bill's intent, and literally brought us together at a reception at the 1997 international watch and jewelry fair in Basel, Switzerland. That was the start of this project, later endorsed by a panel of GIA officials in a meeting with me at the 1997 JCK Show in Las Vegas and then formally approved by GIA's board of governors.

One purpose of this book was to preserve the recollections of people who helped build GIA into the world-class educational institution, grading laboratory, and research organization it is today. I was privileged to interview many of them, and I thank them, again, for the time, comments, and insights they generously provided. Space prevents me from naming them all, but there are some I especially want to cite. They include:

Richard T. Liddicoat, GIA's longtime president and chairman, the industry's respected and beloved "Father of Modern Gemology" who actively supported this project and looked forward to the book's publication. I'm glad he was able to review the entire manuscript before he died in July 2002.

Glenn Nord, a self-described "GIA man" and Liddicoat's right hand in the 1960s and early '70s, who returned to the Institute as president in 1983.

Bill Boyajian, whose entire professional career has been devoted to GIA. As the Institute's president since 1986, he strengthened and expanded its activities as an international educational and research institution into the 21st century, building on the foundation laid by his predecessors.

Al Woodill, nephew of GIA founders Robert and Beatrice Shipley and the longtime director of the American Gem Society (also founded by Robert Shipley), and Dorothy Jasper Smith, secretary to Shipley and later Liddicoat. They were almost the only witnesses left to GIA's beginnings, and thus invaluable sources of information about the Institute's formative years.

Bob Crowningshield, probably the Institute's most renowned gemologist after Liddicoat, and Bert Krashes—like Crowningshield, a longtime GIA vice president. Together, they helped establish the Institute's East Coast school, laboratory, gem identification and grading services, and the "traveling classrooms" that took GIA education to America's grassroots jewelers. Their recollections provided important details about those years and programs.

Essential, too, were insights and information provided in person and by letter, phone, and e-mail by current and former members and officials of GIA, and supporters of the Institute. Among them were Dona Dirlam, Yoshiko Doi, Brook Ellis, Bob Earnest, Chuck Fryer, Michael Grantham, Dr. Edward Gübelin, Gary Hill, George Kaplan, Alice Keller, Kathryn Kimmel, Jim Littman, Janice Mack, Dr. Vince Manson, Dave Morrow, Seung-Hae Moon, Tom Moses, Margaret Orozco, Gary Roskin, Dr. Jim Shigley, Dr. John Sinkankas, Robert Weldon, Tom Yonelunas, and Eunice Miles (through her memoirs).

The preparation of this book involved others, too, in a variety of ways.

Dona Dirlam, director of GIA's magnificent Liddicoat Library, gave me access to the riches of its archives. Her support, optimism and good cheer—and, importantly, the directions and latitude she gave Margot McLaren, the library staff member she assigned to be my research assistant—all provided the framework and support essential for this investigative project.

Margot was invaluable—skilled, always helpful, unfailingly efficient and cheerful. The research data filing system for this book was created by her, and there was no document, no matter how arcane, that she, working in California, couldn't find and promptly dispatch to me, working in Pennsylvania. The foundation of facts and research on which this book stands is in no small measure thanks to Margot.

Victoria Morrison, then the Institute's public relations manager, also aided my research, providing information, GIA press materials, publications, and answers to my many questions about the Institute and its operations. Jan Tilton, then Bill Boyajian's executive assistant, always provided the relevant information I needed and patiently helped me with many administrative details. The professionalism, unshakable efficiency, and friendliness of Vicky and Jan made this project more manageable.

A manuscript is just pages of words unless highly skilled, experienced professionals edit and prepare it for publication. Here I owe much thanks to my two editors. Alice Keller, the talented, multi-award-winning editor-in-chief of GIA's *Gems & Gemology* journal, oversaw this project and worked with me on the book from its start in late 1997. Her prudent editing, patience, astute insights, and perceptive criticisms were invaluable. Stuart Overlin, *Gems & Gemology*'s exceptional associate editor, was instrumental in the book's preparation, copy editing, and illustration gathering, and in working with me on the final revised manuscript. I and the readers of this book owe deep thanks to Alice and Stuart for their editorial expertise, professionalism, and commitment to quality, which made this a better book than it would have been in my hands alone.

Recognition is also due some other talented people, responsible for the visual aspects—"the look"—of this book. They include designer Faizah Bhatti, photo editor Terri Weimer, and production supervisor Richard Canedo, of GIA's Course Development department. Judy Colbert, the library's visual resources manager, helped locate historical images, while Karen Myers, *Gems & Gemology*'s art director, prepared all images for publication. Tom Overton, managing editor of *Gems & Gemology*, was responsible for interfacing with the printer.

In addition, many past and present GIA personnel, and other involved persons, reviewed sections of the manuscript relevant to them, their departments, and/or their roles in GIA's history, and offered useful suggestions and clarifications. My thanks, too, to my past and current colleagues at *Jewelers' Circular Keystone* for their ongoing interest in, and encouragement of, my work on this book.

On a personal note, I dedicate this book to my parents, Lieselotte Ursula Shuster (geb. Lenz) and William Lewis Shuster Jr., who showed me the way, and to my brothers Ronald Shuster and Robert Douglas Shuster, who accompany me on it. I owe special gratitude to my mother for her constant encouragement, patience, wise advice, suggestions, and read-throughs of sections of the manuscript, and to Ron and Bob for their continual, deeply appreciated assistance in many forms (including Ron's computer and Bob's condo) and their encouragement. My family's support was invaluable to me, especially when the project seemed overwhelming. My one regret is that my father didn't live to see this book. I think he's pleased, however, to know that his advice on the need for "system" and personal discipline was invaluable to me in creating it.

Finally, and most importantly, my thanks and gratitude to the Author of our lives, who with each new day provides a new page for our own personal histories, which we compose for good or ill, for now and eternity. *Soli Deo Gloria!*

William George Shuster

1930s | **1940s** | **1950s** | **1960s**

1930 Robert M. Shipley is asked to lecture on gemology at the University of Southern California

1931 Shipley establishes the Gemological Institute of America and introduces correspondence courses in gemology

GIA starts the nation's first gemological laboratory, in Los Angeles

1932 The first GIA Board of Governors (originally the national advisory board) is formally organized

1933 Robert Shipley Jr. joins the GIA staff

1934 Robert M. Shipley founds the American Gem Society, GIA's sister organization

1934 The first issue of *Gems & Gemology* is published

1935 Robert Shipley Jr. creates a handheld polariscope

1935 Frederick F. Thurber becomes GIA's first Certified Gemologist

1937 The first Gemological Conclave is held, in Chicago

Robert M. Shipley is pictured on the front page of the *Los Angeles Times*

The first "resident" classes are taught in Los Angeles to students from overseas

1938 Robert Shipley Jr. appears in a Paramount Pictures film for its "Popular Science" series

The Institute introduces the Diamondscope,

the first binocular gemological microscope with darkfield illumination

1939 GIA is awarded its first patent, for a darkfield illuminator for its microscope

1940 Richard T. Liddicoat Jr. joins the Institute staff

An Eastern office is opened, in Boston

1941 GIA introduces the Diamolite and Colorimeter

1942 The Institute is reorganized as a nonprofit corporation

1943 A $50,000 endowment is raised from the industry to support GIA during World War II

Beatrice Shipley officially retires

1946 GIA tuition is approved under the GI Bill of Rights

1947 Liddicoat's *Handbook of Gem Identification* is published

G. Robert Crowningshield joins the GIA staff

1948 The Institute confers its first Graduate Gemologist (G.G.) diplomas

1949 The GIA Gem Trade Laboratory is established in New York

Bert Krashes joins the GIA staff

1952 Robert M. Shipley retires, and Richard Liddicoat becomes executive director

1953 Liddicoat unveils the GIA Diamond Grading System

1955 GIA moves into its new headquarters on San Vicente Blvd. in West Los Angeles

The Gem Trade Laboratory issues its first diamond grading reports

1956 Crowningshield develops an identification criterion for yellow irradiated diamonds using spectroscopy

Jewelry design is incorporated into GIA's curriculum

1960 The New York offices move to a new location on Fifth Avenue

1961 Glenn Nord joins the Institute staff

1965 GIA courses are accredited by the National Home Study Council, now the Distance Education Training Council (DETC)

1967 The "rapid sight" diamond proportion grading system is added to the curriculum

1970 GIA classes are taught overseas for the first time, in Israel

1971 Institute courses are translated and administered in Japan through an affiliate, AGT

1973 GIA is accredited by the National Association of Trade and Technical Schools, now the Accrediting Commission of Career Schools and Colleges of Technology (ACCSCT)

1970s | **1980s** | **1990s**

1975 William E. Boyajian joins the GIA staff

1976 A formal research department is established under D. Vincent Manson, Ph.D.

GIA moves to new, expanded headquarters in Santa Monica, California

Thomas C. Yonelunas joins the Institute staff

1977 Bob Crowningshield and Bert Krashes are named vice presidents

1978 Robert M. Shipley passes away at the age of 91

1981 A redesigned *Gems & Gemology* is introduced, in full color and a larger format

1982 GIA hosts the first International Gemological Symposium, in Los Angeles, in honor of its 50th anniversary

The Alumni Association is established

1983 Glenn Nord becomes president; Liddicoat is named chairman of the board

1984 The first GemFest is held, at Santa Monica headquarters

1986 Bill Boyajian becomes president

1987 The Institute launches GIA-Net (later known as GIA Virtual Campus), an online education and information network

Tom Yonelunas succeeds retiring Bert Krashes as head of the Gem Trade Laboratory

1988 GIA's Master Plan for the future is unveiled

The Institute library acquires the Sinkankas collection of more than 16,000 books, periodicals, and other items

1989 The Richard T. Liddicoat Gemological Library and Information Center is dedicated

The Gemological Institute of Korea, later renamed GIA Korea, is established

1991 GIA hosts the second International Gemological Symposium, in Los Angeles, in honor of its 60th Anniversary

The Institute hosts its first annual Career Fair, in Santa Monica

1992 GIA Italy is established

GIA Taiwan is established

1993 GIA Thailand is established

1994 GIA Hong Kong is established

1996 The Gem Trade Laboratory launches its "Horizon" Operations Management System

1997 The Institute completes relocation of its world headquarters to The Robert Mouawad Campus in Carlsbad, California

GIA Moscow and GIA Los Angeles are established

1999 The third International Gemological Symposium is held, in San Diego

Robert M. Shipley is named Person of the Century by *JCK* magazine

2000 Commencement 2000, the Institute's first-ever formal commencement ceremony, is held in Carlsbad

2001 GIA London is established

GIA China is established

2002 The School of Business is launched

The Institute unveils the Tower of Brilliance at its Carlsbad headquarters

GIA mourns the loss of chairman Richard T. Liddicoat, the "Father of Modern Gemology"

2000s

PART ONE

creating the legacy

GIA founder Robert M. Shipley (1887–1978) "sold" the gemological idea to jewelers across North America during the 1930s and '40s.

BEFORE THE BEGINNING

1887–1929

The bell above the Midwest jewelry store door jangled as a tall, middle-aged man in an overcoat strode in, the tip of his cane clicking lightly on the floor.

The jeweler quickly sized up the stranger: Thin and neatly dressed, he might be a banker or college professor, an impression reinforced by his finely trimmed mustache, pince-nez glasses, and authoritative manner.

But the jeweler's eagerness at a possible sale on this Depression-era afternoon—not much had sold lately—turned to annoyance when the stranger said he was a salesman. The last thing this jeweler wanted to do was buy.

Still, the stranger kept talking, his deep-set eyes peering intently at the jeweler. He occasionally removed his glasses to gesture as he explained that what he was selling was an idea: correspondence courses, most still unwritten, to teach jewelers about the gems they sold. These courses were the key to a movement to train and thus professionalize the jewelry trade, and to create a national guild of ethical jewelers, he said.

The jeweler's son walked over and both listened, fascinated. There was something about this man that they couldn't ignore. Was it his infectious enthusiasm? His single-minded belief in what he was selling? The amazing extent of his knowledge about gems and the jewelry business?

Time went by and the stranger, as though ending an appointment, thanked the jeweler, shook his hand, and left—with a signed contract for the courses and an $8 down payment. The jeweler, excited and slightly dazed, turned to his son and said, "A guy we never saw before just walked in here and sold us an idea! And he wasn't even wearing a hat!"

THAT "GUY" WAS ROBERT MORRILL SHIPLEY. In the 1930s, the incident was repeated time after time as Shipley crisscrossed the United States and Canada. He covered thousands of miles annually in secondhand cars, aggressively selling—with the single-mindedness of a zealot—the professionalization of the jewelry industry through gemological education. His goal was to create trained jewelers with certified titles who would eventually be united in a national guild.

Shipley's concept was the seed for the Gemological Institute of America (GIA), an organization that would transform the gem and jewelry industry in the United States and, ultimately, around the world.

Robert Shipley's mother, Ida Lima Shipley, nurtured his love of art. She later was associated with him in the ownership of the Vail Jewelry Co. and Vail-Shipley Shops. She died in 1959, at the age of 97. Shipley's father, William Hopkins Shipley, a railroad engineer, died suddenly during his son's junior year at the University of Wisconsin.

Photos courtesy of Robert Shipley III

The history of GIA is as fascinating as any novel. It is filled with a large cast of intriguing characters who struggled for decades to create and build this unique educational and research organization. They did so in the face of obstacles that challenged the growth of the Institute and even threatened its survival. And all of it was played out against the backdrop of the great events that shaped the 20th century.

This is the story, then, of a transcontinental movement that started in the mind of one man and has grown to embrace hundreds of thousands of people and affect millions around the globe.

It isn't the story of Robert M. Shipley alone, but GIA is his creation more than anyone else's, and it is with him that the story begins.

AN ACCURATE PORTRAIT OF ROBERT SHIPLEY in the 1930s and '40s—the first years of GIA and the gemology movement—would show only a blur. He always seemed to be in motion: writing, selling, speaking, traveling, demanding, urging, defending. Today, he would be called "driven," a workaholic. But the early 20th century preferred another phrase: He was a man "out to make a name for himself."

Shipley moved in such furious haste to establish the Institute and the gemology movement because it had taken him until middle age to find a dream of his own to pursue. For the first half of his life, he had measured himself and his success by the goals and plans other people had set for him. And the pressures on Shipley to chase those goals had begun in the cradle.

Robert Morrill Shipley was born February 21, 1887, in Pierce City, a small town in the Ozark woods of southwest Missouri, and grew up in nearby Monett, not far from the Arkansas border. He was the only son of well-to-do parents who expected much of him.

His mother, Ida Lima Shipley, nurtured his lifelong love of the arts and classical music. She was aided by their maid, a college-educated African-American who tutored the child. Shipley's mother blanketed him with affection and encouraged a strong positive opinion of himself.

His father, William Hopkins Shipley, came from a Maryland family of high achievers. An ancestor of his had been Maryland's first governor. His father (Robert's grandfather) was a friend of Baltimore financier and railroad magnate Johns Hopkins (after whom he named his son). Following a brief career as a vaudeville stunt bike rider, William studied engineering and went to work for the railroad.

As a sprouting youth, Robert was sent by his father to St. John's Military Academy in Delafield, Wisconsin, for what he called "toughening up." There, he became a long-distance runner and a sculling oarsman. Participating in these two physically demanding sports taught him patience, focus, and persistence, "traits that served me well later [because] they taught me to stick it out," he said. Sufficiently toughened, young Shipley enrolled in the University of Wisconsin, where he studied his father's profession, railroad engineering.

Then, in his junior year, Shipley's life took the first of many sharp turns: His father died suddenly. The young man left school permanently and returned to the family home, now in Wichita, Kansas, to be with his mother. For the first time in his life, Robert Shipley could decide what he wanted to be and do—and, like young people before and since, he didn't know.

Courtesy of JCK

Robert Shipley as a teenage cadet at St. John's Military Academy in Delafield, Wisconsin.

One thing was sure, though: It wasn't railroading. In Wichita, he tried several jobs—setting type, operating a switchboard, and working for the city's gas and electric company (where he progressed from clerk to auditor in only a few months). Then, romance steered him in a new direction.

Tall (six feet, four inches), handsome, and athletic, young Shipley was "a bit of a ladies' man," as he recalled with a chuckle years later. One of the young ladies he charmed in pre–World War I Wichita was, in true American style, the girl across the street.

Her name was Jeanette Vail, and her family was quite affluent. Her father Edward was an officer of the Wichita Perpetual Building and Loan Association. He also owned the city's oldest jewelry store. Wichita, the one-time cow town and railroad hub, had grown into a prosperous Midwest metropolis. Vail Jewelry Co., founded in 1884, prospered with it. The store

Shipley's sons Edward (left) and Robert Jr. (right), with his father-in-law, Edward Vail.

Courtesy of Robert Shipley III

catered to the expensive tastes of *nouveau riche* cattlemen and oil barons, as well as the blue-collar working men "who received their paychecks on Saturdays."

Like others in the city's upper class, the Vails owned show horses. So, to meet Jeanette—and perhaps impress her successful father—young Shipley showed the first hints of his shrewd and innovative salesmanship: He learned to ride a horse and offered to ride one of the Vails' jumpers in a gala horse show. The young man, who cut such a fine figure in the saddle, caught Jeanette's eye. Her father was impressed, too—with Shipley's initiative.

The young couple's friendship quickly progressed to an engagement and then marriage in 1911. Within a year, their son Robert Jr. was born. Something else was born that year: Shipley's lifelong involvement in the jewelry industry. His father-in-law had just become vice president of the Building and Loan Association and was spending less time with the jewelry store. Vail insisted that his bright young son-in-law come into the shop to fill the gap. To Vail, it was an obvious move. It wasn't so obvious to Shipley. It was one thing to marry into a well-to-do family, but quite another to go into its business.

Despite his appreciation of the arts, Shipley knew little about jewelry and nothing about the jewelry business. Nor did he want to. He already had a good job with the city gas and electric company. But he was persuaded by his wife and in-laws, and possibly his mother, that Vail Jewelry offered a brighter future. Lured by the prospect of wealth and success, he was again following someone else's game plan.

■FIRST SUCCESS

Shipley spent his first months in his father-in-law's jewelry store learning the business from the ground up, and what he learned initially didn't spark a love for the industry. "It seemed like all that I did was polish silverware," he recalled decades later. But when he was given more responsibility, Shipley's talent, drive, and leadership emerged. He didn't really like the jewelry trade yet, but he savored the opportunity to build a business and achieve recognition.

And build it he did. Over the next 15 years, he turned Wichita's oldest jewelry store into its largest and made the company a leader in the Midwest. He opened stores in oil-rich cities in Texas, Oklahoma, and Kansas. He added departments for fine china and giftware, as well as a small jewelry-manufacturing operation.

Watch and clock sales and repair were part of the Vail-Shipley Shops.

In 1920, with financial help from his mother, Shipley bought majority ownership of the Vail Jewelry Co. from his father-in-law. In the mid-'20s, he started a second chain of stores called Vail-Shipley Shops ("For people who appreciate fine things"). The shops featured their own art galleries, porcelains, stationery, and leather goods, plus furniture and an interior decorating service.

Shipley's flamboyant and creative salesmanship also flowered as he cultivated his image as a gem expert. Shipley would sometimes take a wealthy client into his office, ask him to hold out his hand, and drop a few stones into it. "There," he would proclaim. "You are holding $75,000 worth of emeralds!" And in a gesture worthy of a Hollywood agent, Shipley at one point publicly announced that he had insured his eyes for $100,000—because they were so essential in evaluating gemstones and diamonds.

By the early 1920s, Shipley's enterprise was attracting the attention of the local and national press. The *Wichita Eagle* praised him as a "diamond

SHIPLEY TURNED WICHITA'S OLDEST JEWELRY STORE INTO ITS LARGEST AND MADE THE COMPANY A LEADER IN THE MIDWEST.

expert" who had given Wichita "a jewelry store rated second to none west of the Mississippi [and] brought art to the city." *The Keystone*, a leading national magazine for jewelers, called him "one of the rising young businessmen of Wichita" and praised his "remarkable initiative" in building the Vail enterprise.

Meanwhile, Shipley's drive took him into industry politics. He became president of the Kansas Retail Jewelers Association, the Midwest regional vice president of the American National Retail Jewelers Association (the forerunner of Jewelers of America), and a member of ANRJA's tax committee.

In those capacities, he traveled extensively in the Midwest, meeting jewelers and making friends. He also helped found a small, informal group called the Jewelers' Roundtable. These men, representing some of the nation's leading retail jewelry stores and chains, met periodically to discuss business challenges, philosophies, and operations. It was Shipley's first shot at creating a nationwide group of jewelers with mutual aims. The roundtable later evolved into the Retail Jewelers Research Group, whose support would be crucial to the Gemological Institute of America in the 1930s and '40s.

BY THE MID-1920s, Shipley was a solid success by all outward appearances. He owned a thriving business. He was a leader in industry politics, the object of favorable press coverage, and the father of two sons—Edward Vail had followed Robert Jr. But like the nation's own shaky financial situation in the 1920s, Shipley's good fortune was a castle built of sand, and when it began to fall apart, it crumbled quickly.

Despite Shipley's well-crafted public image as an expert, he wasn't very knowledgeable about gems. Although he had read some books on mineralogy and gems and "bragged about my knowledge of diamonds and precious stones," he actually knew very little. The depth of his ignorance was revealed in embarrassing incidents that involved at least two wealthy customers.

One was oil millionaire Dillard Clark, a diamond fancier who had purchased about $250,000 of diamonds from Shipley over the years. But Clark's visit to Europe's diamond-cutting centers in the early 1920s convinced him that his young jeweler didn't know much about what he was selling. Indeed, when Clark returned, he showed Shipley that most of the diamonds Shipley had sold him were actually of poor make (that is, poorly cut). While able to grade diamonds for color or internal clarity, Shipley "knew nothing about how their 'make' affected their beauty and value," he later recalled.

Equally humiliating was a visit with Frank Phillips of Tulsa, Oklahoma, founder of Phillips Oil. Phillips had bought jewelry and diamonds from Shipley for years. He was a man who enjoyed luxury—his Tulsa mansion featured gold faucets, mirrored ceilings, and marble floors—and he expected those in the business of luxury merchandise to be as knowledgeable about their goods as he was about oil.

One day he told Shipley he wanted to buy an emerald ring for his wife. Shipley ordered $100,000 of emeralds on memo and took them to Phillips' home so the oilman could choose the finest for his wife's ring. As they sat in the parlor sorting through the stones, Phillips casually asked, "Well, Bob, how do you know the quality of any one emerald in particular?" The young jeweler was speechless for a moment. Then, he awkwardly offered a few facts gleaned from mineralogy books in the public library. "All I could tell him was what anyone could have read, but that didn't interest him worth a darn," recalled Shipley.

Annoyed, the oilman canceled the order. "He knew I didn't know what I was talking about," said Shipley. "And I realized that I was selling things I didn't know anything about."

Shipley never forgot what he called those "soul-searching experiences." Even though his lack of knowledge was typical of most jewelers at the time, it would later spur his zeal to educate and professionalize the industry.

Despite Shipley's early success as majority owner of the Vail Jewelry Co. in the 1920s, a few embarrassing incidents exposed his lack of knowledge about the gems he sold.

AT THIS POINT IN THE MID-1920S, industry legend and early GIA publicity color Shipley's story—largely because of Shipley, who later reinvented why and how he founded GIA. Acutely aware of how little he and other jewelers really knew about gems, goes the legend, Shipley went to Europe to bring gemological knowledge back to America's jewelry trade. In fact, it was personal failure and illness that propelled Shipley out of Wichita and into a restless odyssey that led—almost by chance—to the founding of the Gemological Institute of America.

SIXTEEN YEARS OF
SINGLE-MINDED
FOCUS ON HIS
BUSINESSES AND
INDUSTRY POLITICS
HAD TAKEN ITS TOLL
ON SHIPLEY.

Sixteen years of single-minded focus on his businesses and industry politics—plus frequent travel as an officer of trade organizations—had taken its toll. The workaholic was suffering from nervous exhaustion, what he later called "a two-year illness." His expanding company was overextended and in debt.

At home, the romance between the rich girl across the street and the dashing young man on horseback had soured. By the late '20s, both were unhappy and reportedly drinking heavily.

In 1927, Robert and Jeanette divorced. She kept custody of their sons. He sold the business and gave the proceeds to her. At 40 years of age, when most men begin to enjoy the fruits of family and professional success, Wichita's most prestigious jeweler was a failure in both marriage and business. He left town and, probably with some financial help from his mother, headed west. Shipley was once again personally and professionally adrift, a wanderer with no set goal—except escape and recuperation.

WHY DID SHIPLEY GO TO CALIFORNIA instead of Chicago or New York? One reason is that he loved the sun and had fond childhood memories of family visits to Southern California. But a stronger motivation was his broken health. Shipley apparently checked into a sanitarium for what he later called "nervous prostration." The stay was brief, and he never discussed it in any detail.

However, recovering in what was then called a "health farm"—a place where prominent people retreated for private recuperation—gave Shipley time to think about his life, about the love of art instilled in him by his mother, and about Europe's great museums. As his health revived, he decided to start afresh—this time heading for Europe.

With money earned from writing a couple of silent film scenarios (possibly for movie people he met at the health farm), Shipley bought a train ticket east, then left America on a ship for Europe. Contrary to industry legend, he wasn't going in search of gemological knowledge. He was going in search of a new life.

And he had no intention of returning.

∎A NEW LIFE

Europe refreshed and invigorated Shipley. He visited glass factories in Belgium and on the little Venetian island of Murano. He toured ceramics factories and art studios in France. In Paris, he took courses at the Louvre.

But his two-year sojourn in Europe did more than revive his spirit. It also sparked three important events that changed his life, incidents that were pivotal in creating GIA. The first was what Shipley always called "the luckiest thing that ever happened to me," a blossoming romance with Beatrice Woodill Bell. This captivating woman, who later became his second wife, would also be instrumental in GIA's survival during its early years.

In Paris, Robert Shipley met the woman who would become his second wife: Beatrice Woodill Bell. Shipley always called her "the luckiest thing that ever happened to me."

Beatrice, a native-born Californian from Riverside, was Shipley's match in many ways. Like him, she was tall and attractive. Like him, she was well educated and cultured. Like him, she was strong willed and resilient. The youngest of seven children of a mother widowed early, and a divorcée whose first husband was committed to a mental hospital, she had learned how to deal with difficulty and adversity—and survive.

But unlike Shipley, who had focused his life on fulfilling his flamboyant ambitions, Beatrice was practical and concerned with helping others, especially young women. (She would spend her later years as an officer of the Girl Scouts of America.) After her divorce, she worked for the Episcopal Church, honing her administrative skills. Then, in the mid-1920s, she joined the exclusive Marlborough School in Los Angeles, a private high school for young women, where she rose to the position of dean.

In 1928, Beatrice led a group of girls on a trip to Paris to visit its artistic and cultural venues. She brought her teenage charges to one of the Louvre museum lectures that Shipley regularly attended. While the girls sat in front, the two tall Americans stood in the back. ("We were always in the back of any lecture group," Shipley recalled years later.) They whispered and chatted about America, Europeans, Paris, art, and their lives.

They began to meet at other lectures. Mutual interests led to friendship and admiration, and then love began to grow again for the two proud survivors.

Beatrice led Shipley into his second life-changing activity in Europe—teaching. Impressed by Shipley's knowledge and enthusiasm, she suggested that he lecture on art and ceramics. Beatrice introduced Shipley to the right people and helped him get lecturing spots at three Paris museums—the Musée des Arts Decoratif, the Cluny Museum, and the Sevres Museum—where he spoke

Shipley and Beatrice whispering in the back of a lecture group at the Louvre museum in Paris. Beatrice had brought a group of teenage girls from the Marlborough School in Los Angeles.

on "decorative arts" (primarily porcelains). He even lectured at the Louvre itself, where he gave talks on paintings. In the process of giving those lectures, Shipley discovered he enjoyed teaching.

Inspired, he began reinventing himself. He advertised his lectures in the Paris edition of the English-language *Herald Tribune* as a two-week school of 24 short courses that he called "The Modern Movement." The lectures would lead American buyers through "the mysteries and trends" in European arts. The subjects ranged from paintings to wallpaper; conspicuously absent from his official curriculum were gems and jewelry.

His new image was well received. "Robert M. Shipley of Paris, an authority on European arts and goods, shows the American how to adapt them to American use," wrote the *Wichita Eagle*. He had, Shipley told the reporter, "spent untold hours in study and historical research" and was "constantly besieged by clients who wished him to accompany them in their buying."

The third important development during Shipley's European sojourn was his introduction to the study of gemology. He hadn't forgotten his humiliation in Kansas, and had resolved even then to enroll in the gemological correspondence course—the world's first—offered by Great Britain's National Association of Goldsmiths (NAG).

At about the same time he met Bea, Shipley finally enrolled. NAG's brochure promised potential students that they would learn to "detect fraudulent gems from real [ones] and be able to clearly explain to an inquiring customer the difference." Here was the guarantee he needed that those blunders in

Wichita wouldn't happen again. Shipley signed up and applied himself to the courses wholeheartedly.

With his enrollment, Shipley's Parisian life split into two parts. By day, he was the authority on European arts, lecturing culturally befuddled Americans on the fine points of porcelains and paintings. By night, the expert became a student, hunched over a table in his garret room in the artists' quarter, intently absorbing gemological knowledge. However, his education wasn't limited to the correspondence course. Shipley visited the famous gem centers in Germany, France, and Holland. He viewed museum gem collections and learned who Europe's gem experts were. It was information that would prove priceless within a few years.

SHIPLEY WENT TO LONDON FOR NAG'S required laboratory and gem equipment classes, as well as for the final examination. On May 23, 1929, says the document he received on passing the course, "Robert M. Shipley of Paris . . . was examined in the theory and practice of gemmology . . . satisfied the board of examiners . . . and was granted the Diploma of the Association." He was only the 129th person in the world to do so.

Earning that diploma meant a great deal to Shipley, both psychologically and professionally. He contacted his hometown paper to report it—"London School Awards Wichitan Gemmology Degree," read the headline. The diploma later hung in his office at GIA, a symbol that he was now an actual gem expert, not just a self-proclaimed one.

But at the time he wasn't ready to return to the retail jewelry trade or even to live in the United States. Gems were only a small part of his new business, he told a *Wichita Eagle* reporter in mid-1929, and he expected Paris would remain his home "for some time to come." Nevertheless, with his "school" in Paris "well underway," Shipley told the reporter that he would "carry his ideas to America for a trial" and spoke of planned art lectures in New York and Chicago.

It was typical Shipley, using the press to his own ends. The "school," after all, was only himself, and it is unlikely that he had scheduled any lectures in America before he left Paris. He certainly gave none after he first returned to the U.S.

In late spring of 1929, Shipley packed his bags and prepared to leave his flat. He finally knew what he wanted to do, and he had the drive and confidence to do it. He had a new business. Best of all, he had met a wonderful woman. "The City of Lights" had illuminated his future path, and the way ahead looked bright.

THE THIRD IMPORTANT DEVELOPMENT DURING SHIPLEY'S EUROPEAN SOJOURN WAS HIS INTRODUCTION TO THE STUDY OF GEMOLOGY.

The homeless and unemployed wait in line seeking shelter in Depression-era New York. Shipley started over again just as the United States slid into its worst economic crisis ever.

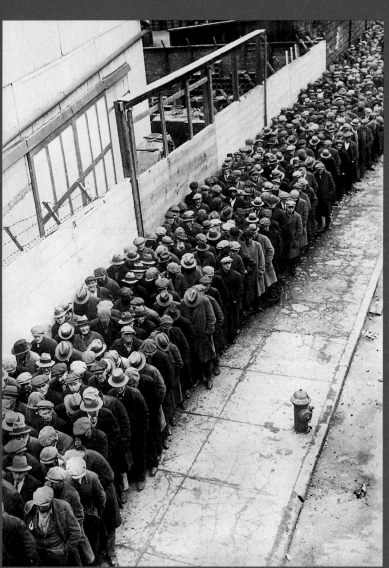

Bettman/Corbis

HARD TIMES

1929–1932

Shipley returned to a country descending into turmoil. The Great Depression was about to overwhelm America, sending millions of jobless workers into the streets and frustrating Shipley's own attempts at a new beginning.

At the same time, consumer confidence in jewelers and gem dealers was at its lowest point in modern history, largely because of rampant gemological ignorance. Indeed, it was so bad that the editor of America's leading jewelry trade magazine felt compelled to editorialize that "the jeweler must know gems" to be successful.

This was one of the darkest periods in Shipley's life, but two encouraging events brightened it—his renewed romance with Beatrice Woodill Bell and a visit from an old acquaintance. This visit in particular would have profound ramifications for Shipley and the gem and jewelry industry.

■STARTING OVER, AGAIN

Shipley couldn't have chosen a worse time for a fresh start.

With the stock market crash of October 1929, America's post–World War I prosperity collapsed like a house of cards, pulling international economies down with it. Within two years, stock losses would soar past $50 billion. Hundreds of companies would go broke. Tidal waves of layoffs would sweep across America. In just 36 months, 16 million people—a third of the total U.S. labor force—would be out of work. In such hard times, no one needed a fine arts consultant or wanted to hear lectures on how to buy luxury wares.

To compound an already daunting situation, the U.S. jewelry industry was in trouble. It wasn't simply the impact of the Depression, which had sent the international gem and jewelry trade reeling. The trade was already shaky from a crisis of its own making: the erosion of public confidence in retail jewelers. In fact, jewelers of the day questioned their own competence. Quite simply, most didn't know much about the gems they were selling. In addition, experienced jewelers rarely shared what they had learned over the years with their employees or family. Shipley's former father-in-law, Edward Vail, was, as one report put it, "extremely close-mouthed" about sharing his wisdom with his own son-in-law. Old retail veterans like Vail believed that since they had learned the hard way, their heirs and employees should, too.

MOST JEWELERS GOT
THEIR INFORMATION
FROM THEIR
SUPPLIERS. BUT
THOSE INDIVIDUALS
WEREN'T ALWAYS
WELL INFORMED,
EITHER.

As George Kaplan, vice president of Lazare Kaplan International, explained half a century later to a group of GIA students, in the early 20th century "jewelers simply didn't know what they were selling. To them, a red stone was a ruby, a blue stone was a sapphire, and a colorless stone was either glass or a diamond!"

Most jewelers got their information from their suppliers. But those individuals weren't always well informed, either. Their facts usually came second-hand from their suppliers, and so on. "With each turn," Shipley said years later, "precious knowledge was diluted and corrupted a little bit more."

By 1930, gemological ignorance in the industry was so widespread that T. Edgar Willson, editor of the *Jewelers' Circular*, the most influential publication in the industry, felt compelled to write an editorial titled "The Jeweler Must Know Gems." In it, Willson wrote that so many jewelers were "so greatly deficient [in gem knowledge] they reflect on the reputation of the trade as a whole . . . it is only the man who can . . . impress his customers with the fact that he *knows* his subject who can reasonably expect to make any impression on a prospective buyer of fine jewelry."

Ironically, as retailers lost credibility, more consumers were taking up rock collecting as a hobby and learning about mineralogy. The result, wrote Shipley years later, was that "the new tribe of rock hounds knew more about colored stones than all but a handful of retail jewelers."

December 1929 found Shipley sitting in his small office in New York. He was broke, discouraged, and lonely. One of those problems could be remedied, at least. For the second time in less than three years, Shipley closed up shop and again headed west toward California—but this time to Bea. He made two stops along the way. The first was in Wisconsin, for a reunion with his son Robert Shipley Jr. at St. John's Military Academy, the same school where his own father had sent him. Then father and son headed to Wichita to spend Christmas with Shipley's mother, Ida.

There, he told a reporter for the *Wichita Eagle*—even in the worst of times, Shipley knew the value of publicity—that the failing economy had changed his plans. Shipley announced his intention to go to California to give lectures for the National Jewelers Publicity Association. Subsequently, he said, he would return to Paris as the "art advisor for a large New York corporation."

IN EARLY 1930, Shipley continued alone to California, where he resumed courting Beatrice. No longer dean of Marlborough, she had opened a small art gallery and studio in Los Angeles. For his part, Shipley rented a small office in Los Angeles. With no firm prospects, he was still a man in search of a professional *raison d'être*.

Happily, he was luckier in love. In June 1930—the very time when Shipley had once expected to be back in Paris—he and Beatrice Woodill Bell were married in Los Angeles.

It was the first chance for the rest of the Woodill family to finally meet him. Alfred Woodill, Beatrice's nephew, remembered Shipley as "very dignified and what we call now a sort of intellectual. I recall my father couldn't quite figure him out!"

Shipley's wedding to Beatrice was the start of a close and happy four-decade partnership, and Shipley began to regain his confidence. While Bea supported them with her art business (they lived on the second floor, over the gallery), Shipley began devising various plans to start a new enterprise.

Courtesy of JCK

Robert and Beatrice Shipley, during their retirement years. Their marriage in June 1930 was the start of a happy four-decade partnership.

He first sent out cards on high-quality paper engraved with red ink that grandly announced, "Robert M. Shipley Associates . . . art consultants [in] planning fine homes and estates [with associates] in Paris, London and New York."

There was no response.

Next, he decided to promote his newly acquired expertise in gemology. He sent out announcements—this time typed on regular paper—for "Robert Shipley Associates, Gem Experts." The announcement assured its readers, "We have lab equipment [a Tully refractometer he brought from Great Britain] for testing precious and semi-precious gems."

Again, no response.

Next, Shipley sent a typed letter to libraries, schools, and jewelers that simply offered "Gemology Service" (for $4 the first month and $1 a month thereafter) that included "valuation, authentical [*sic*], laboratory and reference."

California jeweler and industry leader Armand Jessop paid an important visit to Shipley in 1930. The result was Shipley's 12-week gemology lecture series at the University of Southern California.

San Diego Historical Society Photo Collection

In that letter, he mentioned a book he was writing, based on his experiences and gemological training, titled *Gemology*. (Following the lead of gem expert and author Frank Wade, Shipley Americanized the British "gemmology" by dropping the second "m.") The book, which cost $75, was "a loose leaf [*sic*] of technical gemology on permanent ledger paper—a complete reference arranged especially for the jeweler," said the letter. He promised subscribers "loose-leaf insertions, additional pages on new imitations, substitutes, an up-to-the-minute professional service similar to loose-leaf services provided to physicians, dentists, etc."

But again, there was no response.

Shipley, the master salesman, was discouraged. He was 43, with a new wife who had to support *him*, and his dreams of success were still distant specks on the horizon. Then came the visit that would change his life—and the jewelry industry.

■AN AUSPICIOUS VISIT

Against an unpromising backdrop of widespread misinformation and dwindling public confidence, a leading California jeweler named Armand Jessop, president of J. Jessop and Sons in San Diego, got in touch with Shipley.

Jessop, a jewelry industry leader and advocate of professional education for jewelers, was then president of the Gold and Silversmiths Association of California (predecessor to the California Jewelers Association). He first met Shipley in the mid-1920s when both were regional vice presidents in the American National Retail Jewelers Association. Jessop was convinced that Shipley, with his gemological training and retail experience, was exactly the man that California jewelers needed to hear.

The Shipleys were still newlyweds when, sometime in the middle of 1930, Jessop visited Robert in his cramped Los Angeles office. Jessop asked if Shipley would give a lecture or two for a fee on the "science of gems" to the association's members if a local university or college sponsored the venture.

Without hesitation, Shipley agreed. This was a chance to introduce sound, scientific gemological training to jewelers. In fact, after two failed businesses and months without a job, he felt he had nothing to lose. Shipley didn't expect much from the lectures, except maybe some publicity.

Jessop and Edward R. Allen, the California association's secretary, were more optimistic. Allen arranged with the University of Southern California (USC) to host the lectures one night a week for 12 weeks, as part of USC's evening adult education program.

In the meantime, Shipley began preparing the talks. He met often with Jessop that summer. What they devised, and what Shipley taught, was presented in the proposal for his "preliminary course in gemology," which he submitted to USC for review and approval. Attached to the proposal were a copy of his NAG Gemmological Diploma and a letter from Jessop.

The 12-lesson course, said Shipley's proposal, would include "description and demonstration of scientific principles involved," but no lab work. The introduction covered a history of gems and the factors affecting value. Subsequent lectures concerned the mineralogical nature of gems, the physical characteristics of diamonds and other gemstones, and imitation gem materials. The 12th and final class was an examination.

In the proposal, Shipley promised to provide the class equipment. That included his Tully refractometer, a microscope, a dichroscope, diamond scales, specific gravity liquids, and a chart of the world's diamond-producing areas. The textbook was *Gem-Stones and Their Distinctive Characters*, by British gem expert G. F. Herbert Smith.

Although neither Jessop nor USC had requested it, Shipley was already thinking about offering even more extensive gemology instruction. He called these first 12 lessons a "preliminary course," to be followed by "specialized and laboratory courses."

The university's review committee approved his proposal. USC's president informed Shipley by letter of his appointment to the teaching staff for the fall quarter at a salary of $120 for the course. However, if there were fewer than 10 students, the letter warned, the class would be canceled. Shipley doubted even that many people would show up.

■THE DREAM TAKES FORM

Shipley's first lecture was slated for September 16, 1930, to be held, forebodingly, on the 13th floor of the Los Angeles Transportation Building at Seventh and Los Angeles streets. He entered the classroom hoping to see at

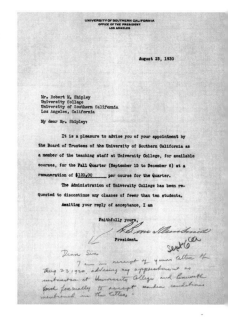

On August 23, 1930, the University of Southern California accepted Shipley's proposal for a gemology lecture series and appointed him to its teaching staff for the fall quarter.

least a couple of people waiting to hear him. Instead, the room was empty. It was probably the most discouraging moment in Shipley's life.

"I really felt desperate," he admitted years later.

After a minute or so, he slowly turned to leave the empty room and go home to Beatrice. As he did, he noticed a small note tacked to the door. The lecture, it said, had been moved to the auditorium.

The auditorium? His heart beating faster, Shipley strode down the hall to the new lecture room.

As he entered, he was amazed to see not one or two people, but a large audience. Jessop and Allen had worked feverishly for weeks to ensure a good turnout, contacting association members and other jewelers as well as the local press. The dozens of students (subsequent accounts ranged from 40 to 90) attested to the success of their efforts.

Robert Shipley's early lectures, coming at a time when education was desperately needed in the gem and jewelry industry, were received with enthusiasm.

Shipley took his place at the podium, spread out his lecture notes, and began to speak. Thus were sown the first seeds for what would become the gemological movement—the most influential in the history of the American gem and jewelry industry.

MUCH LATER, GIA AND INDUSTRY RECOLLECTIONS portrayed those first lessons as polished and comprehensive. In fact, they weren't. A 1931 GIA report called them "mediocre compared to [the] subsequent courses [which are] so greatly improved that students in Professor Shipley's initial classes at USC . . . would not recognize [them]."

Nevertheless, against all logical expectations given the state of the economy, response to those first lectures was enthusiastic and overwhelming. The classes, said jeweler Arthur Dibbern of Glendale, California, enabled the students to "view with broader vision and greater knowledge that which . . . constitutes our life work" and gave them a sense of security in dealing with customers.

Coming when those lectures did—during a period of professional chaos, when jewelers were hungry for what Dibbern called the "authentic knowledge" of gemology—Shipley's lectures must have seemed heaven-sent. Indeed, many of the Institute's early supporters embraced and promoted the study of gemology with a religious fervor. They called GIA training the "gemological gospel" and the "salvation of the legitimate trade," and even labeled their enthusiastic efforts to sign up students as "proselytizing" America's jewelers. Anyone who went out to various groups on behalf of GIA was "a *missionary* for the Institute and not a *salesman*," declared one ardent supporter in a letter sent to Shipley.

And Shipley—who less than a year earlier had expected to return to Paris—now found, to his admitted surprise, that he was quickly becoming the "apostle" of gemology.

SHIPLEY SWIFTLY DEVISED WAYS to reach disciples who were unable to attend courses locally. His brainchild, a correspondence course, has been called the real beginning of the Gemological Institute of America. Shipley's own enrollment in Great Britain's NAG gemology course and his earlier idea for a gemology reference service influenced this approach. However, much credit for the breakthrough that crystallized Shipley's ideas for correspondence courses must be given to one man who was simply tired of driving.

J. E. Peck was a gem collector/prospector/mineralogist who lived in Jacumba, a little town on the California-Mexico border. He attended the first classes in 1930, but the nearly 200-mile car trip to Los Angeles (one way) was simply too tiring to make every week in those pre-superhighway days. So Peck wrote Shipley, pleading with him to mail mimeographed copies of the lectures in return for payment.

Shipley agreed. After all, if one student would pay for gemological knowledge in the form of a correspondence course, why not others? (Shipley never said how much Peck paid, but noted that it was substantial.) And indeed, similar requests began coming in from other California jewelers. Peck's plea was significant. It provided Shipley with the format to extend gemological training beyond the classroom to a wider audience of jewelers.

Peck was not only GIA's very first correspondence-course student, but he also was one of the first to benefit from its content. Soon after completing the course, he tested a supposedly worthless green stone his grandmother had given him and found it was an emerald worth several thousand dollars. He also was an active supporter of the early GIA, and the Institute's gem collection was started by a generous donation from Peck.

J. E. PECK WROTE SHIPLEY, PLEADING WITH HIM TO MAIL MIMEOGRAPHED COPIES OF THE LECTURES IN RETURN FOR PAYMENT.

Always one to seize an opportunity, Shipley pawned a diamond and emerald ring set in chased plat- inum—one of the last reminders of his retail jeweler days—for $75.[1] With it, he rented a typewriter and bought a used Model A Ford road- ster. Like a circuit-riding preacher, he began lecturing to jewelers throughout California and mailing mimeographed copies to those who couldn't attend his presentations.

By year's end, Shipley had expanded his initial 12 lectures into a 40-lesson correspondence course. Tuition was $8 down and $5 per month. Those early correspondence courses, initially intended for California jewelers, were capped by a final in-person class with Shipley and an exam, which led to the title of Theoretical Gemologist.

Demand for the correspondence courses wasn't left to the vagaries of the market—Shipley stoked it, too. Ever the consummate salesman, he mailed promotional postcards directly to Southern California jewelers. ("Equip yourself with this new sale assistance before your competition does," urged one.) He also traveled around Southern California, enrolling jewelers and setting up study groups.

By early December 1930, Shipley had solidified his concept for professional- izing the jewelry industry. At the end of that first semester at USC's evening school, he met with a few selected jewelers who had enrolled in the course at its inception and passed its final examination.

Shipley outlined to them his idea for a guild of professionally educated, ethically minded jewelers, all graduates of a scientific curriculum of gemolo- gy taught through mailed lessons, study groups, and exams leading to a professional title. This organization would lead the industry in restoring the public's trust in the jewelry trade.

The reaction was mixed. "Some were enthusiastic," recalled Shipley, "but others were doubtful. Still others wanted membership to be open to anyone."

---

[1] Shipley eventually bought back the ring, and it has stayed in the family, according to Robert M. Shipley III. "It is still an attractive piece of design, and I still get compliments on it all the time." [Letter from Robert M. Shipley III, February 17, 2000, to *Jewelers' Circular Keystone*.]

Then he had an inspiration that broke the stalemate. "The situation was saved by my suggestion for *two* organizations," he said later. One would be an educational institute. The other would be a professional guild called the Gemological Society. This proposal was immediately accepted by most of those present. Encouraged, Shipley asked them to help him start the Gemological Institute of America by being its first "sustaining members," a select group who would support the Institute with student enrollments, publicity, and donations. Again, most of the jewelers readily agreed, realizing what such a program could mean to the industry's reputation.

The response of these jewelers, and their faith in him and his ideas, deeply touched Shipley. Most of those early students remained steadfast supporters of GIA for the rest of their lives. Typical of them was John Wesley Ware, a San Diego jeweler who was the first sustaining member of the Gemological Institute of America. Ware eventually served four terms on the Institute's board of governors and was an original director of the American Gem Society. When Ware died in 1946, the obituary in *Gems & Gemology*, GIA's quarterly journal, praised him as a man who "participated in the activities of the gemological profession with a religious fervor."

By early 1931, the gemology movement, seeded by Shipley's USC lectures, was starting to sprout. In January, the new Gemological Institute of America opened its first headquarters, a small office just big enough for a lecture room and a laboratory, in the 811 Title Guarantee Building in Los Angeles, although soon thereafter the fledgling Institute (always short of cash in its early years) was moved to 3511 West Sixth Street in L.A., then the Shipley residence.

MOST OF SHIPLEY'S EARLY STUDENTS REMAINED STEADFAST SUPPORTERS OF GIA FOR THE REST OF THEIR LIVES.

GIA's second home was at 3511 West Sixth Street in Los Angeles, shown here in a 1973 photo.

Los Angeles Public Library

23

GIA'S FIRST
LABORATORY WAS SET
UP IN JANUARY 1931
WITH DONATED
EQUIPMENT.

On January 15, 1931, an enthusiastic group of jewelers and diamond dealers founded the Gemological Society. All of Shipley's students—by then about 70 people in Southern California, most of them in the Los Angeles area—were charter members. The society's purpose was the "advancement and practical study of gemology by jewelers and others and the furtherance of a greater appreciation of diamonds and gems on the part of the American people."

The Gemological Society was intended to be the nucleus of Shipley's proposed (and somewhat grandiose) national guild of jeweler-gemologists. But that dream had to wait a while longer, until there were enough graduates of GIA courses to populate such a guild.

GIA issued its first publications and books in early 1931. A short-lived newsletter called *Gemology, Bulletin of the Gemological Institute of America* appeared in January 1931. (It was replaced by a magazine called *Gems & Gemologists* in 1933 for one issue, and then in early 1934 by *Gems & Gemology*.)

The first two books with GIA's imprint were both in loose-leaf format for easy updating. *Gemology, the Authoritative Reference Book* was "as necessary as your scales and tweezers," declared a January 1931 GIA ad. Written by Shipley, it was designed as a "practical means of helping the jeweler build confidence among his customers and efficiency among his salesmen." This was actually a reincarnation of Shipley's earlier idea of a gemological information service. The other book, *Shipley's Gemology*, contained the full course he had given at USC.

GIA's first laboratory was set up in January 1931 with donated equipment. It was used for advanced instruction and original research, and to support GIA's fledgling gem-testing service.

By early 1931, Shipley was teaching several different gemology classes. In addition to the USC evening-school laboratory class for advanced students, he held a "Preparatory Class" at the new headquarters for potential members of the Gemological Society, classes designed specifically for diamond dealers and salesmen, and short courses in general laboratory work and the advanced study of diamonds.

Several study groups sprouted in Southern California, including the Long Beach–Huntington Association and the San Diego Association. These groups met weekly to review and discuss GIA lessons. Shipley often attended these gatherings, conducting their final reviews and examinations.

MEANWHILE, SHIPLEY WAS GETTING INQUIRIES from jewelers elsewhere on the West Coast who had heard reports of his classes. These inquiries and the continued interest in Southern California convinced him that the time was ripe to make this a national movement to educate the jewelry industry. Indeed, as early as January 1931, GIA began to advertise for "young men in every large city to organize study groups in gemology [in return] for free tuition in [the] Correspondence Course."

"Everyone thought I was crazy, even Bea," Shipley wrote two decades later. He had told her about his vision of a national association of gemologically trained jewelers, adding that it would be necessary to sell the idea in person to jewelers throughout North America.

Beatrice must have stared at him for a very long time. She was familiar with what Shipley himself called his "promotional tendencies" and his habit of trying to do too much at once. She had always supported him—emotionally and financially—but this? It seemed too quixotic. Beatrice felt compelled to put her husband's dream of converting the entire U.S. jewelry trade in cold, clear perspective.

"You have as much chance of success of selling this idea to the jewelry industry as you have trying to dig the foundation of the Rockefeller Center with a child's sand shovel," she told him bluntly.

Shipley always listened to Bea's advice—her "wisdom [and] restraining influence" on him were essential to GIA's success, he said years later—but he didn't always follow it. His entrepreneurial instinct told him that now was the time to press the sale. The movement was growing too quickly to ignore this opportunity.

More than that, here was the challenge and the purpose Shipley had sought all his life, one big enough to match his grandest dreams. This was probably his best chance to make his mark. Here was a mission he had launched and led, one with the potential to affect an entire industry. He considered the risk worth taking. "I can build something here," Shipley told his wife. And Beatrice supported him, as she always did.

In February 1931, the Gemological Institute of America was formally registered in Los Angeles as a business partnership owned and operated by Robert and Beatrice Shipley. Bea provided not only her name and personal support, but also considerable financing from the sale of stock she owned.

However, Shipley didn't set off immediately on his cross-continental quest to win over the jewelry industry. He was busy conducting the Institute's first classes and study groups, enrolling more California jewelers in correspondence courses, and soliciting support from state jewelry trade leaders. And he still had to finish administering the advanced evening course at USC.

IN FEBRUARY 1931, THE GEMOLOGICAL INSTITUTE OF AMERICA WAS FORMALLY REGISTERED IN LOS ANGELES.

25

SOME JEWELERS
WERE INDIFFERENT
OR DOWNRIGHT
HOSTILE TO THE IDEA
OF GEMOLOGICAL
TRAINING.

Moreover, he hadn't forgotten Bea's concerns. What guarantee did he have that jewelers outside California would accept his idea of a national guild of jeweler-gemologists?

To test the possibility of national acceptance, he began traveling north, up the Pacific coastline, to seek out "ethical jewelers." Shipley showed them his courses and support materials, and he enticed them with window displays of "Famous Diamonds of the World" and the "Cutting of the Cullinan Diamond" (obtained from the National Jewelers Publicity Association). He loaned these displays free of charge to stores for two weeks for signing up with GIA. While many jewelers listened with interest, it was those displays that were "9-to-1 more appealing than the courses themselves" in signing up jewelers, he admitted wryly.

It certainly wasn't an easy sell, and it set the tone for Shipley's later travels across America. Some jewelers were indifferent or downright hostile to the idea of gemological training. They didn't like the suggestion that they weren't knowledgeable about their trade. Still, many others did appreciate what Shipley was offering. Harry Arold of Hardy & Co. in Seattle, for example, endorsed Shipley's plan in the 1933 issue of *Gems & Gemologists* as "invaluable to any jeweler desiring to improve and hold his position as a leader in his chosen profession."

By year's end, approximately 150 Pacific Coast jewelers were enrolled in GIA's correspondence courses.

CONVINCED NOW THAT HIS IDEA had a chance of succeeding nationally, Shipley stepped up his pace. He had promised an institute endorsed by leaders of the industry, a comprehensive gemology course, and a national association. Now, he had to start delivering. He had to set up governing and advisory boards and garner industry-wide support. At the same time, he had to develop courses that would form the basis for a respected diploma.

Shipley contacted jewelry-industry leaders in California, urging them to support GIA and the gemological movement by enrolling their employees and becoming Institute advisors. One of the first he contacted was Godfrey Eacret—the one man, Shipley would often say later, "who more than any other in the jewelry trade was responsible for the successful establishment of the Gemological Institute of America."

Eacret was president of Shreve, Treat & Eacret in San Francisco, and a leader in state and national jewelry and business organizations. He was also a proponent of gemological education and, at the time, one of the few gem experts among U.S. jewelers; he had the distinction of having examined the Cullinan diamond in its original form as well as the Hope diamond.

Eacret and Shipley already knew each other professionally. When Shipley contacted him in 1931, Eacret was ready to listen. After carefully scrutinizing Shipley's courses, he concluded, "Yours is the first real plan offered to the trade to make our business the profession I think it should be."

Eacret agreed to chair the new board of governors (then called the national advisory board). He also promised to get the support of other jewelers, especially those in the

San Francisco jeweler Godfrey Eacret was the man Shipley would later say was "more than any other in the jewelry trade . . . responsible for the successful establishment of the Gemological Institute of America."

Retail Jewelers Research Group (RJRG). In Eacret's short tenure with GIA— he died suddenly in 1935—he readily donated his time, money, advice, and gem specimens. He persuaded many other jewelers to enroll. Perhaps most importantly, he lent his prestige to GIA at a time when its acceptance by the industry was by no means certain. Shipley later called Eacret "the soul of the gemological movement."

IN 1932, ARMED WITH THE SUPPORT of leading West Coast jewelers and the operations of the tiny Institute underway, Shipley was finally ready to head east on a trek to promote GIA and gemological training. It was the most important selling job of his life, and it would last for years.

Equipped with a battered suitcase, mineralogy books, enrollment forms, copies of the first lessons, and a typewriter to write the next ones, Shipley kissed Bea goodbye and embarked on his journey through the farm towns and big cities of Depression-era America.

His goal, he said, was to personally visit as many jewelry stores as humanly possible, sign up managers and employees as correspondence students, and solicit the backing of industry leaders and the trade press. As Bea predicted, Shipley had set himself—and GIA's tiny staff and small band of supporters— a Herculean task. It was, he admitted decades later, "almost too much for us, financially and physically."

But if successful, Shipley's mission would establish him as one of the greatest contributors to the future of the American jewelry industry.

■EARLY MISSIONARY WORK

In the early '30s, as today, New York City was the center of the U.S. jewelry trade—the home of Wall Street, trend-setting Fifth Avenue jewelers, major gem and diamond dealers, banks, association headquarters, and the trade press. It seemed the logical place for Shipley to promote his plan.

But instead of going directly to the industry's movers and shakers in the East, he made a left turn into America's heartland, to the jewelers of the Midwest.

"Shipley knew his ideas would be shot down in New York," explained Al Woodill in a 1998 interview. He had traveled with Shipley and knew it was no false assumption. Opposition to gemological training was neither casual nor temporary. Woodill recalled having doors literally shut in his face by some firms. "They weren't interested even then in having retailers study gemology," he said. "'We'll tell the jeweler what he needs to know,'" he remembered one dealer saying to him.

Future GIA president Glenn Nord recalled that even in the 1950s and early '60s, wholesalers and traveling salesmen would "discourage jewelers from getting GIA courses. They were afraid of their customers learning too much, and then knowing too much about their operations." The prevailing viewpoint, still held by some decades later, was that knowledge shared with customers would kill business.

Shipley figured the best way to start his national movement was among those who understood him best: his former retail colleagues. Shipley's most important meeting in the Midwest in 1932 was with the Retail Jewelers Research Group, which he had helped start in the 1920s. Its support was crucial. Shipley "had reached the end of his financial rope [and the] funds supplied by Mrs. Shipley," says an unpublished 1980 RJRG history. Also, the group's members included the most respected and influential jewelers in America.

Shipley made the sale, and nine RJRG members were among the first to pledge their support. Thanks largely to such backing, GIA's first national advisory board—which became the GIA Board of Governors—was formally organized in 1932. Most board members remained committed to GIA for the rest of their lives, taking the courses, making donations of money and equipment, directing its operations, and helping form its policies.

GIA'S FIRST BOARD OF GOVERNORS

JAMES D. DOUGHERTY • J. B. Hudson, Minneapolis, Minnesota

GODFREY EACRET • Shreve, Treat & Eacret, San Francisco, California

LOUIS ESSER • Louis Esser Co., Milwaukee, Wisconsin

MYRON EVERTS • Arthur E. Everts Co., Dallas, Texas

PAUL HARDY • Hardy & Hayes Co., Pittsburgh, Pennsylvania

FRANK HEITKEMPER • Frank A. Heitkemper Inc., Portland, Oregon

EDWARD F. HERSCHEDE • Frank Herschede Co., Cincinnati, Ohio

O. C. HOMANN • The C. B. Brown Co., Omaha, Nebraska

FRANCIS A. KEATING • Grogan Co., Pittsburgh, Pennsylvania

WILLIAM G. THURBER • Tilden-Thurber Corp., Providence, Rhode Island

LEO J. VOGT • Hess & Culbertson Jewelry Co., St. Louis, Missouri

With the support of the RJRG, leading jewelers on the West Coast, and a growing number of students, Shipley was ready for New York City. Of Shipley's many stops in the Big Apple, his most important was at *Jewelers' Circular*. There he met with the magazine's editor, T. Edgar Willson. Active in a score of organizations, Willson was a founder and director of the Jewelers Vigilance Committee and, as his recent editorial had made clear, an outspoken proponent of gemological education.

Shipley's message so impressed Willson that he took Shipley into the office of publisher Peter Fahrendorf and had him tell it again. Shipley's plan, Willson later said, brought together "a lot of information that has heretofore been scattered in the hands of a few individuals and not been generally available." Shipley and Willson both faced "rebuffs and discouragements" for promoting gemological training, wrote Fahrendorf in 1952, but Willson strongly believed in Shipley's ideas and "backed [him] completely in our editorial columns [and gave] the most whole-hearted cooperation, from the very beginning." That support included free ads, sympathetic coverage, and space for articles by Shipley during GIA's formative years.

Willson also became actively involved in the young GIA, serving on the board that set the criteria by which students were examined for their Certified Gemologist title. When he, like Godfrey Eacret, died suddenly in

T. Edgar Willson, editor of *Jewelers' Circular* and a founder of the Jewelers Vigilance Committee, was an early supporter of Shipley and GIA.

1935, *Gems & Gemology* praised "his interest in the development of gemological education."

Support from *Jewelers' Circular* continued even after it merged with *The Keystone* and became *Jewelers' Circular-Keystone* (*JCK*) in 1935. However, Shipley's later relations with *JCK* and its editors were sometimes bumpy. He felt they "weren't giving GIA all the publicity needed," while *JCK*'s editors "looked at problems from the overall industry-wide point of view," maintained Fahrendorf. Still, despite occasional differences, Shipley always recognized the magazine's key role in establishing GIA. "It was Willson and *Jewelers' Circular*, and the Retail Jewelers Research Group, who helped me put it over nationally," Shipley said in later years.

Others in the trade press—from national publications like *National Jeweler*, *The Keystone*, and *Manufacturing Jeweler*, and regional ones such as *Pacific Goldsmith*, *Northwestern Jeweler*, and *Midcontinental Jeweler*—followed Willson's lead and promoted the Institute, acknowledged Beatrice Shipley in an August 1933 editorial in *Gems & Gemologists*. With support from the industry in place, she continued, the gemological idea "began to permeate the nation."

AT THEIR FIRST MEETING IN NEW YORK, Willson would introduce Shipley to Meyer D. Rothschild, president of American Gem & Pearls Co. and probably the most important U.S. gem dealer at that time. Rothschild was another advocate of accurate gem information and author of *A Hand-Book of Precious Stones* (1889), which he gave free to his customers. In an environment where many gem dealers challenged the very idea of teaching jewelers about gems, Rothschild's support was essential.

Excited by Shipley's vision, but "anticipating trouble if the big gem dealers didn't approve of what we were doing," Willson called Rothschild and set up an immediate appointment. As he and Shipley walked the few, busy

New York blocks to Rothschild's office, Shipley recounted in 1977, Willson suddenly stopped and looked intently at Shipley.

"You simply can't go to Mr. Rothschild without a hat," declared Willson, himself a stylish dresser. "Let's go into this store and buy you [one]!" This was, after all, the early 1930s, and well-dressed men still wore hats, especially to important business appointments. Shipley's hat had blown off weeks before, as he drove through Iowa cornfields in his open car to visit a jeweler.

Always low on funds in those first years, Shipley was taken aback by Willson's demand. Still, this appointment was too important to lose on a technicality. They went into the store. "Fortunately, it was summer, so I was able to buy a 'straw boater' for just $3, which I paid for myself," he said. And so Shipley literally went hat in hand to ask the most important gem dealer in the U.S. for his support.

Rothschild wasn't a man who suffered fools gladly, and he had seen his share of charlatans in the gem trade. But he trusted Willson's judgment, so he listened politely to Shipley's presentation. However, he showed no hint of enthusiasm. Instead, he told Shipley he would think about it, thanked him for coming, and bid him goodbye.

Willson and Shipley left, mystified. The next morning, Willson phoned Rothschild, who asked, "Can this fellow make any money out of this?"

Willson assured him that Shipley's plan could work. "All right, then," said Rothschild, "I approve." A short time later, he wrote Shipley that he was "very much interested in the objects [*sic*] of the Gemological Institute and wish[ed] you every success," an endorsement GIA publicized. He later donated the numerous color plates from his gem booklet to GIA for its use.

At the end of his tour, a tired but jubilant Shipley returned home. A memo written by San Bernardino, California, jeweler and GIA supporter John Vondey summed up the results: "Mr. Shipley returns after a two-month trip, during which he reports 20 leading firms of America have affiliated with GIA, officers of all retail organizations have endorsed the Institute, two national magazines have pledged assistance and leading scientists have volunteered to be on a national education board."

It was an impressive start.

IN ADDITION TO RECRUITING members of the trade in the early 1930s, Shipley and his supporters sought the help of many pioneers in gemology and mineralogy, including educators, authors, and museum curators. He persuaded

"YOU SIMPLY CAN'T GO TO MR. ROTHSCHILD WITHOUT A HAT," DECLARED WILLSON.

Left: The University of Michigan's Dr. Edward Kraus, co-author of *Gems and Gem Materials* (1925), was one of the most influential gem experts to sign on with GIA in the early 1930s. Right: Dr. Paul F. Kerr, head of Columbia University's mineralogy department, was an important educator in early gemology.

Courtesy of George Kaplan

Mining engineer Dr. Sydney H. Ball (left), pictured with George Kaplan (center) and Lazare Kaplan (right), was a leading diamond authority of the 1930s and '40s.

them to serve on GIA boards and committees, assist in preparing and reviewing GIA's early lessons, and examine title candidates.

Shipley's courtship of scientific experts is one of GIA's most overlooked contributions to the gemology movement. Until then, as *Gems & Gemology* noted years later, "educators and scientists . . . regarded jewelers as tradesmen with little concern for accuracy in their representation of merchandise." Shipley's vision and aggressive recruiting in the early 1930s helped change that, providing what Great Britain's *Journal of Gemmology* called "much needed academic muscle" to the fledgling institute.

Among the educators, gem experts, and authors who signed on with GIA in the 1930s, several stand out. One of the first was Dr. Edward H. Kraus of the University of Michigan, an internationally acclaimed authority in mineralogy, crystallography, and gemstones. Kraus was influential in GIA for many years, starting in 1932 when he accepted Shipley's invitation to join GIA's educational advisory board.

Another important educator recruited by Shipley was Dr. Paul F. Kerr, head of Columbia University's mineralogy department and a well-known expert in the young field of gemology. Kerr was teaching well-attended evening classes in gemstones at Columbia a decade before Shipley launched GIA. He was later president of the Mineralogical Society of America and author of *Optical Mineralogy* (1977). Kerr's status was such that GIA considered his classes equivalent to its own introductory course for gem students preparing for membership in its Gemological Society. He joined GIA's examinations board and remained on it for two decades.

Dr. Sydney H. Ball, a much-honored mining engineer and consultant, was one of the world's leading authorities on diamonds and diamond mining. Ball joined GIA's students' advisory and examinations boards in the early 1930s and served on them for 20 years. He also was one of GIA's most popu-

EDUCATORS AND EXPERTS WHO SUPPORTED THE NEW GIA

In addition to Drs. Edward Kraus, Paul Kerr, and Sydney Ball, several respected scientists played an active role in developing GIA:

BASIL W. ANDERSON, director of the gem testing laboratory of the London Chamber of Commerce, and author of *Gem Testing* (1942)

H. T. DICKINSON, scientific director for De Beers Consolidated Mines Ltd. in South Africa

DR. O. C. FARRINGTON, curator of geology at the Field Museum of Natural History, Chicago

DR. WILLIAM F. FOSHAG, curator of minerals at the National Museum of Natural History, Smithsonian Institution

DR. KARL SCHLÖSSMACHER, professor of mineralogy at Germany's Königsberg University

FRANK B. WADE, a high school chemistry teacher from Indianapolis, Indiana, who wrote books on gems for jewelers

ROBERT WEBSTER, author of *Gemmologists' Compendium* (1937) and *Gems: Their Sources, Descriptions and Identification* (1962)

DR. EDWARD WIGGLESWORTH, director of Boston's New England Museum of Natural History (today the Museum of Science), later GIA's first honorary president and head of its first East Coast office and laboratory

Clockwise from top left: Basil W. Anderson, O. C. Farrington, Dr. William Foshag, and Dr. Karl Schlössmacher.

lar and convivial members, a frequent lecturer, and a contributor to *Gems & Gemology* and other publications.

Other important educators and experts in the U.S. and abroad also signed on in the 1930s (see box). Early GIA boards and committees were composed of virtually everyone who was anyone in the study of gems. It was a stunning endorsement of GIA and the vision of the man leading it.

THE ROOTS OF GEMOLOGY

George F. Kunz

Although others dubbed him "Mr. Gemology," Shipley didn't create its study, nor did he introduce it to North America. The serious study of gemology in the United States and Europe existed more than half a century before Shipley created the Gemological Institute of America.

Books on gem materials have been written for more than 2,000 years. However, a large number of books devoted to gems were first published in the late 19th century in America, England, and Germany. Noted British jeweler E. W. Streeter published *Precious Stones and Gems* in 1896. One of the most influential books was *Gems and Precious Stones of North America* (1890) by George F. Kunz, the American gem expert employed by Tiffany & Co. for whom kunzite is named. Mineralogy professor Max Bauer of Germany's Marburg University followed in 1896 with *Edelsteinkunde* (*Precious Stones*), a monumental reference work.

In the early 20th century, Kunz—one of the most important pre-GIA influences on American gemology—published several more works, including *The Curious Lore of Precious Stones* (1913), which is still used by 21st-century jewelers and gemologists. In 1912, Dr. G. F. Herbert Smith, head of mineralogy of The British Museum in London, published the first edition of *Gem-Stones and Their Distinctive Characters*; Smith's book was the one Shipley used to teach his first gemology lectures in 1930. And in 1903, O. C. Farrington, curator of geology at the Field Museum of Natural History in Chicago, published *Gems and Gem Minerals*.

Early courses in gems followed the first books. At the start of the 20th century, short courses were introduced at Columbia University in New York, by mineralogy professor Dr. Alfred J. Moses, and at the Colorado School of Mines in Golden, Colorado.

But the first serious study of gems in the United States was a course introduced in early 1916 at the University of Michigan by Dr. Edward Kraus. Creating it was difficult, he said years later, because while descriptions of gems and their mineralogical and crystallographic data were readily available, "authoritative information concerning gem cutting, especially for the diamond" was not. Few mineralogists in America or abroad, he noted, had contacts with diamond cutters. There also was very little detailed information about synthetic rubies and sapphires, which were becoming more important. On his own, Kraus visited gem-cutting centers, universities, authorities, and gem collections in Europe (especially Germany and Holland) to get first-hand information. Kraus published his lecture materials in 1925 as *Gems and Gem Materials*, co-authored by E. F. Holden. This text was widely used in America and abroad, and went through many reprintings over the next several decades (with fellow professor Dr. Chester Slawson as co-author of later editions).

In 1908, Great Britain's National Association of Goldsmiths (NAG) adopted a resolution calling for instruction in gemology. With the world's first gemological correspondence course, NAG began awarding diplomas in 1913 and resumed after World War I. This course, which Robert Shipley passed in 1929, provided the model for the correspondence course he created for GIA.

Dr. Max Bauer

In 1931, the same year Shipley founded GIA, the Gemmological Association was organized in England. Holders of diplomas awarded by the NAG became automatically eligible for fellowship in the Gemmological Association.

The Gemological Institute of America and its sister organization, the American Gem Society, became pivotal points for the international gem movement's diverse participants. Virtually all the important authors, experts, and educators in the young field of gemology became GIA advisors, officers, committee members, or supporters.

Dr. G. F. Herbert Smith

And while Shipley did not create the study of gemology, it was he who eloquently conveyed its importance to jewelers and their trade organizations across the U.S. and Canada. In so doing, he changed and professionalized the American—and ultimately the international—gem and jewelry trade.

Shipley's knowledge and enthusiasm for the "gemological gospel" often had a mesmerizing effect on jewelers.

LAYING THE FOUNDATION

1932–1939

Convert America's jewelers and gem dealers to what was called "the gemological gospel"? It was an unlikely mission, perhaps even impossible. But Shipley didn't know the meaning of the word "impossible." Despite industry opposition, he criss-crossed the United States many times during the 1930s, while Beatrice and her tiny staff—initially using the Shipley home as the Institute's "headquarters"—handled its operations and finances.

As the circle of influential supporters in the industry widened, enrollments increased from a few to a few hundred, and the Shipleys began pioneering activities in other areas. Robert Shipley Jr. almost single-handedly created GIA's laboratory services and gemological instruments, while Robert Sr. found time to start a second influential trade organization, the American Gem Society.

By the end of the decade, the Shipleys and their supporters had turned their impossible dream into reality. In the process, they made great progress in restoring jewelers' confidence in themselves and consumer confidence in the jewelry industry.

And it all happened during the depths of the Depression era.

▪ TRAVELS WITH SHIPLEY

Today, in this age of fax machines, cellular phones, and the Internet, Robert Shipley's goal of reaching jewelers across America doesn't sound so grand. But Shipley lived in a different America, one without interstate highways, nonstop transcontinental flights, or national television networks. The closest things to instantaneous communication were airmail letters, which could take days to deliver, or Western Union telegrams, which could take hours. A long-distance phone call was expensive, and the average person—if he or she even had a phone—rarely made one.

In those times, Shipley's goal seemed absurd. Yet he had little other choice if he wanted to persuade America's jewelers. "Everything was pretty much done by correspondence and direct, eyeball contact," recalled Alfred Woodill, who traveled with Shipley as his secretary.

The U.S. of the 1930s *did* have an excellent railroad system. Yet, Shipley—despite growing up in a railroad household—often chose to travel by car during GIA's formative years. The reason was simple: "He could stop in every little town to sign up people," said Dorothy Jasper Smith, who worked with him for 20 years. "He could *really* take the movement across America to every little backwater in the country."

Shipley drove across the Depression-era United States to personally deliver GIA's message to jewelers. This painting by Robert Shipley Jr. depicts the senior Shipley in his used Model A Ford roadster.

Courtesy of JCK

Shipley's journeys in those early years were rarely easy, made even more difficult by the arduous schedule he followed. "I would be at my first jewelry store before the owner in the morning, work all day until the last jeweler I wanted to see closed," he later recounted. "Then, [I would] drive to the next town to be at the next jeweler first thing the next morning."

In the evenings, if Shipley had no scheduled meetings, he would work on new lessons or revisions. On Sunday, he reviewed the lessons, articles, and letters he had worked on that week, and sent them to the home office in Los Angeles to type, mimeograph, and mail.

Travel was often a hand-to-mouth existence for Shipley, especially on those first trips when GIA's finances were so shaky. This cultured man who had socialized with Midwestern millionaires and lectured on art to wealthy Americans in Paris learned to become a "nickel-and-dimer." He used salt from dining tables to brush his teeth, shaved with hotel soap, and wrote notes and lessons on hotel stationery—front and back. Shipley later admitted that he acquired a lifelong reputation for being stingy because of his habits from those days.

AT THE SAME TIME, SHIPLEY WAS FIGHTING BATTLES inside and outside the gemological movement. The Institute's early supporters and officers, who had their own hands full trying to run their businesses during the Depression, didn't always see eye-to-eye with Shipley or respond as quickly as he liked. More than once in the early '30s, he had to urge GIA officials to review proposed appointments, membership rules, and detailed operational regulations.

"It is absolutely necessary to effect a permanent organization or quit," Shipley wrote to GIA's board of governors after an unsuccessful April 1933 meeting in Chicago. Rather than discuss a detailed organizational plan— "the reason for making this trip," Shipley noted pointedly—the board had instead urged him to concentrate on writing courses and enrolling students. "As soon as I can have your cooperation in the work of 'spreading the gospel,'" he wrote, "I *will* be able to concentrate my time as I had originally planned."

Shipley, who certainly could be cranky and imperious, also had to contend with early students and supporters who came to regard him as "a sort of 'dictator'" who promoted himself as a "diamond authority," according to a memo written by Bea Shipley in 1933 or 1934 to squelch such rumblings. "This is an incorrect attitude," she wrote sternly. Shipley's books were compilations of facts and opinions by "most recognized authorities," she continued, while his own opinions were offered as such. Institute policies, she noted, were set by its governors—not Shipley.

Opposition from the greater gem and jewelry trade also continued. In a 1934 confidential memo, Shipley wrote of "an organized effort [by] a small group of pearl and colored gem dealers in New York City to discountenance [the] authenticity and accuracy of the work of [the] Institute." They sought, he said, either "destruction of the Institute or [its] control." In fact, their "determined efforts destroyed constructive results" in some meetings he had held in New York to promote GIA and the gemological movement.

When they couldn't buy the Institute from the Shipleys or take it over, opponents tried to dissuade would-be GIA students. Some suppliers sent hecklers to his lectures. Others sent their salesmen to jewelers ahead of Shipley with propaganda that he was working a get-rich-quick racket. Yes, it was a racket, Shipley sarcastically shot back in a mid-1930s *Gems & Gemology* article, "a racket to increase the happiness of individual jewelers and to elevate the position of the retail trade."

Meanwhile, some jewelers worried that formal education would expose their own limited expertise. There was, for example, a young man in Oregon who was "really excited about the idea of studying gemology," Shipley recalled years later. When the young jeweler was called away to help a customer, Shipley thought he had gained another student. Then the store owner, who was also the young man's father, called Shipley into his office.

"Pack up and leave. You're wasting your time here," he told Shipley bluntly. Surprised, and not a little annoyed, Shipley demanded to know why. "I'll never let my son take that course of yours," came the reply. "I'll be darned if he'll know more about this business than I do!"

Shipley encountered such objections and fears repeatedly in his travels in the 1930s and '40s. "Many jewelers rebuffed my visits," he reflected in 1959.

"I'LL NEVER LET MY SON TAKE THAT COURSE OF YOURS," REPLIED ONE JEWELER. "I'LL BE DARNED IF HE'LL KNOW MORE ABOUT THIS BUSINESS THAN I DO!"

"They felt no need themselves for more knowledge [and] feared at the same time that the courses might benefit a competitor." GIA instructors and officials who followed him later were to encounter similar fears for decades in the wake of new instruments, courses, and grading systems developed by the Institute.

STILL, MANY VETERAN JEWELERS and industry leaders realized that gemological training could benefit both them and the industry. One was sixth-generation jeweler H. Paul Juergens of Juergens & Andersen in Chicago. Juergens enrolled in 1933, after he had already been a jeweler for 37 years.

"I thought I had put schoolbooks aside," he recalled 20 years later. But the training and benefits that Shipley described to him "seemed so interesting that I decided to take the course." Once enrolled, "I became so intensely interested, that I followed it through to the end."

Juergens' new knowledge gave him a confidence he didn't have before, despite decades of experience. "There was no question the public could ask me which I couldn't answer, and correctly," he said. Just as important, "I found my work to be far more enjoyable." Previously, "there was nothing else to say [after] you mentioned price. [Now, there is] the quality and the fashioning of a stone to talk about, and you can go on as long as the customer will listen!" Juergens went on to become a leader in the gemology movement.

By the late 1930s, Shipley seemed to be winning the battle for gemological training. Aiding him was a growing awareness among jewelers that they needed specialized knowledge to compete with credit and department stores, a growing public interest in gems, and a buzz among jewelers and traveling salesmen created by growing debate over the merits of GIA and gemology.

SHIPLEY WOULD HOLD OUT A HANDFUL OF LIKE-COLOR GEMS AND ASK IF THE LISTENER COULD DISTINGUISH THEM JUST BY LOOKING AT THEM.

Shipley now seemed to be ubiquitous, "always selling, making stops all over the country," recalled J. Burton Streeter, a traveling jewelry salesman in the 1930s and later a GIA student and instructor. "I kept hearing he had just been at whatever store I was stopping at."

What was Shipley like on those selling jaunts? "A very striking individual," said Streeter. "He carried a cane and wore spats on his shoes. When he walked in, everyone looked up."

Arthur Jessop—son of the man who convinced Shipley to give the first lectures that led to the Institute's creation—recalled that this self-made son of the Ozarks had "the bearing and dignity of a British diplomat, especially with that mustache and aquiline nose."

By all accounts, Shipley was an inspiring speaker and never better than when speaking one-to-one or in a small group. When this dignified man spoke, you *listened*. His eyes, deep-set in a lean face, peered intently at you as he talked. His tone was mellow but authoritative. He referred to a variety of gemological publications, industry leaders, and business information. He spoke about the jeweler's need for knowledge. With a tactic similar to the one he had used as a jeweler, he would hold out a handful of like-color gems and ask if the listener could distinguish them just by looking at them. (Usually, they couldn't.) As he became more enthused, he would remove his pince-nez glasses and gesture emphatically with them.

Edward Tiffany of Toronto (left) and Carleton Broer of Toledo, Ohio, were just two of the many jewelers who fell under "Shipley's spell" and enrolled at GIA during the 1930s.

The total effect could be mesmerizing, especially for those who were unsure of their gemological knowledge. Edward Tiffany, of Henry Birks & Sons, Toronto, recalled "falling under Shipley's spell" on the GIA founder's first trip to Canada in 1934. Shipley was "so imbued with the gemological gospel and presented it so enthusiastically and dramatically that we really became excited about the whole idea."

In Toledo, Ohio, in 1936, a young jeweler named Carleton Broer was delighted when Shipley walked in. "I was very aware [after nine years in the business] of my need for scientific education about gemstones but had done nothing about it.

"Bob Shipley spent two or three hours that day talking to me about educating jewelers and raising the standards of ethics in the jewelry industry. His enthusiasm was so great and his ideals so appealing that he left with a contract and a check for the first payment on his courses in gemology," wrote Broer, who became a key supporter of the Institute.

■GIA's "BACKBONE"

Despite growing support, GIA in the 1930s was still struggling. It depended on donations for its laboratory equipment and library, and its early resources were modest. Robert Shipley said later, "I had more ideas than money."

Funds were so tight in the beginning that Shipley had to sell at least one course a week to keep operations running. Early supporters recalled Shipley occasionally "passing the hat" for money after talking to groups about the Institute. Those first years were "sure wobbly," said Shipley decades later.

While Robert Shipley was spreading the seeds of the gemological movement, Beatrice stayed in Los Angeles to run the office and manage the Institute's finances.

"We never knew if we would get through it or not!"

Another problem was that the early organizational structure was chaotic. At times, it seemed Shipley created committees and boards merely to accommodate the growing list of supporters. There were in the early '30s, for example, various categories of GIA members, a national advisory board, and dozens more committees and boards of all stripes. Shipley "created such a web of things," recalled Al Woodill. "He wasn't much for minute-keeping or board books. It was all in his head." And sometimes he got things muddled. Colleague Jerome Wiss nicknamed Shipley "Confuse-us" for the tangle of ideas and elliptical explanations he often passed on to supporters.

Clearly, the Institute needed an expert business manager to establish order and financial control. Fortunately, Shipley knew exactly the right person: his wife, Beatrice.

BEATRICE SHIPLEY WAS A PERSON OF ORDER, rectitude, and discipline, an excellent businesswoman at a time when there were few women in business. The former church administrator, school dean, and art gallery owner had honed her administrative and management skills well. She was financially astute, so much so that even during the Depression, investment brokers sometimes called *her* for advice, recalled Woodill.

It was inevitable, then, that Bea should help Shipley steer GIA. She was his most important confidante, the one who "could always express my thoughts and emotions better than I." So, for most of the decade of the '30s, their home was the Institute and the Institute was their home.

In June 1932, Beatrice Shipley closed the art gallery and became GIA's full-time manager. Her formal title was "Registrar and Secretary to the Board of Governors and Advisory Board." But, if Robert Shipley was GIA's "President and Director of Education," Beatrice Shipley was its de facto chief operations officer. While her husband developed the Institute, its courses, laboratory, and equipment, she oversaw its finances and daily operations. During its first years, Beatrice Shipley didn't use her first name or married name. In her early editorials and articles, and in lists of GIA personnel, she went by "B. W. Bell," her first husband's name. The Shipleys may have thought the male-dominated industry was less likely to accept an educational institute whose second-in-command was female. Another reason, suggested Al Woodill, might be that the Shipleys were trying to disguise the fact that the Institute was indeed a "mom-and-pop" operation.

The procedures and standards Beatrice Shipley initiated enabled the Institute to grow. In fact, it's unlikely Robert Shipley could have developed the gemology movement or GIA's courses without his wife's efficient management skills.

Likewise, Bea Shipley's financial astuteness in those Depression years was critical. She was frugal with the Institute's money and always met the payroll, though sometimes it was touch-and-go. Friend and co-worker Dorothy Jasper Smith recalled "running to the bank more than once to make a deposit before we could pay the salaries."

"She was a key factor in the growth and development—even the survival—of the organization," eulogized *Gems & Gemology* at her death in 1973. As Dorothy Smith put it, "Mr. Shipley was a super salesman. He made it go over, but *she* was the one who made sure things got done and that bills got paid. She was the backbone, the one that kept GIA going and made it a success."

Courtesy of Marlborough School, Los Angeles

In addition to serving as the Institute's first librarian, Anna McConnell Beckley was also its director of literary research and editor of GIA's first courses and books.

▪ FRIENDS AND FAMILY

In the beginning, GIA was a family affair. Robert and Beatrice Shipley not only owned and operated it, they also staffed it with relatives and friends. Indeed, the first person Bea recruited (even before she officially joined the Institute) was Anna McConnell Beckley, a friend from the Marlborough School.

A diminutive dynamo with an inquisitive nature and encyclopedic memory, Beckley was a popular instructor at Marlborough, where she taught art history, medieval and modern history, and riding, and co-authored Marlborough's art history course. She also befriended a younger faculty member named Mrs. Beatrice Bell, later to be Beatrice Shipley. After Beatrice left the school, Beckley taught art history classes at Bea's gallery.

As GIA was evolving, Beatrice asked Anna to critique what she and Shipley wrote. By late 1931, Beckley, then almost 60, was so involved that Beatrice asked her to join the Institute. She agreed, retired from Marlborough, and became GIA's librarian and director of literary research. She was also both

Al Woodill, Beatrice Shipley's nephew, performed odd jobs at the Institute while still in high school. He went on to serve as executive director of the American Gem Society from 1947 to 1987.

copy editor and managing editor of the first courses and books.

Beckley was "a fountainhead of meticulous fact," noted one GIA staffer, from Tibetan history (on which she was an authority) to Renaissance pearl jewelry. She was precise in her research, and corresponded regularly with gem experts around the world. Many early lessons were based on material she helped gather or coordinate. Beckley also worked closely with Robert Shipley on his book *Famous Diamonds of the World*, co-authored articles in *Gems & Gemology*, and helped research his *Dictionary of Gems and Gemology*.

ANOTHER EARLY STAFFER who played a lifelong role in gemology was Al Woodill, Bea's nephew. He began working at GIA as a jack-of-all-trades while still in high school. In autumn 1940, after two years at the University of California at Los Angeles, he dropped out when family finances got tight and instead went to school to learn business skills, the tuition paid by his aunt. When he graduated in 1941, the Shipleys gave him a temporary job as Robert Shipley's secretary on a car trip east to visit GIA students and officials in several cities.

Shipley dictated letters as he drove, while Woodill, sometimes balancing a typewriter on his lap, took them down. But travel with Shipley was also instructive. "When he dictated something on gemology, you weren't only to write it down, but to learn it just as fast," Woodill recalled. He also met most of Shipley's major supporters in the industry.

All of it—work at GIA, travels with Shipley, meeting gemology's leaders and students—gave Woodill an education he couldn't have gotten elsewhere. It served him well when he succeeded Shipley as executive director of the American Gem Society (AGS) in 1947.

SEVERAL WOMEN JOINED GIA'S STAFF in its early years, including Dorothy Phebus, Mary Hughes, and Isabel Blanchard. But of them all, Dorothy Morgan's impact was most significant. She came to Los Angeles in

December 1932, seeking work to support herself and her widowed mother. Her search brought her to a little correspondence school called GIA.

After she interviewed with the Shipleys for a part-time secretarial position, Dorothy was "afraid to death" she wouldn't get it. At the time, hundreds of thousands of people were jobless in the Los Angeles area alone. And there she was, a woman and a college dropout, seeking work from this erudite couple.

From 1932 to 1963, executive secretary Dorothy Jasper Smith was in many ways the heart of GIA, indispensable to the Shipleys and, later, to Richard Liddicoat.

She needn't have worried. She made a good impression, and in December of 1932 she was hired. Over the next 31 years, Dorothy Morgan—later to marry and become Dorothy Jasper, then Dorothy Jasper Smith—would establish herself as the heart of the Institute.

Dorothy began as Bea's secretary, but soon became indispensable to both Shipleys. Beatrice was impressed with her diligence, speed, good spirits, and sharpness. As for Robert Shipley, their working relationship evolved into what he called "a long and sympathetic partnership."

Dorothy took dictation, transcribed lessons, mimeographed, mailed and picked up assignments, took them to Shipley for grading, and mailed them back to students. On her own, she began attaching notes to graded lessons, congratulating students on work well done, and urging them to keep trying. She initialed them "DM" (later "DJ," after she married in 1934). Over the next 15 years, until mushrooming post–World War II enrollments made personal notes impossible, hundreds of students came to know those initials and the heartening words that came with them.

She wrote her notes, Dorothy said later, because "we needed every student we could get" in those first years. Equally important for her, the Institute staff was like a family and its students were an extension of that family.

Students began to wonder, "Who is 'DJ'?" Interest in her grew so much that Shipley carried a photo of her to show those who asked. In a few cases, men who saw her photo were smitten. But most simply appreciated that someone at the faraway school was personally interested in them and their success. To

"Hodgepodge Lodge": GIA and its sister organization, the American Gem Society, moved into a small headquarters at 541 South Alexandria Avenue in Los Angeles in 1939. GIA would remain there until 1956.

Canadian jeweler T. M. Little, "Those little personal notations which all students received were really . . . the glue that held the organization together in the early days."

Dorothy's name and initials began to appear everywhere as she took on more roles. She helped organize study groups, wrote occasionally for *Gems & Gemology*, represented GIA at national jewelry trade shows, and eventually became the bookkeeper and paymaster. When Beatrice retired in the '40s, Dorothy was named executive secretary and, in 1948, also secretary to the board of governors. (After Robert Shipley retired in 1952, she became registrar, as well as new director Richard T. Liddicoat's "right hand.") Dorothy was usually the first point of contact for anyone who phoned or visited the Institute. With Shipley on the move and GIA officials scattered around the country, she was "the one who was always there," especially after Bea Shipley retired, said her son William Smith. "If you had a question, you wrote or called Dorothy because you knew she had, or could get, the answer."

The Shipleys came to feel they couldn't do without her, and she reciprocated with loyal service. When pregnant with her second child, she worked until the night before she gave birth, two days before her husband shipped out for World War II service. Later, while she recuperated at home, the Shipleys "brought everything to my house, all the work they had saved up and a typewriter so I could work at home."

Dorothy Jasper Smith's contributions to the Institute continued until her retirement in 1963.

■WORKING FOR GIA

By the mid-1930s, things were beginning to improve a little for GIA. So, pushed by the need for more space, the Shipleys made two important purchases.

One was personal. In 1935, they bought a house in South Laguna Beach overlooking a cove on the Pacific Ocean. "Cliff's Edge" was their escape. Here, Shipley indulged his love for the shore—he was a good surf swimmer, even into his eighties—and built his classical record collection. Bea, meanwhile, indulged her love of cooking and entertaining, and spent hours in her garden.

The other purchase was for the Institute. By the mid-1930s, its operations had grown so much that paperwork literally filled every room, even the bathroom, where lesson materials were stored. So in 1936, the Shipleys bought a lot on Sixth Street and Alexandria Avenue, where they had a two-story, six-unit apartment building constructed. GIA and its sister organization, AGS, occupied three ground-level apartments (each claimed its own mailing address on different streets). The Shipleys lived upstairs in one apartment when they were in Los Angeles. The other two were initially rented out to provide extra revenue.

In early 1939, the staff moved into the Institute's third headquarters in six years. The small rooms filled up so quickly that James Donavan, a major figure in both GIA and AGS affairs in the 1940s and '50s, jokingly called it "Hodgepodge Lodge." It would remain GIA's home for the next 15 years.

Robert Shipley, dictating to Dorothy Phebus in the 1930s. Shipley and his wife demanded much from their small staff.

WORKING FOR THE SHIPLEYS was a little like working for a pair of stern schoolmasters. Business formalities were observed. Beatrice Shipley was never "Bea" to her staff, but Mrs. Shipley. He was never "Bob," but Mr. Shipley or RMS.

As an employer, said early staff members, Mrs. Shipley was smart, charming, and tough. "A beautiful woman, very dignified, very pleasant," recalled one who knew her then. "But she brooked no nonsense. The girls were in awe of her."

"If she didn't like something, you heard about it," said Dorothy Jasper Smith years later. Woodill recalled that his aunt "had a way of chopping your head off if you didn't perform correctly."

Both Shipleys ran hot and cold on individuals, though not each at the same time. One or the other was "either high on someone or off of them completely," said Woodill. Whether it was someone on staff or in the industry, "we were either going into the doghouse or coming out," he recalled.

Sometimes, that made it hard to know what to expect or how to deal with them. "How are you today?" Woodill greeted Bill Collison, a co-worker, one day in the late 1940s. "I don't know," joked Collison. "I haven't seen *him* [Robert Shipley] yet this morning!"

47

Robert Shipley Jr. joined his father's tiny institute in 1933 and quickly left his own mark on gem instruments and research.

■ THE GENIUS OF THE SMOKE-FILLED LAB

There was one other staff member who was to prove indispensable not only to GIA but also to the gem and jewelry trade. He was a bespectacled, quick-tempered young man who liked to drive fast and had a genius for innovation.

His name was Robert M. Shipley Jr., and his creative tinkering forever changed the way jewelers and gemologists around the world did business. The gem-testing equipment he designed made it possible to apply accurate gem-grading standards, and made his father's dream of gemology as an ethical, professional discipline a practical reality. While the father was the magnificent salesman of the gemological idea, it was the son who gave it a solid scientific backing. Indeed, "most of the noteworthy progress made in gem-testing techniques, methods and instruments [in the first half of the 20th century] were outgrowths of his study," noted *Gems & Gemology* when he was made an Honorary Research Member of GIA in 1950.

Born in Wichita in 1912, Bob Jr. in many ways was like his father. He was tall and slender, with sharp facial features and a high forehead. He displayed the same "I don't suffer fools gladly" attitude and the same strong streak of independence. He also had his father's quick, retentive intellect. "He had a very scientific mind and a photographic memory," recalled his step-cousin Al Woodill.

Unlike his father, though, young Shipley was fascinated by technology, especially airplanes. It was, after all, the era of heroic "lone eagles" such as Charles Lindbergh and Amelia Earhart, as well as barnstormers (many of them World War I aces) who flew biplanes at county fairs. During his youth, while his father expanded the Vail-Shipley Shops and his mother brooded over their disintegrating marriage, Bob Jr. escaped through his fascination with flying. He built scores of model airplanes and entered them in contests to win rides in real planes at the local airfield.

In 1930, Bob enrolled in Wichita University to study aeronautical engineering. But by then, he also knew he had poor vision, which greatly reduced his chances of becoming a professional pilot.

Forward to 1932, when Shipley Sr. passed through Wichita on a transcontinental trip for GIA. He invited his son to visit him and Beatrice in California and tour the developing facility. Shipley Jr. was intrigued—especially by the potential for research, lab work, and creative tinkering. When his father urged him to come to Los Angeles and help build the Institute, Bob headed west.

Robert Shipley Jr. joined the staff in early 1933 as "assistant in temporary charge of the laboratory." But the young man didn't remain an assistant for long. Shepherded by his father, he was soon playing a greater role at the Institute.

In addition to testing gems and seeking equipment donations for the tiny lab, he graded lessons, wrote for *Gems & Gemology* (temporarily serving as its editor), and taught seminars. He co-authored the scientific sections of GIA's early colored stones and advanced gemology courses, and helped his father write *Advanced Gemology*, which was published in 1937. That same year, he was named education director (the title held previously by his father), as well as research director. But it was gemological instrumentation, not teaching, that most fascinated him. And it was in instrumentation that he made his most important contributions to gemology.

PRIOR TO GIA'S FOUNDING, there were almost no instruments specifically designed for jewelers, let alone gemologists. Instead, people had to depend on instruments developed for mineralogy or optical physics that were poorly adapted for use in gemology. The petrographic microscope, for example, was used by early gemologists to examine gemstones. Designed to examine thin sections of minerals, its poor lighting made it virtually impossible to see into a cut gemstone to any depth. Not only that, the image from the monocular eyepiece was upside down and backwards.

Robert Shipley Sr. wanted to change this situation, to develop instruments specifically for gemologists. He knew that creating instruments for jewelers and gemologists offered the Institute considerable benefits. Once patented, instruments would be available only through GIA. That exclusivity made being a GIA student and a gemologist all the more attractive, and it provided another source of funds. It also gave the Institute more control over the quality of its professional training.

Encouraged by his father and led by his inquisitive nature, Bob Jr. began tinkering in the lab. His special genius was in devising unexpected solutions to technical problems. But he didn't so much create new instruments as he adapted and improved existing ones for use in gemology. "He wasn't the

PRIOR TO GIA'S FOUNDING, THERE WERE ALMOST NO INSTRUMENTS SPECIFICALLY DESIGNED FOR JEWELERS, LET ALONE GEMOLOGISTS.

A 10x eye loupe that debuted in 1934 was the first gem instrument developed by GIA.

type to 'invent the wheel,'" said co-worker Richard T. Liddicoat later. Rather, he took things and "adapted them to the needs of the gemologist in a way no one had thought of before."

And the more difficult the problem, the more cigarettes he absentmindedly puffed as he worked on a solution. "Bob Jr. never measured time by hours," recalled Liddicoat. "He measured it by packs of cigarettes. I don't think he ever got to 10 packs a day, but he must have been close to five!"

The first successful instrument to come out of that smoke-dense lab was a beautifully simple one, and a basic necessity for any jeweler and gemologist: a diamond eye loupe. Though several loupes were available from European optical firms, Shipley Sr. had written much about the need for a good-quality loupe specifically for gemologists. Research began shortly after Bob Jr. joined the Institute, and in 1934, after another 10 months of experimentation, the "GIA registered diamond 10× eye loupe with a triple aplanatic lens" was offered to the trade for $8.75.

Designed for gemologists, it featured "aplanatic lenses [corrected for spherical aberration] . . . mounted in an individual cell which could be moved to a sleeve in the eye cup . . . to be focused at the will of the user," said Shipley Sr. A GIA registry number was engraved on each eye cup, which was made of lightweight duraluminium—"the metal used in the manufacture of aircraft," boasted Shipley Sr. Thousands of these loupes were sold in the coming years. Two decades later, GIA's loupe was still recognized by the diamond industry as unrivaled in its field because of its superior lightness, strength, and accuracy.

THE DEVICE THAT BROUGHT BOB JR. AND THE INSTITUTE to the forefront of gem instrument development came out a year later, in 1935. It began—typically— with young Shipley's curiosity, in this case about a new thin, plastic material that polarized light. "Sheet polarizer," as it was called, was made of cellulose acetate and contained a colloidal substance that polarized light that passed through it. Photography pioneer and inventor of the Polaroid camera Edwin H. Land was using it in his research. GIA contacted Land in early 1935 and requested samples, which Shipley Jr. began testing.

Al Woodill, then 15 years old, remembers going out one evening onto the balcony of GIA headquarters. "Bob Jr. was out there cutting thin cardboard-like material into little, inch-and-a-half squares. I said, 'What's that?' He said, 'Polaroid material.'

"So, I asked again, 'What's that?' And he said, 'Too difficult to explain. It's for something I'm working on for a polariscope.'

"'Tell me,' I insisted. He gave me a crummy look, but began explaining. 'If you take two pieces of this material and turn one 90 degrees, light goes through the first one but won't go through the second. Then, if you put a gem between the two and turn the stone, you can tell whether it is singly or doubly refractive. And that would help jewelers know if gems were genuine or not.'"

Over the next several months, Shipley Jr. researched the design of a simple gem-testing instrument using Polaroid filters. He also began working with a French tool and die maker in Los Angeles named Raoul Francoeur. Until then, optical instruments were handmade and very expensive. But Shipley Jr. and Francoeur designed their equipment with parts that could be die-cast and mass-produced to lower costs and increase their availability. With Francoeur's help, Shipley Jr. adapted the polariscope (which had existed for 100 years) specifically for gem testing.

By summer's end, after much tinkering, it was done. GIA proudly announced in the September-October 1935 issue of *Gems & Gemology* that it had perfected a device that would become "one of the most valuable gem-testing instruments" in the world: the Shipley handheld polariscope.

With the introduction of the Shipley handheld polariscope in 1935, GIA emerged as a leader in gem instruments.

Fitting easily in the palm of the hand, it had a piece of sheet polarizer set in each of the fixed end caps of its cylinder, which could be rotated. It also contained a beeswax support for the gemstone being tested. Using polarizing film in the polariscope not only increased its working field significantly, but also reduced its cost.

Since users could determine if a stone was singly refractive (like glass) or doubly refractive (like many gem materials), the polariscope's principal value was the rapid distinction of glass imitations from most genuine stones. It did so without compelling the user to resort to destructive hardness tests. Another valuable feature, especially for jewelers who did repair work, was the ability to detect anomalous double refraction in diamonds. Such diamonds are under internal strain and need careful handling, especially with respect to heating.

The Shipley handheld polariscope firmly established the Shipleys and the Institute as leaders in gemological equipment design. Efficient and inexpensive, it remained one of GIA's most popular instruments for decades, becoming standard equipment in gem-testing laboratories.

BUT THE ONE INSTRUMENT THAT would have the most profound change on gemology, gem sales, and gemological research was not far behind. Shipley Jr. had turned his attention to improving another basic device for jewelers and gemologists: the microscope.

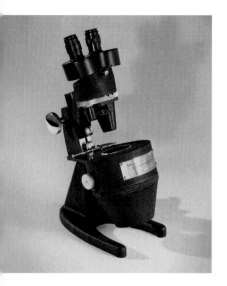

The Diamondscope, with its patented darkfield illumination, was Shipley Jr.'s most profound contribution to gem instrumentation. The instrument's basic design was still being used more than 60 years later.

Darkfield illumination is an optical technique in which light enters a specimen from the side, so that it appears as a bright object against a dark background. Shipley Jr. concluded that jewelers could use it effectively to examine the interiors of cut gems for clarity characteristics, inclusions, and other imperfections. It proved to be a revolutionary idea.

Shipley Jr. designed and added a darkfield base for the microscope, which let a user clearly see internal characteristics of a stone. This made examination and grading, as well as identification of synthetic gems, quicker and more accurate than ever before.

But darkfield illumination was only half the story. The magnification itself had to be improved, too. Until then, the only magnifiers available for gemological work were the simple loupe and the petrographic microscope. Neither was adequate for the purpose. The way to get the most effective use from darkfield illumination, Shipley Jr. concluded, was binocular vision. He bought a stock binocular top from an optical instruments supplier and bolted it to the darkfield base. Binocular vision not only displayed an image right side up and stereoscopically, but it also improved the viewer's field of vision. Next, he added high-power eyepieces and low-power optics, which increased the working distance. This allowed users to examine jewelry with magnification and even use the equipment while performing delicate repair work.

As the *pièce de resistance*, Bob Jr. created a secure stone holder, enabling the gemologist to examine inclusions with less risk of dropping the host gem. The holder was also handy for showing stones to potential customers.

The result was the darkfield gemological microscope, now familiar to jewelers and gemologists the world over. In 1938, Shipley Jr. applied for a patent for the darkfield illuminator, which was approved the following year, the first patent for a GIA instrument. The instrument was introduced as the Diamondscope.

In theory, the Diamondscope was a simple instrument, composed primarily of the magnifier and the illuminator. It took advantage of existing principles of optics, light transmission, and reflection. But in true Shipley manner, the way in which known principles were adapted to gemology was unique. The result was a useful evaluation tool that led to more efficient buying and selling of gem merchandise. Owning and using one swiftly became the hallmark of a credible, well-trained jeweler.

And the instrument's design was so efficient that it was still being used, with only minor modifications, more than 60 years later. Indeed, by the start of the 21st century, the gem microscope had become, reported GIA,

Robert Shipley Jr. at work in the early GIA laboratory on Alexandria Avenue.

"the workhorse of the jeweler's trade, a key tool . . . in diamond grading, colored stone grading, gem identification, pearl grading, and watch repair."

The 1930s were fruitful for the Shipleys and Francoeur. By the decade's end, GIA was not only the exclusive U.S. distributor for all of the important gemological devices made abroad, it also could boast—as it did in one ad— that "if more specialized instruments can be manufactured, we [will] produce them ourselves!"

■THE FIRST GIA LABORATORY

The Institute's laboratory—decades later respected worldwide for its gem-testing, research, and diamond grading capabilities—began modestly, with borrowed equipment.

A "small, practical laboratory," as Great Britain's *The Gemmologist* called it— and the first gemological lab in North America—was part of GIA's first headquarters in Los Angeles. When the Shipley home on West Sixth Street became the second headquarters in 1931, the lab shifted to the dining table and countertops in the Shipley kitchen. When in 1939 GIA finally moved to custom-built offices at 541 South Alexandria Avenue, the gem lab occupied space specifically designed for it.

Throughout the 1930s and '40s, while the Shipleys and their assistants were producing instruments that revolutionized the gem and jewelry

The "Pearl King": Kokichi Mikimoto, founder of the cultured pearl industry, provided support for the GIA laboratory as early as the 1930s. Much of the lab's early work involved pearls.

Courtesy of Mikimoto

trade, the lab itself depended almost entirely on loans and donations to finance its own equipment purchases.

The lab's first instruments were loaned by early supporters John W. Ware and Garfield D. Merner. Its first permanent donations were a polarizing microscope, a pearl endoscope, and some pearl-testing equipment, all contributed by Godfrey Eacret, GIA's first chairman.

Almost every early issue of *Gems & Gemology* cited generous donations to the Institute and its lab. Indeed, a measure of that support—and the state of gemological research at the time—is that by mid-1933, GIA's lab was already "pretty well equipped [and] the most complete strictly-gemological laboratory in this country, outside of a major university," wrote Bob Shipley Jr.

THE LAB PERFORMED GEM TESTING AND IDENTIFICATION for GIA students and AGS members for free—within reasonable limits—and for the public for a fee. Much of its work involved pearls, due to the early support and donations of K. Mikimoto & Co., the Japanese firm that began the cultured pearl industry, and the donation of pearl equipment by Eacret and others. Robert Shipley Jr.'s research in pearl identification in the 1930s resulted in gifts of additional equipment.

The GIA lab quickly made a name for itself beyond the industry. In 1935, the popular magazine *Modern Mechanics & Inventions* featured an article titled "Precious Stones Tested in Laboratory," which provided a fascinating glimpse into the Institute's early research and testing.

"Gemstones from cities large and small on this continent, and in fact from every corner of the world, are sent [to this] completely equipped laboratory," it noted. The gems that came in had "defied local jewelers [who possessed] only limited gem testing equipment at their command.

"Every instrument in the G.I.A. laboratory is either made especially for the testing of gems or has been altered by expert technicians to serve this exclusive purpose. Several pieces of apparatus . . . are available in no other laboratory in the world and others are in the course of experimentation and development.

"It is an amazing experience to watch these scientists fix a costly jewel on the stage of a microscope and study it as intently as a bacteriologist studies a smear preparation."

Significantly, the GIA lab was already considered what the magazine called the "final arbiter on the identity of a gem."

In 1938, Paramount Pictures publicized the Institute with a three-minute color film for its "Popular Science" series. As dance music played in the background, the camera moved in for a close-up of Bob Shipley Jr. at a table spread with instruments, while a voice-over declared, "A new field of investigation—the improved scientific analysis of precious stones!" As Shipley worked, the narrator explained that the lab was "the only one of its kind in the United States where precious jewels are sent from all over the world to be identified and tested for quality and authenticity." The film, which played in movie theaters across America, was a publicity triumph for GIA.

Shipley Jr. demonstrates gem testing at the GIA laboratory in a 1938 film by Paramount Pictures for its "Popular Science" series.

DESPITE ITS WORK IN GEMSTONE AND PEARL IDENTIFICATION, many of the lab's early research accomplishments concerned synthetic gems, already a serious issue in the industry. By the mid-1930s, Robert Shipley Jr. had identified Verneuil synthetic corundum and developed a fluorescence test for identifying synthetic emeralds. In 1937, the lab published reports on unusual inclusions in synthetic rubies.

However, the lab's greatest success in its first 15 years—in the view of many in the diamond trade—was disproving the claims of an American chemist who said he could produce diamonds synthetically and in large enough quantity to be a threat to the gem and jewelry trade. GIA's lab obtained specimens and, in 1938, after much investigation, proved that the synthetic diamond story was false. According to a later Institute report, diamond merchants "could again breathe a sigh of relief." (It is interesting, though, that the manufacture of gem-quality synthetic diamonds would become a real challenge in the 1980s and 1990s, which GIA researchers again met head-on.)

The early GIA lab had another significant effect on the jewelry industry. From the beginning, the Institute offered laboratory instruction for students,

Dr. Edward Wigglesworth was the director of GIA's first Eastern office, which opened in Boston in September 1940.

Courtesy of the Museum of Science, Boston

first to those who lived near its headquarters and later in resident courses and at the gemological gatherings that would come to be known as "Conclaves." This exposure to the effectiveness of gem equipment, plus the accuracy of GIA's lab reports and identifications, impressed jewelers across America. By the end of the 1930s, other gem labs—based on the Institute's model and using equipment sold by GIA—were being set up in scores of North America's leading jewelry stores.

BY 1939, THE INSTITUTE, its laboratory, and the gemological movement itself were large enough and successful enough to become bicoastal.

Shipley had established the Institute in Southern California simply because he was living there when the idea took hold. But although GIA was headquartered in Los Angeles and much of its support was in the Midwest, Shipley and other Institute officials knew that the heart of the trade was on the East Coast. To truly serve the industry, GIA had to be there, too.

Yet its first East Coast office was not in New York—the country's jewelry and financial center—but Boston. It may seem an odd choice now, but to Shipley the reason was simple.

It *had* to be Boston, because that was the home of Dr. Edward Wigglesworth, director of the New England Museum of Natural History (today the Museum of Science) and curator of its mineralogy department. A native Bostonian and seventh-generation New Englander, Wigglesworth was an educator, scientist, philanthropist, and well-to-do gentleman farmer. When he first encountered GIA in the mid-1930s, he was already a leading expert in mineralogy and geology, a founder of the Mineralogical Society of America, and a respected academic. As director and curator of the museum since 1919, he had transformed its mineral display into New England's finest, often using his own private funds to purchase specimens.

Wigglesworth's difficulties in identifying some gems given to the museum in the mid-1930s led him into what a friend called "his last and perhaps most absorbing mineralogical study, that of gemology." Wigglesworth apparently wrote Shipley for information about the gems, and the two men—who shared a zeal for professional training—developed a lively correspondence. By 1935, Shipley knew him well enough to persuade him to lead GIA's newly formed study group for its correspondence-course students in Boston.

Wigglesworth agreed and—though 50 years old and already a respected mineralogist and educator—enrolled in the courses himself. He earned his Certified Gemologist title from GIA in 1939 and that same year was named chairman of the Institute's educational advisory board.

So when Shipley looked for someone to direct the new East Coast branch, he naturally thought of Wigglesworth. The Bostonian accepted immediately and, in an extraordinarily generous gesture, resigned from his post as director of the museum to devote all his time—without pay—to serve as director of GIA's Eastern operation.

THE EAST COAST OFFICE OFFICIALLY OPENED September 1, 1940, at 69 Newbury Street, across from the museum Wigglesworth had just left. Wigglesworth taught individual students—only two at a time could be accommodated— and tutored those who were preparing for their final exams and Certified Gemologist titles. In the lab, Wigglesworth conducted gem testing and research, graded diamonds for use by jewelers as comparison stones, and worked on a system of gem identification that he hoped to make available to all gemologists.

In 1941, in recognition of his selfless support, GIA's board of governors named Wigglesworth the first president of the Gemological Institute of America. He held the honorary advisory post until his death in 1945.

▪GIA AND AGS: TWO SIDES OF THE SAME COIN

Robert Shipley's two goals—to create an educational institute and to develop a national guild of ethical, knowledgeable jewelers—were accomplished simultaneously during the 1930s. First, Shipley's early gemological students founded the Gemological Society of Southern California in January 1931. Next, Shipley planted GIA study groups around the country, which he called the "nuclei of the national professional society." The creation of that society was one of his early selling points when urging jewelers to study gemology.

As more jewelers took GIA courses, alumni became increasingly eager to get together in a formal, organized group. By 1933, the need had become obvious to Shipley. There were still no agreed-upon standards for ethical

WIGGLESWORTH RESIGNED FROM HIS POST AS DIRECTOR OF THE MUSEUM TO DEVOTE ALL HIS TIME—WITHOUT PAY— TO SERVE AS DIRECTOR OF GIA'S EASTERN OPERATION.

SHIPLEY'S GOALS
WERE TO CREATE AN
EDUCATIONAL
INSTITUTE AND TO
DEVELOP A NATIONAL
GUILD OF ETHICAL,
KNOWLEDGEABLE
JEWELERS.

conduct in the industry—such as using 10× magnification and eliminating deceptive terminology for diamonds—and educational requirements for professional titles needed enforcement, he said.

But the main reason Shipley felt a national guild had to be established was that the loose network of study groups he had started was beginning to unravel. If Shipley and his early supporters wanted a professional society, they had to move quickly. In late 1933, Shipley and GIA officials hammered out the *raison d'être* for a national professional society based on guidelines devised by Godfrey Eacret. Then, in 1934, Robert and Beatrice Shipley cashed in their last convertible asset, a life insurance policy, and used the money to organize and promote the American Gem Society.

Among the new society's objectives, declared the AGS news section of *Gems & Gemology*, were to promote professional education among members of the jewelry trade, elevate the ethics and prestige of the trade, and "make America gem and jewelry conscious."

The last point was a major purpose of the new society, because Shipley wanted not only to create a movement of ethical jewelers but also to increase their profits in those Depression years. His campaign urged jewelers to "revive [the public's] dormant love of gems" through ads, window displays, and lectures to civic and educational groups. However, at times it was unclear—at least to some jewelers and those in the trade press—whether the new society was devoted to trade education or to selling jewelry.

Shipley, Beatrice, and GIA's staff assumed the additional duties of running AGS, with Shipley as director and Beatrice as chief administrator. To choose leaders of the fast-growing movement, Shipley set off on a grandly titled "100 Day Tour of America." This "preliminary organization campaign" was officially launched in Cincinnati during the annual convention of the American National Retail Jewelers Association (ANRJA) on September 9, 1934 ("Gemological Day," as it was dubbed by *Gems & Gemology*).

From Cincinnati, Shipley spent the next 10 weeks setting up regional organization committees. He gave educational lectures in 25 cities and held 50 dinner meetings with jewelers to encourage them to support the "Gem and Jewelry" campaign. At the same time, of course, he enrolled more students in GIA programs.

In 1934 and 1935, work also began on defining ethical conduct and gem terminology. The first issue of *Guilds*, AGS's publication, appeared, and the Society adopted its own professional titles such as Certified Gemologist and Registered Jeweler. Regional certification boards and an admissions board were set up to screen potential AGS members. Meanwhile, the initial push to "Make America Gem and Jewelry Conscious" was put on the back burner while GIA and AGS focused on educating jewelers.

IN LATE 1936, SHIPLEY and his supporters decided there were enough GIA students and graduates to convene a gathering. He had "felt for some time that it would be beneficial for those who took his correspondence courses to attend some sort of get-together," wrote Carleton Broer two decades later. There they could see "first-hand some of the things they had been attempting to assimilate by mail."

A two-day Gemological Conclave was scheduled for April 1937 in the Midwest, where support was strongest and its students most numerous. This first Conclave, held at the Palmer House Hotel in Chicago, would prove to be a watershed event in the gemology movement's early history. At the time, though, Shipley was again uncertain—as he was in 1930 before his first USC lectures—hoping that at least 35 people might attend.

Courtesy of George Kaplan

Over 100 attendees at the 1937 Conclave listened as diamond cutter and dealer Lazare Kaplan described how he cleaved the famous Jonker diamond.

Shipley's concerns were unfounded. When the first-ever Conclave finally convened, *Gems & Gemology* reported, there were some 103 GIA graduates and students from AGS groups in 12 different states. *Jewelers' Circular-Keystone* noted how the jewelers had assembled for "precedent-making gem study sessions" and described the Conclave as "an amazing commentary upon the vitality of the jewelry trade." Indeed, at 11 p.m. on a Sunday night, "more than 90 student jewelers were still in their seats and attentively following the discussions."

In addition, there were lectures by Shipley and Bob Jr. on gem instruments and gem identification techniques, talks on diamond mining, an account by famed diamond dealer Lazare Kaplan and his son Leo on how they cleaved the famous Jonker diamond, plus reports by jewelers of how they gained new business with their GIA training.

THE FIRST CONCLAVE, HELD AT THE PALMER HOUSE HOTEL IN CHICAGO, WOULD PROVE TO BE A WATERSHED EVENT IN THE GEMOLOGY MOVEMENT.

With so much happening, fewer than two hours were set aside for AGS business, but "those two hours saw the beginnings of the Society organization as we know it today," wrote Broer. *Conclave* was adopted as the official name for the meetings. Rules governing ethical business conduct by members were approved. Work continued on the organizational framework and on making AGS self-governing, and a national governing committee was formed.

One other action at that first Conclave with far-reaching consequences for the gem and jewelry trade was Shipley's appointment of a diamond terminology committee, composed of diamond retailers and manufacturers, all GIA officers or students. The committee was chaired by H. Paul Juergens, who had helped organize the Conclave. Its purpose, explained Juergens, was to standardize certain terminology for diamonds, which in the past had been deceptive and confusing to the public.

The committee wasted little time. Within six months, based on its recommendations, the AGS urged its members to use *flawless* to describe diamonds instead of *perfect*. "*Flawless*," said Juergens, meant "free from all internal and external blemishes or faults of every description under skilled observation in normal, natural or artificial light with a 10× loupe, corrected for chromatic and spherical aberration." On the other hand, he said, the word *perfect* had become meaningless, adding that it was "questionable whether a scientific profession should use the term at all since nothing in nature can be absolutely perfect."

Acting on the committee's suggestions, AGS also banned other terms then used for diamond quality, including *clean, sound, eye clean, eye perfect, commercially white, commercially perfect,* and *perfect cut*. And so began the first steps toward the standardized gem and diamond nomenclature that would ultimately be used throughout the world.

"WHAT BEGAN AS A PURELY EXPERIMENTAL MEETING ended as a distinct success," reported *Gems & Gemology* shortly after the first Conclave.

"For those fortunate enough to be there, it was an experience never to be forgotten," wrote Carleton Broer, still reveling in the memory 20 years later. "For the first time a large group, all dedicated to the same aims, [was] able to exchange ideas, to come into contact with the leaders of the gemological profession, and to see and use the instruments that they had, until then, only read about."

The first Conclave showed that the gemological movement was taking hold in the U.S. jewelry industry. Still, it was at the second Conclaves ·in April

1938 (in Chicago and Boston) that "the gemological movement came of age," according to *Jewelers' Circular-Keystone*. The first "had the aspect of novelty," it noted, but the second ones were "proof of growth, sustained interest and the individual achievements of students, registered jewelers, junior gemologists and certified gemologists."

Informality and fun leavened the instruction. Those first Conclaves, said Edward Tiffany, did "much to cement relationships among the industry." Through a combination of education and goodwill, they helped knit the thin, widely spread skein of study groups, individual students, and gemologists together as a profession. Friendships with fellow gem enthusiasts from across America created a sense of community and provided cohesion for the still-wobbly national society. Jewelers and gem dealers who had labored on their GIA courses in their offices or homes at night, meeting only occasionally in small study groups, now realized they were not alone, but part of a national movement, one with the scientific tools and equipment to establish them as professionals in their communities.

GIA dominated AGS and its Conclaves from their start in the mid-'30s until the late 1940s. Although Shipley and his associates maintained that the two were separate organizations, in fact they were two sides of the same coin. GIA provided the courses and gemological instruments for AGS members— who were, of course, GIA graduates. The Institute controlled the curriculum and instruction at Conclaves. The same jewelry and gem trade leaders often served as officials of both organizations, sometimes simultaneously, in the early years. The two shared the same building, the same office staff, the same filing system.

These close connections continued until the late 1940s, when GIA and AGS finally set up separate headquarters and officials.

■GIA EDUCATION: A WORK IN PROGRESS

During much of the 1930s, GIA courses were a work in progress, expanding and becoming more comprehensive as Shipley's vision grew.

By 1935, there were basically four parts (with a total of 130 lessons) to the correspondence course: the preparatory course, based on Shipley's USC lectures, which had borrowed considerably from geology texts (dubbed Course No. 012); Colored Stones, or Technical Gemology, with emphasis on gem testing and colored stones; The Diamond, which covered mining, marketing, optics, "aesthetic and investment value," and trade ethics; and Advanced Gemology, also known as the "Certificate Course." Students who finished the first two courses and passed an exam could use the AGS title Qualifying Certified

ALTHOUGH SHIPLEY AND HIS ASSOCIATES MAINTAINED THAT GIA AND AGS WERE SEPARATE ORGANIZATIONS, IN FACT THEY WERE TWO SIDES OF THE SAME COIN.

PART OF SHIPLEY'S
GENIUS WAS HIS
ABILITY TO DRAW
VARIOUS PEOPLE
INTO A PROJECT
AND GIVE THEM
OWNERSHIP OF IT.

Gemologist. Those who passed the entire course and two additional exams earned the professional AGS title Certified Gemologist.

By the late 1930s, the courses were essentially finalized. They remained in the same basic format until the early 1950s.

But most of this curriculum didn't exist in the early 1930s. When Robert Shipley Sr. promoted GIA education, the course he was selling was still being written. Whether in a hotel room, at home, or in his office, Shipley scoured everything in print about gemology.

"I had to study every available book on gem minerals and pearls, not only in English but also in French and especially new ones being published in German," he recalled in a 1959 memoir.

Many in the industry assume that Shipley wrote all of the early courses based on his own gemology training and experience. Early Institute literature reinforced this idea, sometimes assigning sole authorship of the courses to him. But in fact GIA courses were then, and have always been, a collaborative effort. Part of Shipley's genius was his ability to draw various people into a project and give them ownership of it. So, while he did shape and write much of the early content, he was aided in his research and writing by many staff members and associates in the industry.

Robert Shipley Jr. co-authored the scientific section of the advanced courses with his father. Anna Beckley painstakingly verified and coordinated the facts in Institute courses and publications. When GIA gem experts or reference books disagreed on facts, she sent questionnaires to prominent gemologists, authors, mining experts, and trade experts who were members of the Institute's "Committee of 100 World Gem Authorities." A majority opinion was required to settle an issue.

Early supporters and officers such as Godfrey Eacret and John Ware also had a hand in shaping courses. Warren Larter, president of Larter & Sons (a leading New Jersey jewelry manufacturer), reviewed and rewrote most of the jewelry assignments. Thomas Clements, chairman of the geology department at UCLA, helped critique course material.

Major suppliers and associations also assisted. The Sterling Silver Guild contributed to the silverware assignments. De Beers Consolidated Mines Ltd. provided the services of its scientific director and technical advisor, H. T. Dickinson, who reviewed the diamond assignments.

Together, these people and organizations created a curriculum that was stronger, more comprehensive, and more relevant than if it had been the work of one man alone.

IF WRITING THE COURSES was collaborative, then printing and mailing them was "a community effort," recalled office manager Dorothy Smith. On a typical day in the 1930s, she later wrote, "Mr. Shipley would be busy writing and rewriting the correspondence course assignments. The other employees and I would type and retype until it was time to cut stencils to run off the lessons on our small mimeograph machine."

Afterward, it was "quite a sight to see all of us on our hands and knees, gathering together the pages of a new assignment spread out on the floor, with Mr. and Mrs. Shipley helping check and staple!"

Prodding them to work even harder were "eager-beaver students who kept us hopping because they would finish the assignments faster than we could get them ready," said Smith. "We would mail them out and before we knew it, completed questionnaires would be returned to us for grading!"

Isabelle Blanchard (standing) supervises the shipping of early GIA courses in the converted kitchen at "Hodge-podge Lodge."

Some early students felt it took forever to get their next assignments. "I always looked forward to getting it, but one had to wait for Bob [Sr.] to finish writing each assignment before it was sent to us," recalled Milton Gravender, of J. B. Hudson in Minneapolis. Edward Tiffany of Canada remembered waiting "about three months to get the verdict" on his studies. "One kind soul suggested it probably took that long to decipher my writing!"

He wasn't far from the truth. In the first two decades, most lessons and exams used an essay format, which slowed grading and kept student completion rates low. Over time, Institute officials concluded that the essay format was a less effective means of gemological training, and GIA began the shift to multiple-choice questions in the 1950s and '60s.

Those who persevered said it was worth the hard work. "Without doubt, gemology has been extremely helpful to me from the very start," said Gravender decades later, "and I know I have had countless sales consummated due to my work and studies."

Fred Thurber (left) was GIA's first Certified Gemologist, in 1935. H. Paul Juergens (right) followed soon after.

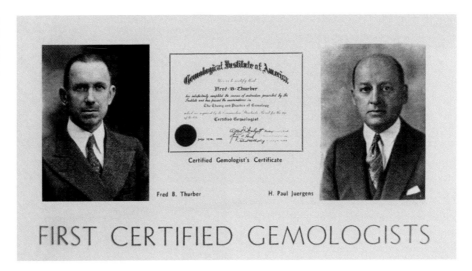

FIRST CERTIFIED GEMOLOGISTS

■ THE FIRST GRADUATES

The year 1935 was a red-letter one for GIA and the gemology movement in America. Seven students received the first Certified Gemologist titles after three to five years of study. These graduates typified the variety of people attracted to gemology in its early years.

1. **Frederick B. Thurber** of Tilden-Thurber Co. in Providence, Rhode Island, was "Certified Gemologist No. 1." By 1935, Thurber was a member of the Institute's board of governors and the ANRJA's representative on GIA's examination standards board.

2. **Richard M. Pearl**, the son of a Detroit jeweler, was a high school graduate who had given up further education. But studying at GIA changed his life. He went on to the University of Colorado, earning a mineralogy degree and becoming a professor there. He also became a nationally recognized author on gemology. "What began as a hobby developed into a profession," he said later.

3. **H. Paul Juergens**, a seventh-generation jeweler, was vice president (and later president) of the Chicago firm Juergens & Andersen. Juergens enjoyed a long career as an officer of GIA and AGS boards, later becoming chairman of the Institute's board of governors and a recognized authority on pearls.

4. **Milton F. Gravender**, at the time with J. B. Hudson of Minneapolis, Minnesota, later joined Lazare Kaplan & Sons in New York City, where his enthusiasm for gemology influenced young George Kaplan—later chairman of the GIA Board of Governors—to enroll in the late 1930s.

5. **Howard S. Smith**, a jeweler from Redlands, California, was vice president of AGS's Southern California Guild.

6. **John F. Vondey**, a jeweler from San Bernardino, California, was a member of Shipley's first USC class in 1930 and an active supporter of gemological training. Vondey was president of AGS's Southern California Guild.

7. **Hans J. Bagge** was a salesman with J. Milhening Inc., a successful Chicago ring-mounting manufacturer. Bagge encouraged hundreds to sign up for GIA courses and helped lead the AGS Chicago Guild.

Sardha Ratnavira of Ceylon (right), a 1940 resident student, was one of the most memorable of the early international students.

IRONICALLY, IT WAS THE GROWING INTEREST of *international* students that led to GIA's first (informal) resident courses—and the first step toward an international educational institution. Almost from its start, the Institute looked beyond America's boundaries. Its early advisory boards included experts from Europe and Asia. Its early work was reported in *The Gemmologist* in Great Britain, and, as early as 1933, students in India, the Philippines, and Canada were enrolled. One of these, a Bombay jeweler named A. H. Mountvalla, even wrote Shipley to say, prophetically, "A day will come when the nations will give first preference to those jewelers who have acquired great knowledge and study in gemstones and who are Certified Gemologists."

After the mid-1930s, a few students from overseas began coming to GIA in Los Angeles to complete their work. That, Robert Shipley said later, led to the first resident course. In 1937, classes were added to help students from abroad. In 1939, the first two-week resident classes were offered to anyone who had completed the correspondence lessons for the Certified Gemologist title and was preparing for the 20-stone final exam.

The international students who attended included gem expert Leopold Kahn from the Philippines, the first graduate of the resident class; Edward Tiffany of Canada; José Beltri, the Mexican government's gem expert; H. Tillander, Finland's diamond authority; and the sons of Asian gem dealers.

One of the most memorable international students was Sardha Ratnavira, a short, handsome young man from Colombo, the capital of Ceylon (later Sri Lanka), and a member of the 1940 resident class. He was sent to GIA by his father, who gave him a number of gemstones, which he kept in a small satchel, to finance his training and pay for his stay in the United States.

Renowned gemologist Dr. Edward Gübelin of Switzerland was one of GIA's first international students, graduating in 1939. Over the next seven decades, he was regarded as a leader in gemological research, especially the study of inclusions in gemstones.

These he sold to gem dealers or jewelers in downtown Los Angeles as he needed money to support himself. But the proceeds didn't all go for tuition, rent, and groceries.

He also bought a new powder-blue Lincoln Zephyr convertible with red leather upholstery. Putting on his white suit and a turban, he would drive up and down Hollywood Boulevard to attract attention and give girls a ride in his car. Then he would return to GIA and relate his adventures to Al Woodill.

With war ravaging Europe and Asia in 1940, and the U.S. close to entering it, Ratnavira's father called him home. Shipley "had a fierce time" finding a safe way to return him to Ceylon, recalled Woodill. He finally sent him back the long way, across the continent to catch a freighter heading east.

But that wasn't the last contact between GIA and Sardha Ratnavira. Their stories were to intertwine again in the next decade.

PROBABLY THE BEST-KNOWN INTERNATIONAL STUDENT who attended the early resident classes was Edward Gübelin of Switzerland, later a world-renowned gem authority and founding member of the Swiss Gemological Association.

Gübelin first heard of GIA in the mid-1930s through promotional material sent to his father, a gem dealer, while young Gübelin studied for his doctorate in mineralogy at the University of Zürich. When his father sent Gübelin to his partner's New York City firm to improve his English and learn salesmanship, Gübelin wrote Shipley. Within weeks, Shipley sent him his first course assignment, and Gübelin started his studies.

"The deeper I delved [into them], the more enthusiastic I grew," he recalled in 1997. "The courses were outstanding and excellently balanced between theoretical gemmology and a practical application."

After meeting Shipley at the April 1939 Conclave in Boston ("I immediately felt great respect and liking for him"), Gübelin came to Los Angeles in July to complete his studies, attend the first resident class, and pass his final exam.

Shipley encouraged him to continue his research into gem inclusions and to write a book to benefit all gemologists. Returning to Switzerland, Gübelin examined each stone in his father's inventory and urged gem polishers to bring him samples from around the world so he could study their inclusions. After the start of World War II, knowing that *Gems & Gemology* needed authors and new material, he wrote up his observations and sent his photomicrographs to Shipley for publication. It was the start of a long-running series of *G&G* articles by Gübelin about gem inclusions, with emphasis on differences among gems from varying localities. In 1953, Gübelin published the book he had first discussed with Shipley in 1939, the landmark *Inclusions as a Means of Gemstone Identification.*

Robert Shipley and early GIA supporter John W. Ware on the front page of the *Los Angeles Times* in 1937. Publicity for Shipley's gemological movement was in high gear by the late 1930s.

The renowned gemologist was to earn many honors in his field. Looking back at his student experience at the Institute, Gübelin said, "I do not exaggerate when I say that my studies with GIA had the greatest impact on my professional gemological career. I gained all the necessary knowledge for a practical jeweler and a keen gemologist. I learned more in those seven months than I might have in 10 years of commercial life."

■THE REASON WHY

By the end of the 1930s, Shipley, GIA, and their growing legion of supporters and students had done the impossible: The U.S. gem and jewelry industry had regained public respect—and their own confidence—through the gemology movement.

There were now hundreds of GIA correspondence-course students in North America and abroad. Scores of industry leaders were serving on various boards and committees that were building the movement. They and many others were preaching the gemological message in their hometowns and across the continent to civic and industry groups. A national society of ethical gemologists had been set up. Conclaves were bringing together jeweler-gemologists annually, empowering the movement. Gem experts, suppliers, and wholesalers in the U.S. and abroad were helping create lessons to train jewelers and gem dealers. New gemological instruments were regularly emerging from GIA's laboratory, which was considered the final authority on gems for the industry.

In the face of incredible odds, Shipley—a failure at 40—had successfully changed the gem and jewelry industry by the time he was 50. But how? Why was he able to achieve his audacious dream? There were several reasons.

He was tenacious, of course, a "super salesman who believed in what he was selling," as Dorothy Smith had observed. Shipley himself, in moments of modesty, attributed his success to the times. "It was the Depression," he would reflect in his twilight years. "There weren't many customers coming in and interrupting the jeweler when I started my spiel!"

Yes, the times were certainly a factor, though not in the way Shipley meant. "The mysterious 'spirit of the age' was fighting on Shipley's side," wrote his friend and GIA advisor Basil W. Anderson, director of the London gem testing laboratory. Embodied in that *Zeitgeist* was "awareness of the *necessity* for gemmological knowledge in the jewellery trades of the world, threatened by the advent of and rapid spread of cultured pearls and [synthetics]." Another factor was a growing public demand during the Depression era for professionalism in various industries.

"The confidence status of the jeweler in his community—once equaled only by that of the banker—could only be restored by professionalizing his vocation," Shipley explained later. "Like the physician, the architect and the engineer, the gemologist must complete prescribed studies and examinations in order [to be] of exceptional service to the public [in] the new profession of Gemology." Early GIA ads reinforced that idea. "This scientific and sales course . . . lifts you above jewelry store competition to the status of a professional man," assured one in 1934.

Shipley also recognized the value of publicity and marketing in building the Institute. The two publications he launched in the mid-1930s—*Gems & Gemology* for GIA and *Guilds* for AGS—strove to keep the trade informed about the gemology movement. He advertised both GIA and AGS heavily in trade magazines. By the mid-1930s, the Institute was sending press releases to local newspapers about the growing number of professionally trained jewelers in their communities. In addition, Shipley and other leaders in the

From the beginning, Robert Shipley sought counsel from gem and jewelry industry leaders, who served on advisory boards and committees. Facing (from left) are Leo Vogt, Godfrey Eacret, and Shipley.

movement encouraged GIA graduates and AGS jewelers to approach schools, fraternal organizations, and community clubs with lectures and slide shows to explain the "Gemological Idea."

Also contributing to GIA's early growth was Shipley's wisdom in developing it as an organization of and for the industry, one that the industry could support. He never saw the Institute as "a one-man show." Rather, he brought industry leaders in with him to help build it.

"Uncle Bob had a way of winning people," recalled Al Woodill. "His belief in what he was doing was contagious. He made people whose help he was soliciting feel they had as much a part in creating this project as he did."

So from the very first, GIA boards and committees included not only educators, curators, and gem experts, but also members of the retail and wholesale segments of the industry, its major associations, and the trade press. These leaders came from all over the U.S. and Canada, and from abroad as well.

But what was the fundamental reason for GIA's success? It was Shipley himself, lecturing to groups, meeting industry leaders, signing up small-town jewelers, and (in the words of a 1943 *Guilds* article) "preaching his gemological message on the avenues of cities and at remote crossroads."

It wasn't easy—but it was as simple as that.

A young mineralogist named Richard Liddicoat Jr. arrived at the Institute in 1940.
Liddicoat would leave an indelible mark on modern gemology.

THE WAR YEARS

1940–1945

Times were good again in 1940 and '41. The Depression years were gone, and the jewelry business was bouncing back. The Gemological Institute of America was firmly established, with a new headquarters, hundreds of enrollments, growing laboratory services and instrument sales, and the prospect of financial security.

Then everything changed. On a Sunday morning in December 1941, a faraway U.S. naval base in Hawaii was bombed, and America entered World War II, which was already raging in Europe and the Pacific.

The jewelry trade was devastated. Business dropped, and millions of young men went overseas to fight for Uncle Sam. Among them were Shipley's right-hand man — his son Robert Jr. — and a young mineralogist named Richard Liddicoat, who had been hired, ironically, as an interim replacement while Bob Jr. was in the service. So many men went to war that the Institute's survival seemed at risk — until its supporters from the industry stepped in with a proposal that changed the operation of GIA forever.

Other things changed, too. More women began studying gemology, while a largely female staff kept the Institute going despite tight finances and few new students. And an important figure in the GIA story left.

For the Institute then, as Charles Dickens once wrote, "It was the best of times, it was the worst of times."

■ "A TEMPORARY REPLACEMENT"

Robert M. Shipley Sr. had a problem at the start of 1940.

It wasn't the Institute. Its future—and that of the gemology movement— seemed secure. Hundreds of students were taking GIA courses, and there were already close to 100 Certified Gemologists. Jewelers were ringing up their best sales since 1929, thanks to a surge in marriages and demand for bridal jewelry and gifts. Shipley and GIA officials estimated, based on projected enrollments, that by 1945 the Institute would be financially sound. Indeed, the Shipleys were finally recovering some of their original investment in it.

Robert and Beatrice Shipley, both over 50, began thinking about turning the Institute over to the next generation: Robert Shipley Jr., whom Shipley had named director of education and research in 1937. The Shipleys assumed he would take over GIA when they retired.

With Robert Shipley Jr. departing for active duty in the Army Air Corps, Shipley Sr. needed a "temporary replacement" at the Institute. This led to the hiring of Richard Liddicoat in June 1940.

However, the flames of war engulfing Europe and southern Asia were melting America's isolationism, and U.S. involvement seemed ever more likely. Though President Franklin D. Roosevelt pledged not to send U.S. boys to a foreign war, the country was already aiding European allies and building up its own armed forces.

Growing numbers of young men were being drafted or enlisting. So many jewelers were already leaving that in 1941, months before the attack on Pearl Harbor, *Jewelers' Circular-Keystone* magazine added a monthly section called "They're in the Army Now," which listed those who had joined and where they were serving. In 1940, Army reservist Bob Shipley Jr. volunteered for ski patrol duty on Mount Rainier in Washington State, and it seemed likely that official orders calling him to active duty would arrive soon.

So Robert Shipley Sr.'s problem was clear-cut: He needed a replacement for Bob Jr., someone to fill in for him until he finished active military service. To find that person, Shipley wrote to a few of GIA's educational advisors, asking them to recommend someone with gemological or mineralogical training.

CHESTER B. SLAWSON, professor of mineralogy at the University of Michigan and a GIA advisor, puffed on his cigarette as he read Shipley's letter. Then he walked down to the basement office of his affable, recently married teaching assistant. The earnest young man, then preparing for his Ph.D. in mineralogy, glanced up at his mentor.

"I don't think you're interested in this, but you might want to take a look at it," said Slawson as he handed him the letter and sat down. The young man read the letter silently, while Slawson quickly described GIA and the gemology movement.

"I had never heard of the Gemological Institute of America or of Robert M. Shipley," recalled the young mineralogist, Richard T. Liddicoat Jr., almost half a century later. "But I said, 'Yes, the idea does appeal to me.' "

That ready "Yes" was a pivotal moment, not only for Liddicoat but also for GIA and the future of gemology during the next half century.

Richard Liddicoat Jr. was born in Kearsarge, Michigan, in 1918. He was the son of Carmen Beryl Williams and Richard Thomas Liddicoat, who was an engineering professor at the University of Michigan for 41 years.

IN HINDSIGHT, Liddicoat seemed fated to become involved with the Institute. His fascination with gems and minerals was "in my blood," he once joked. Both his grandfathers had mined copper in Cornwall, England, before migrating to the copper-rich mining region of Keweenaw Peninsula in northern Michigan in the late 1800s. Richard Henry Liddicoat, his paternal grandfather, was a hard-driving "scrappy little guy with a Napoleonic ego driven to be number one in his work," his grandson recalled. He passed on his drive to the boy born in Kearsarge, Michigan, in 1918 to Carmen Beryl Williams and Richard Thomas Liddicoat.

Young Liddicoat was especially close to his mother's father. William Williams was a marvelous storyteller, affectionately nicknamed "Captain Billy" by his neighbors. He was also a serious rock collector, and his rock-hunting jaunts and collection of Copper Country minerals captivated his grandson. "By age five, I was already poking around in mining dumps looking for mineral specimens," recalled Liddicoat.

His father, Richard T. Liddicoat Sr., was a scholarly, well-mannered man with a strong sense of personal loyalty to others, traits his son inherited. Liddicoat Sr., a World War I veteran, became an instructor at the University of Michigan, in Ann Arbor, after completing his Ph.D. in engineering there. He stayed on as a professor of engineering for 41 years, becoming a respected authority in his field and authoring a widely used textbook. He also encouraged his son's curiosity about the world around him.

Mineralogy professor
Chester Slawson of
the University
of Michigan, a key
academic advisor to
GIA, recommended
Richard Liddicoat
to Shipley.

"We used to argue playfully when I was young," recalled Dick Liddicoat. "I would ask him endless questions, and he would always answer them very specifically."

WHEN IT CAME TIME FOR RICHARD TO GO TO COLLEGE, the natural choice was the University of Michigan, where his father taught. Uncertain of the career path he wanted to follow, Liddicoat signed up for the business course but took just enough math to keep engineering open as an option. To satisfy the science requirement, he took a class in geology, a casual decision that would have far-reaching consequences.

The class fascinated Liddicoat. In his sophomore year, he took a two-semester mineralogy course. That did it: He was hooked. He changed his major to geology and did so well that he was given an assistantship in the mineralogy department for his junior and senior years. Although Liddicoat was unaware of the significance at the time, Professor Slawson and Dr. Edward Kraus, a dean at the university, had co-authored *Gems and Gem Materials*, a widely used and respected textbook. Both were advisors to Shipley and GIA almost from its start, and they taught a popular class in gemology at the university (which Liddicoat never took).

When Liddicoat graduated in June 1939 with a bachelor's degree in geology and a minor in mineralogy, he was still uncertain about a career. He decided to try "geophysical prospecting"—hunting for oil—and applied for a job that summer with the Seismograph Service Corp. in Tulsa, Oklahoma. He was hired as a trainee and given one week to learn seismographic data, which he later likened to "being given a 100-page document in Sanskrit and told to translate its first 20 pages" in the same time span!

He joined a geophysical prospecting crew in Louisiana. It was grueling, monotonous work. The crew would camp in a field for several weeks, dig lines of holes, set off dynamite charges in them, use sound-wave equipment to measure the repercussions, and look for evidence of underground geological structures associated with oil. Then they moved to another field and did it all over again.

It was also lonely work, and Liddicoat thought often of Imogene ("Gene") Hibbard, his high school sweetheart. Then "an amazing night at the movies," as he called it, sparked his decision to marry her. That Saturday at the small theater in Marksville, Louisiana, was "Bank Night," where Depression-era movie theaters offered prizes to increase business. The theater manager pulled the winning stub and tried to read the winner's name but couldn't pronounce it.

"I figured out he was trying to say 'Liddicoat!'" the Michigan native said later. "I went up and won the magnificent sum of $95. It was enough to convince me that if I saved a bit more money, I could get married that fall. So I went right out, phoned Gene, and asked her to marry me!"

As the long summer wore on, going back to his sweetheart and to Michigan to pursue a graduate degree in mineralogy became even more appealing. Liddicoat returned in September 1939 and secured another assistantship in the mineralogy department. Then he married Gene and settled into newlywed life, working on his master's degree and assisting Slawson with his classes.

And that was the situation in early 1940, when Liddicoat said "Yes" to his chain-smoking mentor—and to GIA.

Richard and Imogene "Gene" Liddicoat married in 1939.

GIVEN THAT LIDDICOAT HAD NEVER EXPRESSED any interest in gemology, Slawson was a little surprised by the response. But Liddicoat knew geophysical prospecting wasn't for him, and the only other real option for a Ph.D. in mineralogy then was to become a college professor. His recent marriage made the GIA opportunity even more attractive. As a graduate teaching assistant, Liddicoat made only $300 a year. Gene, who was in charge of a large Ann Arbor engineering office, earned $135 a month. The prospect of his wife having to support them for three more years while he finished his doctoral studies in mineralogy made Liddicoat uncomfortable.

Besides, he explained later, "working with beautiful gemstones had great appeal to me," as did the Institute's Southern California location, which was very attractive "when compared with the winters—and summers—in Michigan!"

Cincinnati jeweler and GIA Board of Governors chairman Edward Herschede joined Shipley in interviewing Liddicoat for a position at the Institute.

So Slawson wrote back to Shipley, giving Liddicoat a glowing recommendation, which Dean Kraus affirmed in another letter. Impressed, Shipley invited the young man to meet him and Edward F. Herschede (then chairman of the GIA Board of Governors) in May at the Frank Herschede Co. in Cincinnati, Ohio. And, wrote Shipley, "Bring your wife, too."

"They wanted to see us both," explained Liddicoat later, amused, "because GIA was a very small organization and they wanted to judge whether we would fit in."

Borrowing his parents' car, he and Gene drove down to Cincinnati that spring. While Liddicoat was waiting to see Shipley and Herschede, he admired the gemstones in a display case. When he saw an especially eye-catching pale blue stone, the young mineralogist said to the salesperson behind the counter, "That's a nice labradorite."

"No, sir," the salesperson replied. "It's a star sapphire."

"I was glad the chap wasn't Mr. Shipley to hear that," chuckled Liddicoat.

When the founder of GIA and its chairman—both well over six feet tall—did come out a few minutes later, Liddicoat, who was five feet seven inches, was "immediately impressed" with both.

Shipley explained to Liddicoat that he needed someone to fill in for Bob Jr. while he completed military service. No specific title was offered, but Liddicoat's appointment as assistant director of education was implied, assuming he proved satisfactory.

The session, including their meeting with Gene, went smoothly. Indeed, the fact he was married was a point in his favor, since it seemed unlikely that married men would be drafted anytime soon.

"Shipley just wanted to confirm what he had been told and to see if I had what it takes," said Liddicoat. Apparently, he did. Shortly afterward, Shipley sent him a telegram offering him the job.

THE LIDDICOATS AGREED that Richard should make the trip to California alone, while Gene stayed in Ann Arbor. "We had to make sure this was the right thing for us before she gave up a very fine job," said Liddicoat. "Also, I wanted to be sure this wasn't another situation, like oil prospecting, with which I wanted no part."

He decided to give the GIA opportunity "two or three months—a get-acquainted period for both Shipley and myself"—before deciding whether to move permanently to California. "I needed to know if I liked gemology," he said, "and Shipley needed to know if he liked me."

◼A NEOPHYTE'S EDUCATION

Liddicoat arrived at the Institute on June 28, 1940. Shipley Sr. greeted him, introduced him to Mrs. Shipley and the dozen or so staffers, and explained his role. For his part, Liddicoat wasn't thinking about succeeding Bob Jr. "I was just a neophyte," he said, "trying to prove myself worthy of staying on the staff!"

Liddicoat was given a desk just a couple of feet from Bob Jr. ("a very bright individual, but a little irascible," Liddicoat remembered). His primary task, initially, was grading the lesson assignments sent in by GIA's correspondence-course students (then about 200 to 250 questionnaires a week), tracking students' progress, and staying in touch with them.

Ironically, though, Liddicoat had barely started the course himself.

Shortly after Liddicoat's interview in Cincinnati, Shipley offered him a job at GIA.

SHIPLEY HAD SENT HIM THE COURSE IN LATE SPRING, before he left Michigan. But completing work for his master's degree and preparing for California had left Liddicoat little time for anything else. When he arrived at GIA, he had only finished six assignments out of 128.

Shipley was *not* pleased. He told Liddicoat to complete the coursework as quickly as possible—on his own time, like any other student, after work, at night, and on weekends.

And he did, with astonishing speed. In his first of many achievements at the Institute, Liddicoat finished the entire course—which took the average jeweler working under similar constraints a minimum of two and a half years, and some as many as six—in *two months* while working full time and becoming acclimated to GIA. Shipley was impressed with this early demonstration of Liddicoat's intellect, persistence, and ability to deliver under pressure.

What Liddicoat learned at night in his studies was reinforced during the day by the assignments he evaluated. It was slow, tedious work. He also

Richard T. Liddicoat, circa 1940, when he arrived in Los Angeles to begin work at GIA.

maintained the students' files, kept track of their individual progress, and wrote letters to them, answering questions and encouraging them to continue their studies.

Liddicoat also learned an important lesson as a correspondence-course educator. He intended for his letters and comments to establish a rapport, so that students "would study on a regular basis knowing there was an 'Uncle Fudd' sitting in Los Angeles, anxious about them, and that their failure to study would make them feel guilty." He soon found, though, that this approach didn't really work.

"I learned the hard way that people make all sorts of promises, but seldom honor them. If someone is attuned to doing home study, they don't need much prodding, while the others promise the moon and you still don't get completed lessons from them.

"So I concluded that a certain amount of early follow-up to jog people into studying is worthwhile, but that heavy work is a lot of expense and wasted time."

LIDDICOAT'S OTHER DUTIES INCLUDED helping Bob Shipley Jr. teach the summer resident classes, testing gemstones in GIA's lab, and assisting with equipment development. During 1940 and early 1941, he helped the Shipleys, father and son, put the finishing touches on two new instruments that went far in setting accurate standards of diamond color grading, a longtime industry goal.

One was the Diamolite (later renamed the DiamondLite), a device for color grading diamonds with a lamp that simulated daylight as closely as possible. It also could control the intensity and direction of light falling on the stone, eliminating "confusing reflections from surrounding walls or objects." With

it, jewelers thousands of miles apart could grade diamonds at any time of day with identical results.

For advice, the Shipleys contacted lighting pioneer Norman Macbeth, who in 1915 had developed the first illumination system to simulate natural daylight. "They turned to him for help in designing equipment as close to natural daylight as possible in an enclosed environment," said Liddicoat. By the end of 1940, they had developed the original Diamolite. Although the result was in actuality only a partial daylight equivalent, it provided illumination that possessed most of the characteristics of north daylight. (A later version of this instrument used fluorescent tubes to more closely simulate natural north light.)

The second instrument—about the size of a loaf of bread—was the GIA Colorimeter, a device for grading diamond color against a constant standard (essentially a graduated scale of colorless to yellow quartz). An important feature was its use of a numerical scale, from zero to six, to correspond to diamond color grades, rather than trade terms.

This was a significant step forward. Interpretation of the terms then used to describe diamond color—such as *White, Blue-White, River* (for colorless) or *Wesselton* (named after a diamond mine in South Africa)—varied so widely that it was virtually impossible to use them as industry standards. As early as 1934, *Modern Mechanics and Inventions* noted, "The often-heard

Liddicoat, shown on the left teaching the use of the GIA Diamolite, helped design the instrument. The Diamolite (later renamed the DiamondLite) was designed to afford a controlled light source as close to daylight as possible, thus providing standard conditions for color grading diamonds. On the right, Shipley Sr. grades a group of stones on the Diamolite.

The GIA Colorimeter, introduced with the Diamolite in 1941, provided a method of comparing diamond colors against a standard scale.

term 'Blue-White Perfect Diamond' has been used to describe so many grades of diamonds (some of them actually quite yellowish and not at all perfect) that it has come to mean nothing at all."

Use of the Colorimeter scale as the industry standard was authorized by AGS in 1941. Thus, it became the first widely acceptable diamond color-grading yardstick. Creation of the Colorimeter also led to the development—by Shipley Jr., assisted by Liddicoat and Dorothy Jasper Smith—of the first master stone diamond comparison sets for color grading diamonds. "Using this device and the human eye, the original GIA master set was put together," recalled Liddicoat.

The two instruments—the Diamolite and Colorimeter—were described in Liddicoat's first bylined article for *Gems & Gemology*, in fall 1941. Titled "A Solution to Diamond Color Grading Problems," it confidently—perhaps too confidently—stated that "the problem of the relative color of the [diamond] grades seems to have been largely solved" for the jeweler who had key stones graded on the Colorimeter "yardstick" and who did his own color grading under the consistent light of the Diamolite. What would be most important in the years to come was the contribution these developments made to the establishment of a consistent, accepted standard for the color grading of diamonds.

BY FALL 1940, SHIPLEY WAS SURE that Richard T. Liddicoat was the right man to be assistant director of education. Indeed, a report in *Guilds* late that year said Liddicoat had "proved exceptionally capable [and was] already supervising the work of a large number of students."

"It is expected," the article predicted, "that Mr. Liddicoat will be especially popular among staff and students alike."

And Liddicoat was now sure he wanted the job. "From the beginning, I really enjoyed what I was doing," he recalled. "I enjoyed working with students, many of whom I already knew on a first-name basis. It was fun working with gemstones, and there was a good spectrum of activities. No two days were alike. There was growth potential, and a lot of excitement.

"Everything seemed to be saying, 'This is it. Stay here.'"

Something else happened that fall. An unexpected romance blossomed between Robert Shipley Jr. and his (and Liddicoat's) secretary, Mary Hughes. Their initial relationship was so abrasive that when they announced their engagement, everyone was surprised, recalled both Liddicoat and Woodill. In November, they married.

Courtesy of Robert Shipley III

Mary Hughes, secretary to both Robert Shipley Jr. and Richard Liddicoat, married Shipley Jr. in November 1940.

But less than two weeks after he married, Bob Jr. received orders to report to the ski patrol duty for which he had volunteered early that year. Those orders were unexpectedly canceled shortly afterward—possibly because young Shipley had gotten his Army commission transferred to the Army Air Corps (predecessor of the U.S. Air Force). Six months later, in April 1941, he received new orders to report immediately to Wright Field in Dayton, Ohio. He went into the Army Air Corps as a lieutenant, working in photographic surveillance.

As the Shipleys said goodbye to Bob Jr. that spring and Liddicoat promised to take care of things until he returned, none of them knew that they were also saying goodbye to the Shipleys' dream of handing GIA to Bob Jr. or that within a few months everything would change, forever.

LIDDICOAT IMMEDIATELY TOOK ON BOB JR.'S DUTIES, and the senior Shipley began to rely on him. In fact, Liddicoat was responsible for two changes in GIA's education program between 1941 and 1942.

One was to raise the bar. In GIA's early years, 65 percent was a passing grade on the written tests. That wasn't good enough, thought Liddicoat. He persuaded Shipley that such a grade was "inadequate [if the intent was to] protect the consumer in any way." Shipley agreed, and the passing grade was raised to 75 percent, where it has remained ever since.

Something else that needed fixing, thought Liddicoat, was GIA's introductory course—Course 012. It actually discouraged jewelers from wanting to take the rest of the GIA courses: "They resented it because it was *too* fundamental."

Liddicoat's solution: present it as a one-week course. He felt that would improve the chances of getting them interested in the balance of the program.

This time, Shipley was more difficult to convince. He doubted that 22 lessons could be covered adequately in six days. So Liddicoat, who was determined to sell Shipley on the idea, suggested a test class, which he would teach at the 1942 AGS Conclaves in Philadelphia and Chicago. Shipley agreed.

On the first day of the Philadelphia class, Liddicoat was certain that Course 012 could be effectively taught in six days and that six of his students would easily pass the exam. The problem was the seventh student, "a really delightful old gentleman named Charlie, who was as vague as anyone I ever encountered in all my years of teaching," recalled Liddicoat. "I would ask him a question in class and get an answer that had no relationship to it!" Old Charlie would have great difficulty passing the exam— if he passed at all.

Six of seven students passing the course would have convinced Shipley to okay Liddicoat's plan. But the 23-year-old assistant director of education was "determined to have 100 percent of the class [pass], and to do it honestly." So, he enlisted the help of the other students. Since all seven took their meal breaks together, Liddicoat asked the six to keep asking each other and Charlie "every question that might appear on an exam to insure they were firmly planted in his mind."

During the exam, Liddicoat was as nervous as the students and even momentarily regretted convincing Shipley to raise the passing grade. But everyone passed, with Charlie barely squeaking by with a 75.

After that, the success of the Chicago class—all 13 pupils passed with grades in the 80s—was anti-climactic. Convinced, Shipley added the one-week class. And Liddicoat had made another significant change to GIA's education program.

■ "FIGHT TO KEEP THE INDUSTRY ALIVE"

The United States' entry into World War II on December 8, 1941, had a profound effect on the jewelry industry. Jewelry production from Europe and Asia withered. Melee and "acceptable qualities" of smaller diamonds became difficult to get after Holland and Belgium were invaded (though supplies of one-quarter to one carat sizes were reasonably good). Due to wartime taxes, demand fell for larger fine-quality diamonds normally bought by affluent customers.

There were shortages of colored gems from East Asian sources in war zones, as well as shortages of strategic and precious metals. At a time when the United States was still a leader in watch production, U.S. watch factories converted to wartime applications, ending production of "civilian" watches until peacetime. Meanwhile, imports of watches and watch parts from Europe, including Switzerland, had become "uncertain and fragmentary" by early 1942, noted *Jewelers' Circular-Keystone*.

What a reversal of fortunes! During the Depression, many jewelers had too much product and not enough demand. Now, with war raging, many found it difficult to get even enough basic merchandise to meet demand.

"We had standing orders for as many watches and as much sterling flatware as we could obtain," recalled Sioux City, Iowa, jeweler

In 1942, during World War II, Richard Liddicoat left GIA to join the U.S. Navy. He eventually served as a weather officer on the aircraft carrier USS *Wasp*. Liddicoat was aboard the *Wasp* during the Battle of Leyte Gulf in October 1944, the largest naval battle in history.

and GIA student Wilson T. Clark. "We could create a line of customers a block long just by advertising alarm clocks! That was true of almost everything we sold."

Many jewelers became anxious. Indeed, as early as January 1942, G. H. Niemeyer, president of Handy & Harman, urged his fellow industry leaders to "fight to keep the industry alive!"

Even so, by 1943, a growing number of jewelers bowed to merchandise and employee shortages and went out of business or sharply reduced their operations. Hartwell Jewelry Co. in Oklahoma City shut its doors after 43 years. Others, like Thomas E. Bufton in Union Grove, Wisconsin, closed for the duration of the war. Bufton, a jeweler for 55 years, said he would reopen when his son Malcolm came home from overseas.

THE WAR'S IMPACT ON THE INSTITUTE was immediate and troublesome. Limits on travel and gasoline rationing forced GIA and AGS officials to suspend the gemological Conclaves, which did not resume until 1947. The two-week resident classes were cancelled, as was production of gem instruments (due to the government's first-call on primary materials for wartime use). AGS activities practically ceased, and the society went into hibernation.

Worst of all, the war shattered Shipley's and GIA officials' vision of financial security for the Institute, as they saw hundreds of thousands being drafted

ON THE FRONT LINE

RICHARD T. LIDDICOAT JR.

Based on his scientific background, the Navy sent Richard Liddicoat to the California Institute of Technology (Cal Tech), where he earned a Master of Science degree—a requirement for being a "Naval Aerologist" (meteorologist)—in eight months. He was assigned to the aircraft carrier USS *Wasp* as an assistant meteorologist and joined the ship in July 1944 in Pearl Harbor, Hawaii.

The *Wasp* was involved in "The Second Battle of the Philippine Sea" to retake the Philippines from the Japanese in October 1944. Also known as the Battle of Leyte Gulf, it was the largest naval battle in history. During one critical moment, on October 13, 1944, the *Wasp* was attacked by a dozen aircraft. One of her escorts, the USS *Canberra*, was hit by two torpedoes meant for the *Wasp*.

Liddicoat vividly remembered one night during the battle. "We had to make 38 emergency turns to move around the wounded battle cruisers. And then a Betty (the Allied code name for a Japanese bomber) came diving in, and I thought, 'It's headed right at us!'" Anti-aircraft fire from the *Wasp* was able to "knock out an engine, forcing the plane to turn and it crashed [into the sea] just off the bow of the ship."

The battle virtually finished the Japanese Navy as a serious threat in the Far East.

ROBERT M. SHIPLEY JR.

Bob Jr.'s engineering talents were used by the military to develop photographic reconnaissance equipment for the Air Corps and to adapt aircraft to use them.

into wartime service. Indeed, the Institute estimated it would lose up to 65 percent of its annual income as "young men in jewelry stores from coast-to-coast dropped all thought of gem study [because] Uncle Sam called them to arms," reported *National Jeweler*.

"The siphoning of younger men into the services reduced GIA's potential for new students to the point where it was doubtful if the Institute could survive without some help," said then-member of the board of governors, Carleton Broer.

Then, in 1942, Shipley's worst fears were confirmed: Richard T. Liddicoat Jr., the popular assistant director of education and research, resigned to enter military service.

He began his military service months before the U.S. entered the war in the Photography Laboratory of Wright Field (now Wright-Patterson Air Force Base) in Dayton, Ohio. He was next sent to the Army Air Corps headquarters in Washington, D.C., where he oversaw development and production of the aircraft photographic equipment. Among his achievements were conversion of the P-38 into the photo plane F-4, and modification of B-25s for photographic surveillance in the famous "Colonel James Doolittle raid" over Tokyo in April 1942.

ALFRED L. WOODILL

Al Woodill volunteered for Army Air Corps cadet training in fall 1941, and went into active service on December 18, 1941. Stationed in North Africa and piloting a B-26 Marauder bomber, he flew more than 40 raids over Italy. He remained on active service until August 1945, when he was discharged with the rank of captain following the Japanese surrender.

BERT KRASHES

Later to become director of the GIA Gem Trade Laboratory in New York and a vice president of the Institute, Bert Krashes served as a bombardier in the 8th Air Force. He was shot down over Germany, seriously wounded, and taken as a prisoner of war. He later received the Purple Heart.

Expecting to be drafted anyway, Liddicoat had applied for a naval officer's commission to ensure that his wife had an adequate income. It was a logical decision: A draftee got $30 a month, an ensign $300. In August 1942, he resigned from GIA to work in a shipyard in Alameda, California, building warships until he heard from the Navy.

Now, in late August 1942, as Bob Shipley Jr. had a year earlier, Liddicoat said goodbye to GIA, the Shipleys, and the friends he and Gene had made. Nobody knew if he would return to the Institute when the war was over—if he survived the war.

"It wasn't a sure thing," said Liddicoat. "First, you had to finish the war—and then GIA itself had to survive."

■ A GIFT TO THE INDUSTRY

In just 10 years, the Institute had significantly raised the standards of the U.S. gem and jewelry industry, and had increased the public's respect for the trade. Much of the information for the Federal Trade Commission's fair trade practices for the industry came from GIA and AGS, and the nation's Better Business Bureaus regularly called on the Institute for assistance.

GIA had become a valuable resource for both the industry and the consumer. "No other continent has developed such an organization," noted *Guilds* in 1943, "and rarely, if ever, have the active boards of an organization been comprised of as many representative members of its industry [and] most representative educators in one branch of learning."

If the Institute was to survive the wartime slump, the leaders of the gemological movement had to act quickly. The solution, decided Shipley and officials of GIA, AGS, and the trade in mid-1942, was to change the Institute—still owned by the Shipleys—into an industry-controlled, nonprofit organization with an endowment.

It was a generous act on the part of the Shipleys, and Robert Shipley Sr. would often say later that "giving" GIA to the industry was a longtime goal of his. Ironically, the pressures and mandates of war, and their threat to the Institute's existence, made it a necessity.

THE FIRST STEP WAS RAISING THE ENDOWMENT FUND. The AGS—then still the unofficial alumni association of GIA—led the effort. The goal was at least $20,000. In less than four months, the jewelry industry donated more than $50,000. It represented, said the leader of the endowment fund committee, Percy K. Loud, the industry's belated thank you to Robert M. Shipley, whose "untiring efforts over a period of years . . . established an educational institution which is known and respected throughout the world by every firm or individual who believes in absolute truth in selling based on scientific knowledge of merchandise handled."

That $50,000 "saved the trade's leading educational institution from becoming a war casualty," declared *National Jeweler* in February 1943. The endowment fund provided the stability—both financial and psychological—that the Institute needed to survive.

By 1943, the process of converting GIA to nonprofit status was complete. On October 8, 1942, the Gemological Institute of America, Inc. was formally chartered as a nonprofit corporation in Ohio (home state of then-chairman Edward F. Herschede). Its purpose, said the charter, was to further gemological education by various means and methods as decided by its board of governors.

As for GIA's greatest asset, Shipley signed two other contracts with the board that would keep him as the Institute's executive director until at least July 1, 1946. The agreements also permitted him to retire or "engage in a more profitable activity" once he had trained a successor.

Beatrice Shipley, here conducting a jewelry fashion show at an AGS Conclave, remained an important influence on GIA and AGS after her retirement in 1943.

WHILE ROBERT SHIPLEY STAYED ON, his wife and partner decided to withdraw. Beatrice Shipley had been as essential to the establishment of GIA as her husband. Her managerial skills, financial acumen, and organizing talent "contributed largely to the rapid growth of the Institute," noted *Guilds* in 1943. But by the early 1940s, the foundation was laid and, like a proud mother whose child has grown up, she decided her work was done.

In June 1943, Bea officially retired and redirected her energies and skills to philanthropic and social service work, eventually becoming president of the Los Angeles Council of the Girl Scouts of America. But her resignation didn't erase her concern for the organization she had helped nurture. Shipley continued to seek his wife's opinion on Institute matters. *The Loupe*, which began as GIA's student newsletter in 1947, reported that even after retiring, Bea's "interest and sincere concern for both students and employees [continued to] influence the policies of the Gemological Institute."

▪THE FIRST WOMEN OF GIA

GIA's students and officials were virtually all male during its first decade, reflecting the composition of the gem and jewelry industry. Indeed, noted

Eunice Robinson, later known by her married name of Eunice Miles, was one of the first female gemology students. In the 1950s, she became the first female gemologist at the GIA Gem Trade Laboratory in New York, starting a distinguished career at the Institute.

National Jeweler in the early 1940s, "There are few outstanding women in this industry. From the mining of gems [to] making jewelry, the work passes largely through masculine hands."

That began to change as more women became interested in gemology and enrolled at GIA. One pioneer was a plucky young woman named Eunice Robinson, whose fascination with gemstones began as a child, when she was entranced by her grandmother's mineral and gem collections.

While studying geology in college, Robinson went to Dr. Edward Wigglesworth, then director of Boston's New England Museum of Natural History and curator of its mineralogy department, and told him she wanted to learn as much as she could about gems and minerals. Women at that time, she recalled, "simply were not accepted in the field [of mineralogy]." Wigglesworth took her on as his assistant. He taught her basic mineralogy and gem testing, and sought her ideas on redesigning the museum's mineral, rock, and gem exhibits.

Then the Massachusetts Institute of Technology offered her a scholarship after she gave an impressive extemporaneous speech to the Geology Society of Boston. She happily accepted—and found she was the only woman in her MIT classes.

Meanwhile, Wigglesworth was introducing Robinson to important people in mineralogy and geology. In early 1938, one of those was Robert Shipley Sr. Like Wigglesworth, Shipley was impressed with Robinson's enthusiasm and knowledge and offered her GIA's gemology course at a two-thirds discount. It was, he said, his way of repaying Wigglesworth for his help. Eunice, though, suspected the influence of Mrs. Shipley in the offer. "She was in favor of gemology as a career option for young women," she said later, and "definitely had a great deal of influence" at the Institute.

Eunice Robinson—later known by her married name Eunice Miles—went on to carve out an impressive career in gemology. She wrote a number of articles on gemology with Dr. Fred Pough, curator of minerals at the American Museum of Natural History in New York City. Miles joined GIA in 1953 as the first female gemologist/researcher in its Gem Trade Laboratory, where she had a long and distinguished career.

Top: Lala Penha of Los Angeles graduated from GIA in 1937, becoming the first female Certified Gemologist. Bottom: Virginia Hinton, the first female jeweler to hold the title of Certified Gemologist, served as GIA's director of education from 1944 until 1946.

THOUGH ROBINSON WAS AMONG THE FIRST FEMALE gemology students, she wasn't the very first one. By the early '40s, there were already a dozen women with the AGS title of Registered Jeweler. Nor was she the first female Certified Gemologist.

That honor belongs to Lala Penha, of Los Angeles, who in 1937 became the 25th C.G. in the world. She was also a Fellow of the Gemmological Association (FGA) of Great Britain. In 1940, Shipley asked her to help teach GIA's second resident class.

The first female jeweler to hold the C.G. title was Virginia V. Hinton, who became a mainstay at the Institute during the war years. An unpleasant incident while working at an Atlanta jewelry store in 1930 put Hinton on the path to gemology. It was noontime during Christmas rush when a young man walked in to buy a diamond ring and peppered her with technical questions she couldn't answer. Embarrassed, she vowed to learn all she could about gemstones.

After marrying and settling in Houston, Hinton began taking the GIA courses. She received her Registered Jeweler title in 1939 and became a Certified Gemologist in 1943.

Hinton was not only one of the few professionally trained jeweler-gemologists in the United States, but she also had one of the finest and best-equipped private laboratories in the country and a comprehensive gemological library. She studied crystallography and gem materials at Harvard University, the American Museum of Natural History, and the Field Museum

This photo, taken at Alexandria Avenue shortly after the end of World War II, illustrates the important role of GIA's female staff in sustaining the Institute during the war years.

of Natural History. In 1944, she became a Fellow of the Gemmological Association of Great Britain.

That same year, Shipley appointed Hinton director of education at the Institute. In that role, she supervised correspondence courses, oversaw *Gems & Gemology,* and co-authored the U.S. edition of *Introductory Gemology* with Robert Webster. Hinton held the post until early 1946, when she returned to Houston.

■THE HOME FRONT

Ironically, the war led the Institute to expand its gem identification services. By 1944, U.S. newspapers and trade publications were reporting that servicemen in North Africa, Europe, Asia, and the South Pacific were being "cheated" by scam artists who sold them synthetic stones and cultured pearls as genuine goods. GIA's governors were concerned that purchase of these bogus gems by servicemen at "considerable portions of their pay" would continue unabated if their families had no way of ascertaining whether or not the stones were genuine. So, the Institute expanded its identification services to "the layman." For a $5 fee, its labs evaluated the stones and provided a signed identification report.

However, the most significant gemology lab work during the war came out of the Boston lab. GIA president Edward Wigglesworth helped Shipley compile the *Dictionary of Gems and Gemology*, published in 1945, and created a system of gem identification, listing on cards each gem's physical properties and comments by leading mineralogical and gemological authorities. The cards were used as references in instruction and research.

IN 1945, THE YEAR THE WAR ENDED, things became especially difficult. First, Wigglesworth died in May. His death put GIA's East Coast operation in limbo. There was no one else of his stature to take it over. Even if there had been, the Institute probably couldn't have afforded it. Wigglesworth had operated the lab and conducted classes, research, and testing voluntarily—without pay—five days a week for years. Who could GIA have found to do the same thing? Without him, there was no East Coast branch.

Second, there were continuing money problems. Despite the security of the endowment fund, GIA still had to stretch its finances to make ends meet and tried a variety of ways to increase enrollments and revenues. In late 1943, for example, it added a postwar scholarship program by which its courses could be purchased for study at "a more convenient time in the future." The plan was specifically designed for veterans to use when they returned home, for postwar employees of jewelry firms, and as gifts for disabled veterans.

Nevertheless, by 1945, GIA couldn't stretch its finances any further. After holding the line for years during the war, the Institute found it impossible to continue its pre-war fees for its courses. Early in the year, it announced a nominal increase for its basic and advanced courses.

Thus the war ended for GIA as it did for millions of people around the world—finally, and just in time.

CHAPTER 5

Bettmann/Corbis

President Franklin D. Roosevelt signs the GI Bill of Rights, which provided broad educational benefits for World War II veterans. The Institute's correspondence course was accepted under the GI Bill in 1946, paving the way for an enormous surge in enrollments.

YEARS OF CHANGE

1946–1952

The postwar years marked tremendous growth for the Institute. Course enrollments mushroomed. There were major changes in curriculum, a new East Coast office, a new laboratory, and new leaders. Meanwhile, GIA and its sister organization AGS separated.

It was a time, said Gems & Gemology, *of "phenomenal success and rapid development of the Institute's activities." Not until the mid-1970s would GIA again experience such unbridled expansion and change.*

■ RETURNING SONS

Champagne flowed, people danced in the streets, families reunited. The war was over, and its ending changed everything for GIA. But this time, the changes were for the better.

The first was the return of Richard Liddicoat. He had left in 1942, uncertain whether he would be back. He returned now, certain he would never leave.

The Navy discharged Liddicoat in January 1946, and in February he was once again at the Institute. Shipley immediately named him director of education and, shortly afterward, director of education and research. By March, he had plunged deeply into the Institute's operations—teaching, grading, writing, and helping develop the curriculum.

"I loved what I did there," Liddicoat explained. "I had found something I really enjoyed, and I was keen to keep on doing it."

AS IF LIDDICOAT DIDN'T HAVE ENOUGH TO DO, Shipley asked him to write a book on gem identification. Although several authoritative works were already available, for the most part these had been written for scientists, primarily mineralogists and geologists.

By the late 1940s, interest in gemology—thanks largely to GIA—had spread far beyond academic circles. Now the public needed, as Liddicoat later described it, a book that gave "both the jeweler and the layman with limited equipment an outline for making the simple and often conclusive tests that identify gems."

Just as important to Shipley was that the Institute have its *own* text rather than continue to use someone else's. Although Liddicoat was dubious about

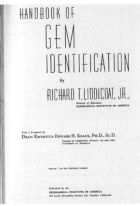

The first edition of Liddicoat's *Handbook of Gem Identification*, published in August 1947. Now in its 12th edition (4th printing), it is one of the most widely read textbooks in gemology.

his qualifications to write such a book, Shipley waved away his concerns. "If you work hard enough on it, it will serve us," he said.

So Liddicoat began his first major contribution to gemological literature. Above all, he wanted it to be basic and accessible. To this end, he organized it "like a cookbook, starting out with all stones that are red, then all that are blue and all that are green, then dividing them into transparent or nontransparent."

The volume took almost a year to complete. When finished, it described the essentials of gem properties, discussed gem-testing instruments, and presented clearly and in detail the procedures for identifying gemstones and separating them from their "manufactured" counterparts. The 250-page first edition of Liddicoat's *Handbook of Gem Identification* came out in August 1947. The book remained in print into the 21st century, becoming a standard in the field. It went through more than 12 editions as the science of gemology evolved.

IN EARLY 1945, ANOTHER CHANGE OCCURRED. Bob Shipley Jr. returned to California—but not to GIA. Bob's real interests were in researching, designing, and creating instruments, not running the Institute. Following a medical discharge in late 1944, Bob joined the Curtis Laboratory in Los Angeles, where he specialized in designing optical instruments. He rejoined GIA in early 1946, but the jobs he held before the war—director of education and director of research—were now handled by Liddicoat and newcomer Dr. George Switzer. And the Institute had no immediate need for new instruments. So Shipley Jr. taught, graded students' papers, and wrote for *Gems & Gemology*.

In January 1948, he left again—this time for good—to start his own company in Glendale, California. Eventually he did design and create more gemological instruments. Those included a new gem refractometer about the size of a cigarette pack, the Binocular Gemolite microscope, and a stock record camera (for maintaining records of jewelry merchandise). Although he continued to be a technical consultant to GIA, he never again was an official employee.

■CLASSES AND DIPLOMAS

In contrast to its lean war years, the Institute was overwhelmed by new students after the war ended. By early 1946, there was already tremendous interest from returning servicemen who wanted to enroll.

The lifting of wartime restrictions on the gem trade, reunions between loved ones, and a surge in weddings unleashed a pent-up demand for jewelry and gemstones. That in turn triggered booms in the retail gem and jewelry industry, "but many of the people hired had no knowledge of gemstones," Liddicoat noted. In addition, "a lot of people in the industry who hadn't studied the courses were now anxious to get involved, so we had to get things rolling again, quickly."

In 1946, Shipley and Liddicoat began a period of educational change for GIA as they expanded its curriculum to meet the greater demand. In April, they launched the first resident class since 1942, a four-week, five-hour-a-day gem identification laboratory class. And in June, GIA introduced its first evening classes, at the request of Los Angeles students who wanted to supplement correspondence-course assignments with lectures and laboratory work. In July, it added a new course for advanced study of colored stones and gem identification; on completion, students were expected to identify 200 gems.

In 1947, the Institute launched two traveling classes—the equivalent of modern-day "extension" classes—Gem Appreciation (for non-GIA students in the jewelry business) and Laboratory Practice (for correspondence-course students). Over 14 months, the tour covered virtually the entire country.

ALTHOUGH EARLY ON GIA ALLOWED its students to use a professional title (Theoretical Gemologist, Certified Gemologist), it gave up that right to the American Gem Society after its creation in 1934. Non-AGS graduates of GIA could hold only a Certificate of Completion (added in 1944), which conferred no title.

But with the sharp increase in enrollments, industry-wide clamor for formal recognition of the professional knowledge obtained from GIA grew. In 1948, the Institute authorized use of the title Gemologist for all of its graduates. Two titled diplomas were created for students who successfully completed its curriculum: *Gemologist* could be used by anyone who successfully completed the entire correspondence course and written exams; *Graduate Gemologist* (G.G.) was reserved for those who also successfully completed the resident classes and passed practical tests in diamond grading and gem identification.

Granting of these titles worried AGS officials and members. With the new GIA titles, of what value was the Certified Gemologist title AGS conferred on those who successfully met its requirements for admission (including passing

THE INSTITUTE WAS OVERWHELMED BY NEW ENROLLMENTS AFTER WORLD WAR II ENDED.

GIA courses)? As an AGS report put it delicately, "Members of the Society might not readily appreciate the reason for [the Institute's] action."

To avoid a squabble that could split the gemology movement, GIA submitted its plans to AGS for review. Institute officials explained that the new diplomas shouldn't be construed as "a certification" of a GIA student's firm or business practices, as the AGS titles were for its members. The diplomas were simply "a statement of educational knowledge."

The AGS International Committee ultimately agreed that a student "deserved and should receive *individual* recognition" for successfully completing gemological studies "whether such student was a member of the Society or not."

■ THE GI BILL

The greatest impact on the Institute's postwar enrollment, courses, and fortunes came from the Servicemen's Readjustment Act of 1944. Commonly known as the GI Bill of Rights, this legislation promised that the federal government would pay the educational costs for any veteran who wanted to go to a school or take a correspondence course. In view of GIA's financial struggles during the war, Liddicoat felt that being on the list of approved schools was critical to boosting enrollment and revenues.

But Shipley didn't want GIA involved. He worried that the federal government eventually would intrude on the Institute's operations. Nevertheless, Shipley—after "grumbling about it," according to Liddicoat—was persuaded to give the GI Bill a try. To get on the list of approved schools, GIA asked its students and graduates, as well as AGS members, to urge the Veterans Administration to approve its courses. In September 1946, the Institute announced that its correspondence course had been accepted under the government's GI Bill of Rights.

According to the terms of its contract, the federal government reimbursed GIA for veterans' tuition costs. Thus, a veteran could get a complete gemological education worth $975 (in 1946 dollars) without paying a penny, plus three months' subsistence payments for resident courses. Now former servicemen could enroll at little or no cost to themselves, which made gemology training available to a lot of people who couldn't have afforded it otherwise.

THE GI BILL HAD A PROFOUND EFFECT on both GIA and the jewelry industry. "Once we went under the GI Bill, enrollments came in *huge* numbers," said

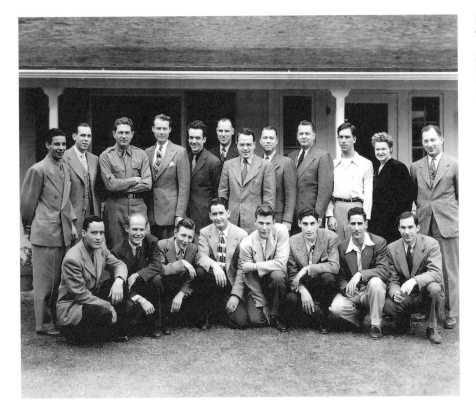

Liddicoat (center) and a graduating class from 1947. Between 1946 and 1949, more than 2,500 students enrolled at the Institute under the GI Bill.

Liddicoat. The program was so successful and important for GIA that in 1949 the Institute renewed its contract for the duration of the bill, which ended in 1951.

Between September 1946 and early 1949, more than 2,500 veterans enrolled in the correspondence courses. By early 1951, that had almost doubled to 4,755. The effect on GIA's revenues was also significant. Its gross income for 1945 was just over $70,700; by 1946, it was almost $186,000. Thanks largely to GI Bill enrollments, in 1952 GIA's annual gross revenues topped $300,000.

Some in the industry worried that the GI Bill let too many potential competitors—to put it bluntly—into the trade. But in fact, the program revitalized the industry and enabled veterans who were jewelers as well as would-be jewelers to get the high-quality, professional training they could not have afforded otherwise.

Arthur Gleim, a jeweler in Palo Alto, California, enrolled under the GI Bill and went on to become chairman of GIA's board of governors.

"That's why I took it," recalled Arthur Gleim, of Gleim the Jeweler Inc., Palo Alto, California. "Here I was, just out of the Army, making $78 a month, and I could get a free course. So I took it!"

And it changed his life. "GIA made me a jeweler-merchant, instead of a watchmaker sitting in a store," said Gleim, who remained an active supporter of the Institute, eventually becoming chairman of its board of governors.

Robert Shipley, too, came to see that the GI Bill was good for both GIA and the trade. These young men, survivors of a grim and bloody war, were "obtaining from their courses with the Gemological Institute of America fresh ideals and high hopes for their own future and that of the industry," he said in 1947. That, he predicted, would be "a most constructive force in the industry" in the coming years.

■ DIVISION AND GROWTH

New classes and bulging enrollments weren't the only changes during those postwar years. The Institute also made significant changes in operations.

One of the first was separation from its sister organization, the American Gem Society. There had long been confusion in the jewelry industry, ever since Shipley launched the Society in 1934, over where one organization ended and the other began. Despite repeated efforts by AGS and GIA to articulate their differences, most in the industry still thought of the two as a single entity—with some justification. Both organizations were started by Shipley, who served as executive director of each. The two associations shared several of the same employees, the same industry leaders alternated as their officials, and jewelers had to pass GIA courses to qualify as AGS members—making AGS virtually a GIA alumni association.

But in 1946, AGS was benefiting from its own surge in activity. The return of its members from war and the many young men entering the jewelry field gave renewed momentum to the Society, after several moribund years. It was large enough now, said officers and members, for what *Guilds* called a "natural" separation.

The break began that year. First, at a joint meeting it was agreed to "divorce activities" of the two organizations and to begin looking for separate housing for their respective headquarters. Then, in May 1946, Shipley submitted his resignation as executive director of AGS, a post he had held since its founding in 1934.

The two organizations officially divided in 1947, and the following year the separation was formalized when AGS moved to its own headquarters on Wilshire Boulevard in Los Angeles. "For the first time," later wrote Carleton Broer, an AGS chairman, "the Society was in its own home and completely on its own feet. . . . One era had ended, and another begun."

That message was underscored at the 1948 Conclave in Washington, D.C., where Shipley delivered his valedictory message to AGS. "Jealously support protection of the public as the measure of your every policy and act," urged the man whose creation of both organizations had raised the ethical and professional standards of an industry.

IN 1948, NOW 61 YEARS OLD, Shipley dropped the other shoe. Having given up his duties as AGS executive director, he also wanted to slip off his mantle as director of GIA and retire, he told the Institute's board of governors. After all, he had agreed in 1943 to stay on only as long as it took to find a qualified replacement after the war. He had one now in Liddicoat.

But the board was reluctant to let him step down with so much still to be done. Published reports of the board's 1948 meeting in Chicago say it obtained a contract from him to stay on until December 1951, and that the contract was "accepted by the executive director with the understanding that he be permitted to retire at that time."

WITH HIS RETIREMENT now less than three years away, Shipley focused attention on training his successor, Richard Liddicoat.

"He thought I needed more grooming," recalled Liddicoat, "and once he decided to retire, he was careful to make sure I had opportunities to learn the operations." That spring, Liddicoat was promoted to assistant director of GIA and assumed all of Shipley's administrative responsibilities, while he continued to supervise the education and research departments. Dorothy Jasper Smith took over some of Shipley's projects, including coordination of students' progress.

The shift in duties was so abrupt that *The Loupe* had to reassure students and supporters, "None of these changes mean that Robert M. Shipley, founder of the Gemological Institute of America, has relinquished his position as Director of the Institute." He would continue as "its head and advisor" until he retired.

"JEALOUSLY SUPPORT PROTECTION OF THE PUBLIC AS THE MEASURE OF YOUR EVERY POLICY AND ACT," URGED SHIPLEY AT THE 1948 AGS CONCLAVE.

Kay Swindler joined GIA in 1946 as manager of the publications department. She served as editor of *The Loupe* and associate editor of *Gems & Gemology*, and oversaw advertising and publicity activities.

■CRAMPED QUARTERS

Burgeoning enrollments and the growing numbers of classes in L.A. and elsewhere in the country quickly put a strain on GIA's staff, operations, and facilities.

The Institute's administrative and instructional staff started expanding almost as soon as enrollments did. In 1940, when Liddicoat was first hired, the staff totaled less than a dozen, including the Shipleys. By 1950, there were 50 full-time employees. Some had been with GIA since the beginning, such as Dorothy Jasper Smith, Dorothy Phebus, and Isabelle Blanchard. The rest were part of the postwar staff buildup.

They included Kay Swindler, who joined GIA in 1946 as manager of the publications department, editor of *The Loupe*, and associate editor of *Gems & Gemology*. She was also responsible for all advertising and public relations activities until she left the Institute in late 1953. In addition, Swindler was a GIA historian. Her account of the Institute's founding and growth appeared in the Summer 1951 issue of *Gems & Gemology* on the occasion of GIA's 20th anniversary.

Some of the people hired after the war became pillars for decades to come. One was Clare Verdera, a former Broadway actress. She helped on a part-time basis in the late 1930s and early '40s before joining the staff full-time in 1946. A buoyant personality, she performed many roles over the next 18 years, including personnel director and managing the Institute's mailing, shipping, purchasing, and printing operations.

Another was Margaret Orozco, who joined GIA straight out of high school in 1949 as an "errand girl." She moved up to working in the mailroom, and then—thanks to her energy and initiative—to management of student records and disbursement of course materials. When Verdera retired in 1964, Orozco was named supervisor of management services. She was responsible for GIA's printing, shipping, purchasing, personnel, and mailroom, plus all incoming/outgoing laboratory identifications, student stones, and book sales! She and her staff did what would one day require "a host of directors and managers in seven different departments," noted the Institute's alumni magazine *In Focus* in 1994, the year before she retired.

But she did it well for 15 years, expanding those operations as GIA itself expanded.

In 1979, Orozco turned her attention to a longtime pet project: creating a full-service bookstore for the Institute. She managed the bookstore during her final 16 years at GIA, building it into one of the world's largest sources of publications in the fields of gemology, jewelry, and watchmaking.

THE POSTWAR EXPLOSION OF STUDENTS put a serious strain on the Institute's facilities. As early as 1946, GIA had to lease space in a nearby school for some classes, and the board of governors began seriously thinking about a new headquarters.

"By the late 1940s, we held classes all over the Wilshire District," recalled Liddicoat. "In a nearby church, in a glorified gazebo, in storefronts, and across the street, where we had offices next to a Ralph's supermarket."

The Institute's self-proclaimed "International Headquarters" was bursting at the seams. The building that seemed "like heaven" to Dorothy Smith only a few years earlier was "just a tiny little house" in 1948, noted one staff newcomer.

Even the Shipleys were affected by the staff's relentless need for more space. GIA's founders had kept their second-floor apartment at the headquarters, though Bea had long since moved permanently to their Laguna Beach home and Shipley himself—after turning most of his duties over to Liddicoat and Smith in 1948—only came to the headquarters on Mondays and Tuesdays.

Each time he left, the staff encroached a little more into the apartment. One day Shipley arrived to find it completely filled with desks and staff. All that was left to him was a small bed in the bedroom. He was, to put it mildly, very indignant.

With some trepidation, education supervisors Lester Benson and Kenneth Moore told him bluntly, "We're desperate for space. We absolutely need this apartment!"

Personnel director Clare Verdera (above, far left) also supervised mailing, shipping, purchasing, and printing operations at the Institute for nearly two decades. Four-decade veteran Margaret Orozco (left) assumed those responsibilities after Verdera's retirement in 1964.

Top to bottom: War veterans Ward Cook, Joe Phillips, and Joe Murphy all enrolled under the GI Bill and went on to become GIA instructors.

▪ "GI" GEMOLOGISTS

The impact of the GI Bill of Rights on enrollment and revenues was obvious. But that legislation also had a far-reaching effect on GIA's staff and the gemology movement. Among the thousands of veterans who used their benefits to enroll with the Institute were several who became instructors and molded the thinking of future gemologists. Others became GIA officials who influenced the Institute's future direction.

As enrollments boomed in the late 1940s, the need for knowledgeable instructors became urgent. So Shipley and Liddicoat paid special attention to GIA students, hiring the best to become teachers, staff gemologists, and managers. "We were looking for people all the time. Standout students were offered jobs immediately," said Liddicoat. It was a smart idea, and the Institute adhered to it so closely that only in the late 1970s did it begin hiring technical people who *weren't* GIA graduates.

There was, for example, Ward Cook, a former chemical engineer, who was one of the first veterans to enroll at the Institute under the GI Bill. An honor student, he was hired as an instructor immediately after he graduated in 1947. Cook assisted Liddicoat with resident classes and also brought GIA's laboratory practice classes to cities around the nation.

Joseph Phillips and Joseph Murphy were two other GI Bill students hired in the late 1940s. Phillips, an instructor, assisted Liddicoat in developing GIA's diamond grading system, and also tinkered with instrument research and development. He worked on early versions of the electronic Colorimeter and a ProportionScope. Murphy went on to become, said Liddicoat, "one of the Institute's best home study instructors."

ALSO AMONG THE MANY GI GEMOLOGISTS HIRED between the late 1940s and early 1950s were several who significantly affected GIA's development.

Lawrence L. Copeland's fascination with gems began with his grandfather's mineral collections and watching him work at his foot-operated stone-polishing wheel. As a teenager, Copeland became an avid gem collector, bought his own lapidary machine, and taught himself how to cut and polish gemstones.

While working in jewelry stores in New Mexico and Colorado, Copeland learned about GIA and used his veterans' benefits to enroll. He was hired as an instructor in 1948, but it was his writing skills that were quickly put to use. Within a year, he was director of the correspondence courses—a post he held for more than a decade—keeping lessons revised and updated, and

Left: Lawrence Copeland, initially hired as an instructor, later became associate editor of *Gems & Gemology* and coauthored several books published by GIA. Right: Kenneth Moore created new gem-testing equipment in the 1950s and eventually headed GIA's GEM Instruments division.

overseeing major rewrites and reorganization every four years. Copeland was associate editor of *Gems & Gemology*, and he wrote a regular column for *The Loupe*. He also authored *Diamonds—Famous, Notable and Unique* (a trade standard on famous diamonds) and co-authored *The Jewelers' Manual* and *The Diamond Dictionary*. Copeland served as GIA's research librarian until he retired in 1970.

Kenneth M. Moore spent four years as a pilot in the European theater. In postwar Berlin, Moore's visits to a gem market sparked his interest in stones. On a trip to London, he visited Basil Anderson, head of the London gem testing laboratory. Anderson, an Institute advisor, recommended some gemology books—and GIA courses.

Back in the United States, Moore visited GIA headquarters in 1947. A resident class was about to start, so he signed up. A year later, after successfully completing the curriculum, he was hired as an instructor but soon took over administration of the correspondence courses. An exceptional organizer and administrator, Moore went on to head GIA's Gem Instruments division through the 1960s and '70s.

Lester Benson was the Institute's own Renaissance man, capable of doing almost anything and doing it well and with ingenuity. Indeed, if there was one word that his colleagues used to describe him, it was "genius"—but it was genius that only fully blossomed in the greenhouse of GIA.

Benson, a Colorado native, was inducted into the Army in 1942. His high marks on the intelligence test set him apart for officer training, but in 1944, shortly after getting married, he was sent to the Philippines with a tank unit. After being wounded, he was sent home and discharged in early 1945.

Lester Benson, an Army veteran hired in 1947, was the Institute's Renaissance man: teacher, inventor, illustrator, and author.

His wife, who was interested in gemstones, had enrolled in GIA home study during the war. Her enthusiasm rekindled Benson's childhood interest in gems and jewelry. He resumed designing and making jewelry—a hobby from his high school days—and together they opened a small jewelry firm in Denver. Aware of his own lack of training and impressed by his wife's GIA lessons, Benson enrolled in 1946. After graduating from the resident class, he was hired in 1948 by Liddicoat to be an instructor. "He was a standout," said Liddicoat, "a superb and charismatic teacher."

Within months, Benson was doing much more than grading papers. He illustrated Liddicoat's *Handbook of Gem Identification*, and did all the photomicrography for the Institute. He performed gem identification in the laboratory and redesigned the camera on the X-ray diffraction unit (then the only one in the world dedicated to testing cut gemstones). He also completed a catalog showing the X-ray pattern of each gem material. Soon, Benson was promoted to director of resident class training, and by 1952 he had a staff of 10 instructors.

As a teacher, one topic that fascinated Benson was appraisals. In the early '50s, he began gathering gem prices to teach appraising more effectively in his classes. Later, he and some colleagues devised easy-to-understand colored stone price charts for the home study courses. As early as 1952, "his important contributions to [gem] identification problems, as well as an effective colored stone appraisal system, had made him known to most members of the trade," noted *Gems & Gemology*.

ANOTHER GI BILL GRADUATE had an enormous impact on the Institute, more so than anyone else except Richard Liddicoat. His story was interwoven with that of GIA and its laboratory for more than a generation, and his influence on the jewelry industry and gemology continued to ripple into the 21st century. However, G. Robert Crowningshield took a most circuitous route to GIA, one that hinged on a chance encounter at an unplanned stop half a world away during wartime.

Crowningshield was first attracted to the beauty of gemstones as a youth, though studied botany, not mineralogy, at San Diego State University. It took World War II to really kindle his interest in gemology. After joining the

Navy in 1942, Crowningshield was assigned to a troop transport that was going to Australia. To relieve the tedium during his spare time, and satisfy his curiosity about gemstones, he took a couple of books to browse: F. Rogers and A. Beard's *5,000 Years of Gems and Jewelry* and Slawson and Kraus's *Gems and Gem Materials*.

On a subsequent voyage to Calcutta, Crowningshield gained his first awareness of the differences in the quality and value of gems from native dealers who came to the port to sell to U.S. sailors. He began collecting gems and became something of a shipboard advisor to those who wanted to buy stones when they were in port in India or Ceylon. He also began designing gold settings for gems bought by his shipmates. But it was his budding interest in star sapphires that led to a casual detour—one that, in hindsight, was momentous for Crowningshield and GIA.

IT HAPPENED TOWARD THE END OF THE WAR. The captain of Crowningshield's ship hadn't bought a gift to take home to his wife. The ship was near Ceylon, the home of star sapphires. Crowningshield, the ship's navigator, suggested a quick, unscheduled stop at the capital city of Colombo, where he would help the captain choose some gems for a necklace. "We had to get permission from the U.S. government to make the stop," Crowningshield recalled. "The captain told them we were low on provisions, and we got the Navy's okay!"

In Colombo, they went into the first jewelry store they saw near the docks, attracted by a display of star sapphires in the window. They decided the necklace should be comprised of seven star sapphires, graduated in size. As Crowningshield inspected the stones placed before them and discussed each with his captain, the young man behind the counter asked him in English, "Are you a gemologist?"

"No," said Crowningshield. ("I didn't even know what the word meant," he laughed years later.)

"You should be," said the young man. "You show a lot of interest in it." Then he continued, "I am a gemologist. My father wanted me to learn as much as I could about gemstones, and right before the war he sent me to a school called the Gemological Institute of America in Los Angeles."

The young man was Sardha Ratnavira. Fate had brought together that stylish member of the Institute's first resident class in 1939 and the soft-spoken botanist who—because of this chance meeting—would become one of the world's greatest gemologists. Ratnavira's suggestion "planted

A chance encounter in Colombo led G. Robert Crowningshield to enroll at the Institute. Crowningshield would play a key role in the growth of GIA over the next several decades.

SHIPLEY FELT "WE *HAD* TO BE REPRESENTED THERE [NEW YORK] IF WE WERE EVER TO BECOME AN IMPORTANT FACTOR IN THE INDUSTRY," SAID LIDDICOAT.

the seed in my mind that I should go there," said Crowningshield. "Gradually, it dawned on me that there was a career in the knowledge of gemstones."

Discharged in San Diego in 1946, Crowningshield immediately drove to Los Angeles. There he met Shipley and Liddicoat, and saw what GIA offered in gemological training. "My life was sealed at that point," he said.

Six months later, Crowningshield used his veteran's benefits to enroll in the correspondence course, where he made an indelible impression on his instructors. He "stood out as one of the top students in his class, a natural at gemology," said Liddicoat of the lanky ex-Navy man years later.

In August 1949, Shipley invited Crowningshield to join the staff, and he did. He spent his first few months grading papers, working in the lab on identifications, and assisting Kay Swindler on the *Gems & Gemology* column "Seen in the Laboratories."

In early 1948, GIA's governors approved opening a new branch on the East Coast. The following year, Shipley and Liddicoat asked Crowningshield if he wanted to go, and he replied with an enthusiastic "yes." His decision would have a huge impact on gem identification and gemological research.

▪ GIA GOES TO NEW YORK

No Eastern branch had existed since Wigglesworth's death in May 1945, and reestablishing it was a top priority for Shipley. This time, though, the Eastern office would be located in the heart of the gem and jewelry trade, in New York City. Shipley felt "we *had* to be represented there if we were ever to become an important factor in the industry," said Liddicoat.

By 1948, GIA was ready to reactivate its East Coast presence, and Shipley had found just the person to do it—though he had to look to South America to find him.

GEORGE SWITZER, GIA'S DIRECTOR OF RESEARCH from 1946 to 1947, had been GIA's "token" Ph.D. When Switzer left to join the U.S. Geological Survey, Shipley quickly sought another Ph.D. to replace him—Dr. Mark C. Bandy, a geologist with a Harvard doctorate in mineralogy, who was then working in Bolivia. Although Bandy had spent most of his career working for oil, steel, and mining companies in Mexico and South America, he spent much of his free time collecting minerals for Harvard and the Smithsonian Institution. By 1947, he wanted to return to the U.S. When Shipley offered him a job as GIA's director of research, he accepted.

It was Bandy, then, whom Shipley tapped in early 1948 to head the new East Coast operation, with Crowningshield as his assistant. To introduce the new East Coast director to the trade, Shipley took Bandy with him to the March 1948 AGS Conclave in Washington, D.C. At least that was the official reason. In actuality, with Al Woodill now director of AGS and Liddicoat busy as assistant director of GIA, Bandy became Shipley's unofficial secretary—and it drove Bandy up the wall.

The problem was that Shipley had his own capricious agenda when he traveled. "He would say, 'On Wednesday I want to see Cliff Josephson in Moline, Illinois, and if I do that, I can go to Chicago and see Charlie Peacock. Then I can go to Cincinnati and see Ed Herschede,'" recalled Liddicoat. "But if Ed wasn't there, or someone else couldn't make an appointment, Shipley kept changing his plans." Liddicoat was accustomed to this; the new lab director was not.

"Poor Bandy," Liddicoat said. "I could see his growing distress."

Bandy's distress was to have a dramatic effect on GIA's operations within a short time.

Dr. Mark C. Bandy was picked by Shipley to be director of GIA's new East Coast office in New York, which opened in August 1948.

IN JUNE 1948, GIA OFFICIALLY ANNOUNCED that it would open a new Eastern branch later that summer. In early August, Bandy and Crowningshield set off for New York. The new East Coast office was located at 5 East 47th Street, a small building at the corner of Fifth Avenue. The office/lab itself was on the sixth floor, at the end of the hall in a tiny room "that couldn't have been more than 30 feet by 30 feet, and had some partitions," recalled Crowningshield.

With his typical good sense of publicity and timing, Shipley scheduled the official opening for August 9, 1948—just before the annual convention of the ANRJA in New York. Any GIA students "as well as all in the trade" were invited to visit the new facility, read the announcement.

Almost immediately after the opening, Crowningshield began writing a chatty column for *The Loupe*. Initially, it detailed visits and events in the new branch. But soon it carried opinions, test results, discoveries, and findings in the East Coast lab. Initially called "Overheard in the Big City," and then "Through the Lens at the Gem Trade Lab," the column—together with Crowningshield's later "Development and Highlights at the Gem Trade Lab in New York" column for *Gems & Gemology*—became a diary of gemology achievements and minutiae for GIA students, graduates, and other gemologists, and an important contribution to the gemological literature.

The GIA Eastern lab in New York in the late 1940s. From left: Gilbert Oakes, Richard Liddicoat, and G. Robert Crowningshield.

BUSINESS AT THE NEW EASTERN OFFICE was slow initially. "The trade would send people by with queries, but we learned as much if not more from them as they did from us," recalled Crowningshield.

Then, in September, Mark Bandy dropped a bombshell. He sent Shipley a letter with his three-month notice, saying he had accepted an offer to run the Paris office of the U.S. Atomic Energy Commission. The GIA job, he said, was not for him.

"Shipley was startled and furious," recalled Liddicoat. "It was devastating. Here we had just sent this man to open our new office and lab in New York City with a neophyte to be his right hand. The question was, 'What do we do now?'"

Shipley's answer: Send Liddicoat. Though Crowningshield was quickly named director of education in New York, Shipley worried about leaving him in charge alone because of his inexperience and lack of industry recognition. This was, after all, the Institute's Eastern presence, its bid for attention in the heart of the U.S. gem trade.

Crowningshield understood Shipley's feelings and agreed. "I had just joined GIA, straight out of its program. I was bright-eyed, bushy-tailed—and didn't know a damn thing," he recalled with a chuckle.

If there was a plus side, thought Shipley, it was that this would give Liddicoat a chance to test his management and administrative skills. "Shipley wanted me to make it go, to develop a viable function for it in New York, to make it self-supporting," and to run the operation until Crowningshield could do it himself, explained Liddicoat later.

But Liddicoat didn't want to go. He had barely unpacked his bags from recent trips east. Back in California, he was teaching more resident classes, giving talks on gemology to the public, and, as the new assistant director of the Institute, attempting to master its daily operations. There was much that required his attention in Los Angeles.

But Shipley promised him it would only be for five months at the most, and Liddicoat reluctantly agreed. In fact, it would be 14 months before Liddicoat could finally return to L.A.

ON CHRISTMAS EVE 1948, Richard and Gene Liddicoat set off for the cross-country drive to New York, stopping for Christmas Day dinner in a "greasy spoon" somewhere in New Mexico. They reached New York on New Year's Day and got to work almost immediately.

A new series of three-week resident classes, taught by Liddicoat and Crowningshield, started January 10. In addition, Liddicoat shrewdly added free evening classes in the basic course that was the entry into GIA curriculum. That got jewelers' attention, and enrollments picked up.

Among the first students at the little school was a tall, genial New Yorker named Bert Krashes, a combat veteran of World War II. On his return from the war, Krashes worked for an architect in preparation for joining his father-in-law in the construction business. But then his father-in-law died suddenly. To supplement his income, Krashes took a part-time night job with a retail jeweler in New York. He found, though, that he enjoyed the jewelry business, so he went to work full-time as a jewelry salesman.

Bert Krashes, hired as an instructor/gemologist at GIA New York in 1949, went on to head the GIA Gem Trade Laboratory with G. Robert Crowningshield.

In 1948, a fellow salesman told Krashes about GIA. Intrigued, he signed up for the second resident class in New York. Liddicoat was impressed with the "excellent work and keen questions" of this earnest student. In September 1949, he offered Krashes a job as an instructor/gemologist in New York. His initial jobs were identifying gems and pearls, teaching, and grading correspondence papers.

Krashes would go on to become one of the Institute's most popular instructors and, with Crowningshield, lead New York's laboratory to international prominence.

"THE AMENITIES OF THE NEW YORK CITY FACILITY were modest, to say the least," recalled Krashes. The facility was only "about the size of a present-day classroom. It had sliding industrial partitions, and was painted in a very warm, lovely battleship gray. On one side of the partition was the 'executive suite,' with two desks, one occupied by Richard Liddicoat and the other by his wife Gene—who was the entire clerical staff! The rest of the space

LIDDICOAT AND
CROWNINGSHIELD
WORKED SEVEN DAYS
A WEEK TO GET
THE EAST COAST
BRANCH GOING.

belonged to us peons," joked Krashes, "and there were folding chairs and folding tables when classes were in session."

Gene Liddicoat was invaluable to them. Like a good manager, she made sure everything got done in good order. Often at the end of a long day (usually 8 p.m. or later), Krashes recalled, Liddicoat would "sit back, stretch, and say, 'Okay, we've had it,' but Gene would say, 'No, you've got to get this one more letter out first.'"

They worked seven days a week. There was no air conditioning in the summer, and in the winter the building's heat was turned off on Friday nights, weekends, and holidays—whether the GIA staff was there or not. Still, despite the hardships and uncertainties, those days in New York City "were a lot a fun," recalled Liddicoat years later.

Within months, the teaching activities of the East Coast branch were successful, but the lab itself was virtually ignored by the New York City gem industry. Liddicoat pondered how to change that.

Then opportunity quite literally came knocking at GIA's door with an offer to take over the nearby Gem Trade Laboratory.

■THE GEM TRADE LABORATORY

When the Institute established its gem-testing lab in the early 1930s, it was the only one in the United States, but it received little support from gem dealers and importers in New York. Indeed, at the time very few New York gem importers even acknowledged the validity of, or need for, scientific testing of gemstones.

By the mid-1940s, however, there were hundreds of GIA-trained jewelers and private gem laboratories in scores of leading jewelry stores. That convinced a growing number of New York gem and pearl dealers that they, too, needed their own "national" lab. What began as informal discussions culminated in 1945 in meetings that involved the city's entire gem and pearl trades. "The unanimous feel," reported *Jewelers' Circular-Keystone*, was that "such a laboratory would be in the best interests of the industry [and] to proceed with the project."

The initiative was supported with annual dues from the sponsoring firms, contributions from sympathetic parties, and fees charged for testing pearls and gemstones. The Gem Trade Laboratory was incorporated in New York and began operating in January 1946 at 36 West 47th Street. This "new" lab was actually an expansion of one started by the Pearl Associates in 1940 and operated by Dr. A. E. Alexander, one of the world's best-known pearl authorities, who now stayed on as director of the laboratory. However, testing colored stones would be a departure for pearl specialist Alexander.

Pearl authority Dr. A. E. Alexander was director of the original Gem Trade Laboratory, which was officially consolidated with GIA's East Coast office and laboratory in October 1949.

BY 1949, ALEXANDER'S LAB was beginning to struggle financially. Though called the Gem Trade Laboratory, most of its work still involved pearls, so much so that it was known informally as "the Pearl Associates Lab."

The Gem Trade Lab simply wasn't getting the support from the trade and the public it had hoped for. But it did have something GIA wanted: the technology and techniques, developed by Alexander, to differentiate between cultured and natural pearls. Alexander agreed to provide these in exchange for a $2,000 "contribution" to the lab. In effect, his lab was so desperate for cash that it was willing to trade away one of its few weapons in competing with GIA—the secret of detecting cultured pearls.

Alexander showed Liddicoat and Crowningshield the X-ray equipment and operating techniques he had developed to identify and distinguish cultured from natural pearls, using a combination of X-radiography and fluorescence. After that, "things got a lot more active around the New York office," said Liddicoat.

They would soon get even livelier.

IN THE SUMMER OF 1949, TIFFANY & CO., the luxury jewelry retailer and a Gem Trade Lab client, offered Alexander a job as colored-stone buyer.

"Perhaps Alexander heard the footsteps, and so he took the job," said Liddicoat. But first Alexander came knocking on the door of GIA's East Coast offices and told Liddicoat and Crowningshield he was leaving the Gem Trade Laboratory.

Here was another opportunity that had to be seized immediately. GIA officials, including Liddicoat and Shipley, immediately contacted the Pearl Associates, who knew that without Alexander they didn't have a gem lab. "They had no place else to turn," said Liddicoat. "They asked if we would take over the lab."

Would they? "We jumped out of our shoes!" recalled Liddicoat. He believed that owning the Gem Trade Laboratory, together with Alexander's pearl-identification equipment and methods, was the first step toward validating GIA's New York lab in the eyes of the trade.

On October 13, 1949, the Gem Trade Laboratory was officially turned over to GIA and consolidated with the Institute's New York branch. The combined operation was renamed "The Gem Trade Laboratory of the Gemological Institute of America." It had a staff of three: Liddicoat, Crowningshield, and GIA instructor Gilbert Oakes. The new lab offered the jewelry trade and the public in general "the most complete identification facilities in this country," proclaimed *The Loupe*.

Until 1953, though, the lab's primary business remained pearl identification. In its first year of operation, GIA's Gem Trade Lab identified more than 50,000 pearls but only about 3,600 gemstones, and the city's gem trade paid little attention.

■TRANSITIONS

Richard Liddicoat was getting fidgety in early 1950.

Alexander's Gem Trade Laboratory had been successfully consolidated with GIA's New York lab. The New York class schedule was set, enrollments were rising, and home study lessons from East Coast students were ably handled by education director Robert Crowningshield and new GIA instructors Bert Krashes and Gilbert Oakes. So, with Shipley's retirement only 23 months away, Liddicoat was anxious to get back to Los Angeles to resume his duties there as assistant director and to continue his preparation as Shipley's successor.

"I kept telling him, 'Hey! I want to come home,'" recalled Liddicoat. "I assured him Bob was competent and well able to take over the New York office full time."

Shipley finally agreed, and Liddicoat returned to GIA headquarters in February 1950. There he re-familiarized himself with the operations, details, and responsibilities. "As his assistant director, Shipley expected me to start making a lot of the decisions," said Liddicoat. "That made the transition much smoother."

But Shipley also wanted Liddicoat to travel and meet the industry's people face-to-face in their stores, as he had done in the 1930s when he started GIA and AGS. So after the August 1950 ANRJA convention in New York, Liddicoat began a nationwide goodwill tour to promote the Institute to the jewelry trade.

"I picked up an auto in Detroit and traveled all over until the first of November," said Liddicoat. "Then, after the AGS Conclave in 1951, I drove around the Midwest for several months."

On those trips in late 1950 and the first half of 1951, Liddicoat called on many jewelers and spoke to groups of GIA students and others interested in gemology. "The uninformed jeweler is no match for the partially informed layman," he warned them. Thanks to the GI Bill, he remembered that tour as "one of the easiest selling trips I ever made. People were quickly convinced since it didn't cost the veteran a nickel."

Liddicoat made some observations on his trips throughout the U.S. in the middle of the 20th century. Despite the many mom-and-pop stores in the jewelry trade, the people enrolling in GIA "were mainly male." He was also surprised, and impressed, by the distance some people traveled to attend study group meetings. One Iowa jeweler, for example, regularly traveled 210 miles round trip for the Minneapolis group meetings. Two other men traveled 160 and 130 miles, respectively, to attend those in Indianapolis. He heard similar stories from attendees of the Philadelphia and Detroit groups.

"The high regard for the Institute's courses not only among students but throughout the industry was especially gratifying," said Liddicoat. And by the time he took over from Shipley, Liddicoat had become well known to the trade around the country.

AS SHIPLEY'S RETIREMENT NEARED, the gem and jewelry industry bestowed tributes on the man who had helped change them from uninformed traders of diamonds and colored stones into a profession of respected, ethical, skilled gemologists.

Congratulatory letters and telegrams came from friends, graduates, and industry leaders throughout North America and the world. Organizations and trade magazines honored Shipley's contributions. In response, *The Loupe* noted, "Not often does one live to see the fulfillment of a life's dream and altruistic ambition, or receive the grateful thanks of those whom he has benefited. Such, however, has been the repeated privilege of GIA Director, Robert M. Shipley, father of gemological education on the North American continent."

The most touching tributes for Shipley came from the organizations he founded and the people with whom he had established the gemology movement. In 1949, AGS made him its first honorary Certified Gemologist at the Boston Conclave, citing his "personal initiative and persistence [and] contributions to the jewelry industry [which] have been tremendous."

ONE IOWA JEWELER REGULARLY TRAVELED 210 MILES ROUND TRIP FOR THE MINNEAPOLIS STUDY GROUP MEETINGS.

Robert Shipley at his retirement dinner, seated between Beatrice Shipley and master of ceremonies George Houston.

Appropriately, the last tribute, in May 1952, came from the first group to actively support Shipley's idea of gemological training. The Retail Jewelers Research Group honored the Shipleys at its annual meeting in Chicago. The group gave them an album of testimonials and thank-you letters from industry leaders around the world.

Shipley refused to accept all the credit for GIA's success. He graciously acknowledged the invaluable service and help of Beatrice Shipley, Robert Shipley Jr., and "those men who in the difficult beginning . . . accepted the burden of helping me establish firmly first the Institute and later the AGS.

"Without the many jewelers and numerous educators who helped in the development of the gemological profession," he said on the eve of his retirement, "there could not have been a successful industry-controlled school for the jeweler."

He asked the staff to "continue to teach GIA students not only ethics, but culture and a bit of philosophy." New developments in the science of gemology were "outstanding and gratifying," he noted, but students needed "more than the means by which to make more money and gain prestige through the scientific ability to test gemstones and grade diamonds.

"Give them something to make their lives happier, and their surroundings more beautiful," he urged. "Give them something to live by."

Shipley certainly looked forward to retirement. He was in good health, and happy that he and Beatrice could enjoy their later years together.

AT ABOUT THE SAME TIME, another Shipley left gemology. In 1951, a year after being named an Honorary Research Member by GIA and shortly before his father's retirement, Bob Shipley Jr. cut most of his ties with the gemological profession he had helped build. He sold his gem instrument company to the Institute and returned to the research lab at his farm in the rural town of Cloverdale, California, north of San Francisco, where he lived with his wife and two sons.

His last contribution to gemology came between 1953 and 1955, when he developed and built 75 models of an electronic diamond Colorimeter for the

Over two decades, Shipley recruited a formidable group of academics to the gemology movement. Seated, clockwise, at a 1947 GIA advisory board meeting in Chicago are Elizabeth Brown, Dr. C. S. Hurlbut Jr. (Harvard University), Slawson, Liddicoat, Frank Wade, Dr. George Switzer, Dr. W. D. Shipton, Dr. Ralph Holmes (Columbia University), Dr. W. F. Foshag, Shipley, and Kraus.

AGS. After that, Shipley Jr. devoted his considerable intellect to creating equipment for other industries. He successfully developed agricultural harvesting equipment in the late 1950s and early 1960s. Toward the end of his life, he turned to solar energy research.

When Shipley Jr. died in 1982, *Gems & Gemology* praised him as "a genius in instrumentation," whose work helped transform the gemology movement and benefited jewelers, gem dealers, and collectors around the world.

THE EXITS OF ROBERT SHIPLEY AND HIS SON, following the departure of Beatrice Shipley a decade earlier, marked the end of an era for GIA and for gemology. The founders who had transformed one man's dream into a practical, rewarding reality for many thousands were gone.

"We owe a great deal to the Shipleys," wrote Percy Loud of the GIA Board of Governors in 1952. "The brilliance and ethical principles of one family have touched the jewelry industry in every city and hamlet in our country!"

But it was ultimately Robert M. Shipley Sr. who deserved the laurels. His successor, Richard Liddicoat, expressed it well:

"The results of your intensive efforts during the past two decades are evident in all divisions of the industry today," he told Shipley on his retirement. "The inestimable value of the trade institution you have created will live on to influence the industry through generations to come."

PART TWO

building the legacy

Shipley's successor, GIA executive director Richard Liddicoat, is surrounded by the Los Angeles staff at the 1955 groundbreaking for the new headquarters on San Vicente Boulevard. The building officially opened in February 1956 and would remain the Institute's headquarters for the next 20 years.

FACETS OF A REVOLUTION

1952–1960

On April 1, 1952, Richard T. Liddicoat Jr. took over as executive director. His work was cut out for him: a complete overhaul of GIA's curriculum, establishing the New York lab within the gem trade, and relocating the cramped Los Angeles headquarters.

But he faced a more immediate problem first: The Institute's survival was again threatened. The way in which Liddicoat and GIA dealt with this challenge would have far-reaching consequences.

■ THE GIA DIAMOND GRADING SYSTEM

In 1951, during Shipley's last year at the Institute, GIA faced a crossroads due to, of all things, the GI Bill of Rights. The very legislation that had revived enrollments after World War II now threatened to shatter the Institute.

The GI Bill's benefits were due to end July 25, 1951. Liddicoat called that last group "the worst bunch of students we ever enrolled." Many said they were "anxious to be gemologists," he explained. "Yet they waited until the last minute to enroll—and then did nothing!"

The new students left just as quickly as they had signed up. Many didn't even meet the minimum GIA and GI Bill requirement to submit a completed lesson within the first 120 days. "They dropped like flies," said Liddicoat.

That last burst—and bust—of enrollments made the Institute's precarious situation all too obvious to its staff. The GI Bill had radically altered the makeup of the student population. By early 1947, veterans made up 60 percent of GIA's 1,500 students. By the summer of 1951, when the bill's benefits ended, 95 percent of the students were veterans. The impending end of the bill's coverage would erase that source of students and income. There were enough GI Bill students to carry GIA into 1953, but unless something was in place by then to consistently bring in more students, "we were going to wind down quite rapidly," said Liddicoat.

Institute officials saw the answer to this problem in improving its diamond evaluation training. Although diamonds were emphasized in the courses, GIA training had what one trade magazine called a "refractive index/specific gravity orientation" geared toward identifying colored stones. Now, with jewelers demanding better knowledge of diamonds to buy and sell them more effectively, the Institute sought to respond with the right courses. First, though, teachers and students alike had to speak the same "diamond

GIA COLOR SCALE

COLORLESS
D
E
F

NEAR COLORLESS
G
H
I
J

FAINT
K
L
M

VERY LIGHT
N
O
P
Q
R
S

LIGHT
T
U
V
W
X
Y
Z

language"—that is, use terms and concepts acceptable and understandable to all. At that time, there was no such common industry standard. Indeed, diamond grading was chaotic and inconsistent because there were so many systems then in use—and misuse. This left industry dialogue about a diamond's features, and therefore its relative value, open to interpretation.

Liddicoat and his staff knew they needed to create a new diamond grading and appraisal system, designed specifically for use in the courses. The new system was intended as a teaching mechanism, not a commercial system. Designing that grading system as quickly as possible took precedence over everything else. GIA's groundbreaking new focus on diamonds had begun.

IN EARLY 1952, about the time he took over the reins of the Institute, Liddicoat and his colleagues—primarily Lester Benson and Joe Phillips, with input from Crowningshield and Krashes—began work on the diamond grading system. It would have three main segments: color, clarity, and cut.

Color grading (and nomenclature) was a major focus because of its inconsistent application in the industry. There was widespread "soft grading"—that is, careless upgrading—of diamond color by dealers, retailers, and appraisers. Terms such as *Rarest White*, *River*, or *Top Wesselton*, once reserved only for "top color" diamonds, were now regularly used with customers to describe stones of somewhat lower quality. Adding to the confusion, many diamond firms cobbled together their own in-house systems—based on three colors, five colors, 10 colors, or even more. Often they used multiple "A" grading, with their best stones designated as "A," "AA," "AAA," "AAAA," or even "AAAAA"! Yet each firm differed in the term and parameters used to designate their top grade. The result: color-grading Babel in diamond houses and at sales counters.

So GIA began working on an accurate, consistent color-grading system for colorless to light yellow diamonds, which represented the majority of diamonds

The D-to-Z diamond color-grading system, using the GIA Color Scale above, was developed by Liddicoat and introduced in 1953. Diamond master stones (right) are used to determine a diamond's color grade based on the relative absence of color.

Tino Hammid/GIA

on the market. They wanted a system based on "absolutes" and opted to use the alphabet—rather than numbers or vague industry terms—for precision and simplicity. But instead of *A* for top white or colorless, they had the novel idea of starting with *D*. It seemed an odd choice to others at the time because *D* was, and still is, used in U.S. education and business to represent subpar quality, with the letter *A* indicating top quality. But GIA chose the letter precisely because *D* had such a poor reputation. Using *D* as the top grade meant the Institute's new system was unlikely to be misinterpreted or misused.

The result was the GIA Color Scale, which began with D (colorless) and continued through the alphabet to Z (light yellow). Each letter grade designated a range of color appearances—or more accurately, the relative absence of color—in a diamond table-down as seen by a trained grader working with controlled lighting and a (pre-graded) master color set of diamonds for comparison.

ANOTHER MAJOR AREA WAS CLARITY GRADING (or "imperfection grading," as GIA first called it), still a source of confusion in the trade. The terms *flawless*, *VVS* (very, very slightly imperfect), *VS* (very slightly imperfect), *SI* (slightly imperfect), and *imperfect* were used in the industry by the early 1950s, but not by everyone. Many, for example, still used *perfect*, noted Krashes later. "There was ambiguity and confusion when it came to diamond clarity, so there was a need for GIA to create a new clarity-grading scale."

Liddicoat and Benson decided that the new clarity scale needed to be more precise than the one currently being used. "There weren't a large enough number of grades to fit the market," said Liddicoat. "We had to have more." So GIA's clarity yardstick divided each category below flawless in two for pricing purposes—VVS_1, VVS_2, VS_1, VS_2, SI_1, SI_2, I_1, and I_2.[1]

"Such exactitude was possible using microscope-based instead of loupe-based clarity grading," noted *Modern Jeweler's* David Federman in 1985. "The shift from loupe to microscope grading was a GIA innovation."

BUT LIDDICOAT WASN'T FINISHED YET. There was a third issue to address if the Institute was to offer a practical grading and appraisal system: diamond "make" (proportion and cut) and its effect on a diamond's value.

GIA CLARITY SCALE

| FLAWLESS |
| INTERNALLY FLAWLESS |
| VVS_1 |
| VVS_2 |
| VS_1 |
| VS_2 |
| SI_1 |
| SI_2 |
| I_1 |
| I_2 |
| I_3 |

VERY VERY SLIGHTLY INCLUDED
VERY SLIGHTLY INCLUDED
SLIGHTLY INCLUDED
INCLUDED

In the modern GIA Clarity Scale, clarity is divided into 11 grades, ranging from Flawless through three levels of Included (originally "Imperfect").

[1] The clarity-grading system was further fine-tuned in subsequent years. In the 1970s, GIA added IF, the internally flawless grade, which would include minor surface blemishes. It also inserted I_3 for diamonds with large inclusions and surface faults that were obviously disfiguring.

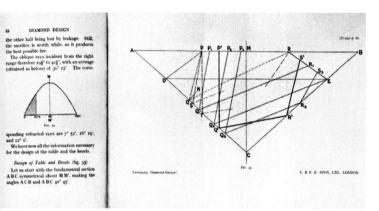

Diamond "make" (proportion and cut) was also incorporated into Liddicoat's grading system. Belgian mathematician and diamond cutter Marcel Tolkowsky's recommended proportions, known since the early 20th century as the "ideal cut," served as the basis.

Surprisingly, GIA's diamond grading and appraising system appears to have been the first to take the impact of make into account, even though it was at the heart of a serious concern in the industry. Simply put, why did top-color stones of like clarity differ so significantly in price per carat?

The reason wasn't just markup; rather, it came back to the way different diamonds were cut and polished—in other words, their make. And some makes allowed more weight retention than others. Liddicoat wanted to clarify this for the jewelry trade with a make-grading system that jewelers could use to relate prices to proportions and enable meaningful comparisons between different makes. The main factor was the degree of weight retention or loss, because the feeling in the trade was that better-proportioned diamonds lost more weight from the rough, and thus were more expensive to produce.

Liddicoat started from a particular set of diamond proportions suggested in the early 20th century by Belgian mathematician and diamond cutter Marcel Tolkowsky, which was subsequently called the "ideal cut." The new make-grading system calculated what a diamond would have weighed had it been cut to "ideal" proportions and then made percentage deductions for proportions that deviated from that. These deductions were totaled and applied as a reduction to the present weight of the stone to determine the "corrected weight" (what the stone would have weighed if cut to "ideal" proportions). This corrected weight was then the weight used for the rest of the evaluation. Last, Liddicoat devised a formula to translate the corrected weight into a reduction from current prices for a top-quality, "ideal cut" stone.

All told, Liddicoat and his staff spent almost 18 months working on GIA's diamond grading system. In the end, they created a "language of diamonds" so simple and effective that any jeweler or dealer could know sight unseen the quality of a diamond just by its letter designations, and could consistently estimate its price based on the grading data for color, clarity, and make.

By early 1953, Liddicoat and his staff were ready to unveil the diamond grading system. They decided to do it in New York City, in the heart of the diamond district. In April 1953, Liddicoat and Crowningshield taught the first one-week Diamond Grading and Evaluation class at New York City's Roosevelt Hotel. Students recorded their observations on a number of diamonds and in turn were evaluated on how skillfully they graded their stones using the new system.

An important part of the class (though since discontinued) was the translation of grading information into diamond value. At the time, Liddicoat explained, most retailers "didn't have much of a clue as to whether they were buying diamonds accurately or effectively, or if they could get the same goods elsewhere for less. So they were delighted when they arrived at the same dollar amount we had calculated. This gave them reassurance and raised their confidence."

WORD-OF-MOUTH ABOUT THE CLASS and grading system spread quickly among local jewelers and diamond dealers. The waiting list of enrollees was so great that the Institute had to schedule one, then two, then four additional one-week Diamond Evaluation classes in New York in the next four months. Jewelers and GIA students on the West Coast wanted the training, too, and the first class in Los Angeles was taught by Liddicoat in late summer.

GIA quickly added its new diamond grading system to the curriculum, and offered Diamond Grading and Evaluation classes. Here, Crowningshield poses with a 1957 traveling class in Columbus, Ohio.

■SPREADING THE NEWS

GIA had a success—a big success—on its hands.

"The fact we had a diamond grading system that arrived at a specific price really appealed to the small retailer," noted Liddicoat. At that time, most small jewelers relied on their diamond dealers for "quality analysis" of the merchandise they purchased. Now, the Institute promised that retailers could accurately evaluate and price their own diamond merchandise, without relying on someone else's judgment.

GIA ADDED THE NEW DIAMOND GRADING SYSTEM to its regular curriculum in 1954. Early that year, the Institute started to take its new diamond grading system directly to towns and cities across the U.S. and Canada, to the grassroots of the jewelry industry—the independent, mom-and-pop jewelers. The first on-the-road classes were taught alternately by Crowningshield and Krashes. They traveled as far north as Toronto, as far west as Hawaii, as far south as Puerto Rico, and back and forth across the continental U.S.

Peter Johnston/GIA

Crucial support for the GIA diamond grading system came in 1955, when De Beers chairman Sir Ernest Oppenheimer authorized the donation of more than 1,500 carats of rough diamonds for use in the Institute's new Diamond Grading and Evaluation classes.

Those on-the-road classes were an eye-opener for many jewelers. "We created a whole new world for jewelers who up to that time had relied only on a loupe," said Krashes. "Can you imagine their delight when we showed them what they could do with a microscope and other diamond-grading equipment?"

For Tony Roskin, the diamond grading class was "like an informal laboratory." Roskin applied his training as soon as he returned to his father's store, Gilbert Roskin Jewelers in Marion, Indiana. The Roskins sold a nationally advertised line of mounted diamond goods that claimed their center stones were "perfect." But after his diamond course, Tony knew they weren't. "We returned many of their pieces for replacement or credit. We also began returning stones and mounted goods to other suppliers."

IN ITS FIRST YEARS, GIA'S DIAMOND GRADING TRAINING received a significant boost from an important trade organization—the Diamond Corp., a part of the De Beers international diamond syndicate. De Beers had been a supporter of GIA from its earliest days. Now, in mid-1955, it gave GIA more than 1,500 carats of rough diamonds for use in its resident and traveling diamond evaluation classes. The donation was personally authorized by De Beers chairman Sir Ernest Oppenheimer.

The sparkling gift, dubbed the "Oppenheimer Student Collection," was made up of diamonds in a variety of shapes, sizes, qualities, and colors, weighing from one to 23 carats. Most of the crystals were industrial quality, but about 200 carats were of a size and quality suitable for cutting so they could be used by the classes. Much of the diamond cutting was donated by the renowned New York diamond firm Lazare Kaplan & Son. As a result of the Oppenheimer donation, students in the diamond grading classes could evaluate a variety of diamonds similar to those available on the market. Equally important, it enabled GIA to offer the popular course throughout the country.

IN 1955, ALMOST ONE-THIRD OF GIA'S DIAMONDS COURSE was revised to include the new grading and evaluation material. A few years later, in 1958, when the correspondence course was completely rewritten, an important—and at the time, highly unusual—feature was added. Before, students had been asked to grade their own stones and send them in for checking. But many of the correspondence-course students couldn't afford to remove diamonds from their own inventories to ship to GIA. So with the new 1958 course, the Institute started mailing "practice" diamonds to students to study and grade.

"People expressed amazement that we would do this. A lot of them said we were nuts!" recalled Liddicoat years later, laughing. "I don't know if we were naive, but it seemed to me that the jewelry industry is based on trust, and we had to take a chance and trust the students."

It was trust well placed. Over the years, losses were virtually nonexistent, and invariably they were due to problems with the mail, not with the students.

The Institute also began providing something else to its diamond students in the late 1950s— diamond price charts, periodically updated, for use with GIA's diamond appraisal system. It did so until the mid-1970s, when the diamond investment boom inflated prices so rapidly that the charts became irrelevant almost as soon as they were printed.

■ THE GIA DIAMOND REPORTS

It began innocuously, with a few mimeographed worksheets. Students in the early diamond evaluation classes used them to record their observations on the diamonds they inspected. At the time, neither teachers nor students gave those worksheets a second thought.

Yet, as Donald S. McNeil, editor emeritus of *Jewelers' Circular-Keystone*, later wrote, those pages "would trigger an upheaval that continues to shake the diamond world." They were the forerunners of the GIA Diamond Grading Reports, the seeds of what would become the Institute's diamond grading service. Ultimately, these reports would set the international standard for objective quality analysis of diamonds.

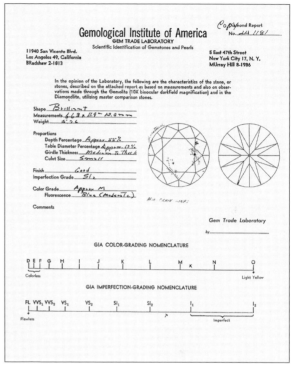

An unintentional by-product of the diamond grading system was the Diamond Grading Report, first issued by the GIA Gem Trade Laboratory in 1955. These reports, which began as student worksheets, were introduced in response to industry demand.

SEVERAL FACTORS IN THE LATE 1950s AND EARLY '60s transformed those wispy little worksheets into arbiters of diamond quality and value. First, jewelers who took GIA's diamond evaluation traveling class or correspondence course wanted to be sure they were using the new system correctly. Soon, students were sending their diamonds to the Institute in New York and Los Angeles for comparison grading. "What they sent us in the beginning were the ones that were most troublesome," added Liddicoat, "to help set them straight."

The new diamond grading system generated far greater awareness of the GIA Gem Trade Laboratory and the Institute at large. Here a 1950s client submits a piece of jewelry for examination, as Crowningshield waits behind the window.

But eventually jewelers found it easier simply to send their diamonds to GIA to be graded rather than do it themselves. "Inevitably," said Liddicoat, "requests for grading became quite common."

MEANWHILE, WORD SPREAD that GIA had created a precise, consistently reliable grading system. Some of New York's diamond cutters, dealers, and retailers began bringing their diamonds to the Gem Trade Laboratory. The "grading" at that point was little more than a friendly gesture.

"It wasn't anything formal," recalled Krashes. "We jotted down facts about the diamond, such as round or emerald cut, on the same type of worksheet the students used in practice grading."

Then, in 1955, GIA issued its first diamond reports. The Institute consciously decided not to use the word *certificate*, because it would appear to validate the diamond itself, as opposed to objectively reporting information about the stone.

Those original reports included weight, clarity grade, color grade, degree of ultraviolet fluorescence, and a description of the stone's proportions (depth percentage, diameter, girdle thickness, and culet size). There was no charge to students for the reports. If the work was done for a company, "we charged a ridiculously small amount in terms of the time spent," Liddicoat said.

As the trade's awareness of the grading system and terminology grew, and as more dealers or their employees began taking the class in the late '50s, "cutters and brokers would bring stones in that they had pre-graded, hoping they would be D, E, or F," said Crowningshield. "If they weren't, we didn't issue a report. It was still just a consultation."

AT THE SAME TIME, TRADE MEMBERS LEARNED that a positive evaluation couldn't be "bought" from GIA. It took a while for some to get the message. In the early days, Crowningshield and Krashes were each offered substantial amounts of money—equal to more than a year's salary—to raise the grade on a diamond. "Obviously, we turned it down," said Krashes.

In Crowningshield's case, a man came into his office with a report that he wanted altered. Attached was a $1,000 bill. Crowningshield—a tall man— stood up and shouted at him, "If that's the way you think we operate, why should we even look at your diamonds? GET OUT OF HERE!" As the client scurried through the doorway, colleague Eunice Miles rushed in. "I've never heard you raise your voice like that before," she exclaimed.

Such incidents were important turning points for the Gem Trade Laboratory, said Krashes. "When word got out on the street that we couldn't be 'had' for any amount of money, confidence in our reports skyrocketed."

The laboratory was swiftly earning a solid reputation for objectivity, accuracy, and integrity. Important industry figures began consulting GIA for evaluations of the diamonds they bought and sold.

One of the first retailers in New York to request GIA's reports on a regular basis was luxury jeweler Harry Winston. He used them, recalled Crowningshield, to "assure customers overseas that they were getting top-rated stones—and to avoid sending stones overseas if potential sales were uncertain." Winston was the laboratory's biggest diamond grading client, and his routine use of the service lent it further credibility.

Among the New York diamond dealers who sold overseas, one of the first to have his stones graded by the Gem Trade Laboratory was Arthur Reik, a specialist in fancy-color diamonds. Reik used GIA's reports to document the quality of the large diamonds he sold.

One of Reik's clients was a Milanese diamond dealer. The cultured Italian gentleman visited New York regularly to inspect the diamonds Reik had selected for him and to review the accompanying grading reports. He would compare the stones with the reports and choose the ones he wanted. But as the dealer aged, his vision began to fail, and he could no longer use a loupe effectively. So in the late 1950s, he told Reik to "let the professors grade them." Reik was to send him the GIA reports—in which he now had fullest confidence. Based solely on those reports, he chose the diamonds he wanted.

The Italian dealer was the first person in Europe known to use GIA's grading reports to sell his diamonds. As stones began to circulate accompanied by reports, European dealers and clients began to take notice. More of them asked to have their stones graded by GIA and requested copies of the diamond reports.

Security spurred foreign and domestic use of the reports as well. Gems sent overseas sometimes disappeared on the way, even if sent by registered air mail. (New York's John F. Kennedy Airport was an especially risky spot in the mid-'60s for diamond merchandise in transit.) That led more overseas buyers to demand GIA diamond reports from their suppliers in lieu of the stones themselves. By the late 1960s, many people were buying stones simply from the reports rather than after seeing the actual gem itself. It was a development that would have significant implications within two decades.

Peter Johnston/GIA

During the 1950s, legendary "Jeweler to the Stars" Harry Winston became the biggest client for GIA's diamond grading services.

The Institute's board of governors had its doubts about the way the industry used GIA's diamond grading system. Some members believed the Institute should teach jewelers how to grade their own diamonds, not offer an actual diamond grading service. "They said we were in the business of training jewelers, not in the business of doing jewelers' work for them," said Crowningshield. Some also thought the service looked a little too much like an appraisal business, which they wanted GIA's labs to stay out of.

But most of the opposition to the grading system and reports came from the diamond trade itself. According to Krashes, in the late 1950s and '60s many in the New York diamond houses grumbled, "Who are they to grade diamonds? What do they know about diamonds?"

"That was an understandable reaction," he added. "These diamond people had been in their field all their lives. So when we introduced our consistent system of grading, they were initially defensive."

Some suppliers also objected to providing jewelers with the means to determine prices for themselves. The antagonism lessened over the years as GIA's diamond grading system and terminology were absorbed into the industry. But even at the end of the 20th century, decades after the system was introduced, some resentment lingered.

"There are still some people who don't want to be told how to evaluate a diamond," said Krashes. "But in the main, the industry has come to recognize the value of GIA's grading system."

GIA HAD CREATED ITS DIAMOND GRADING SYSTEM to attract more students as the Institute faced a financial challenge. And it achieved that objective, making the correspondence and traveling classes considerably more popular, while strengthening the diamond merchandising expertise of professional jewelers. As its language became the norm in retail and wholesale sectors in the U.S. and around the world, the GIA diamond grading system finally provided what the trade needed most: a widely accepted standard for diamond evaluation. Within a quarter-century, GIA grading reports became the benchmarks of diamond quality, respected globally by trade and consumer alike.

Not only that, the diamond grading system improved GIA's standing in the industry. While the Institute had been respected for its theoretical training and gem equipment, "until we went into grading and appraising in such detail, there was a feeling that GIA wasn't relevant" to the trade's practical daily needs, Liddicoat commented.

But with the advent of the diamond grading system and reports, people in the trade began to think of the Institute "as *part* of the industry, rather than an ivory-tower institution, and that is what has really differentiated GIA from all other gemological training in the world."

■ THE EARLY YEARS OF THE NEW YORK LAB

In 1953, a gemologist who would later become known as "The *Grande Dame* of Gemology" joined GIA's New York staff.

Eunice Miles had impressed Shipley and Edward Wigglesworth in the late 1930s with her interest in gemology, and had gone on to become one of the first women gemologists. In the decade between earning her C.G. in 1944 and joining GIA New York, she made some impressive additions to her resumé. She assisted Dr. Fred Pough of the American Museum of Natural History and created the black-and-white illustrations for *Petersen's Field Guide to Rocks and Minerals*. She lectured on gems to civic groups and classrooms, appeared on television, and wrote a number of articles on gems and gemology.

Eunice Miles, here flanked by Bob Crowningshield and Bert Krashes, became one of the stalwarts of the GIA Gem Trade Laboratory in New York during the 1950s and '60s.

Miles exemplified "what can be accomplished when training is coordinated with imagination and initiative," wrote *The Loupe* in announcing her hiring in late 1953. Still, despite her credentials, Miles' gender was an obstacle in the 1950s. The jewelry trade itself—except for the mom-and-pop shops—was male dominated.

Not long after Miles joined the staff, two dealers brought in an important diamond that they said they wanted "the boys"—Crowningshield and Krashes—to see. They went into Crowningshield's office, set up the microscope on his desk, and proceeded to examine it. Then Miles' colleagues invited her in to take a look. She did—and immediately found a pinpoint inclusion that the men had missed. The diamond dealers were astonished and appreciative. It was her introduction to the city's diamond trade and her symbolic initiation into the laboratory staff.

"After that," Miles said, "the door to the Gem Trade Lab was always open to me . . . and 'we' became 'three.'"

THE DIAMOND
DEALER STARED AT
EUNICE MILES IN
DISBELIEF. "WHAT
CAN A WOMAN KNOW
ABOUT DIAMONDS?"

But widespread acceptance by the diamond trade took longer. In one instance in the mid-'50s, a member of the Diamond Dealers Club (DDC) was annoyed with the results of a diamond report. He saw two sets of initials on it, "GRC" and "ERM." The dealer recognized "GRC" (Crowningshield) and went to the lab, where he told Miles—whom he took to be the receptionist— that he wanted to see Bob Crowningshield. But when Miles explained that Crowningshield was away, the dealer loudly demanded to see "the other man who signed this report."

"Sir," replied Miles calmly, "you are speaking to the 'other man.' Those are my initials."

The diamond dealer stared at her in disbelief. "What do you mean?" he demanded angrily. "You are a woman! What can a woman know about diamonds?"

As time went by, more people came to recognize and respect her initials on the diamond grading reports. But Miles knew she was truly accepted on "The Street" when she was invited to visit the DDC by its president as a personal guest. He cordially greeted her at the door and took her to a trading table to observe transactions between club members; many were Hasidic Jewish men who couldn't even shake hands with her for religious reasons. But Miles wasn't offended. Instead, she said later, sitting there and watching gave her a better understanding of the diamond dealers. And throughout her long GIA career, Miles said, "the dealers always treated me with respect."

IN CONTRAST TO ITS BUSY SCHEDULE IN LATER YEARS, the first years of GIA's New York office were slow paced and low key. Business was sporadic. Indeed, there were many periods when there were no stones at all to test. "When the phone rang, we all got up to answer it," said Krashes. "If someone knocked at the door, we all got up to see who it was, to see the stone a client brought, and to talk to the person who brought it!" The small staff used the time to grade correspondence papers and study gemology. "We tore into every stone and pearl that came in," said Krashes. This knowledge, he said later, helped equip them for the future.

Throughout the 1950s, it was common for lab staff to casually interrupt a class—the lab and classroom were separated only by a door—to show students an especially beautiful or unusual gem.

But students weren't the only ones interested in the lab's work. During the early years, curious construction workers next door often peered in through the windows. One worker tapped on Crowningshield's window and was invited in. The worker said he was from Russia, and that his mother had worn a Russian alexandrite when he was a child. He asked to see one of GIA's alexandrites.

Crowningshield produced a Brazilian alexandrite, which turned from bluish green to purple. The fascinated Russian said his mother's had turned from green to red. "It was his first lesson in gemology," Eunice Miles said, "that the same gem variety can vary in color according to its geologic origin."

Satisfied, the worker thanked Crowningshield and said with a smile, "I'll take the Russian kind." With that, he went back out the window.

The spectroscope (foreground) was the gem identification tool that set the stage for several important discoveries at the Gem Trade Laboratory during the 1950s.

DESPITE THE INFORMALITY, valuable work was being accomplished at the New York lab. Crowningshield, Krashes, and Miles tracked trends, conducted gemological research, and tackled important identification problems, particularly those involving synthetic and imitation gems and pearls. Still, the gem trade paid little attention to these activities at the New York lab. "Until we accomplished something that meant something to them, we didn't interest them," Crowningshield said.

That "something" would revolutionize the burgeoning field of gem identification and establish GIA's reputation in diamond research.

■DISCOVERIES IN THE REALM OF LIGHT

G. Robert Crowningshield used the spectroscope so effectively—changing the world of gemology in the process—that his international reputation is inseparable from it.

A spectroscope is an instrument that separates the white light that passes through or is reflected from a gem into its component spectral colors. The wavelengths of visible light absorbed by the gem appear as black lines or bands on the spectrum; these features are called "absorption bands." The position and number of these bands are constant for stones of the same chemical composition, making the spectroscope a useful identification tool.

Ironically, the man who was to open up new worlds of gemological research and understanding with the spectroscope didn't have the foggiest idea how

**CROWNINGSHIELD
WORKED WITH THE
SINGLE-MINDEDNESS
OF A MAN POSSESSED.**

to use one early in his career at GIA. In New York, Crowningshield periodically tried to use a Beck handheld spectroscope in his lab work. "I just couldn't get the hang of it," Crowningshield said.

The epiphany came after Bert Krashes joined the staff and Liddicoat had returned to California. Crowningshield and Krashes were tinkering with the Beck spectroscope one day in 1950 when Hans Myhre—a gemologist and wholesale jeweler from Oslo—stopped by. Myhre, learning of their frustration, slipped a garnet in front of the instrument and spent the next half-hour demonstrating how to use it. That casual incident was a life-changing moment for the young Bob Crowningshield, and a history-making moment for gemology.

USING A HANDHELD SPECTROSCOPE, Crowningshield began studying the absorption patterns of every gem that came into the lab for identification—and any other gem he could get his hands on. He began recording the spectra he observed, developing his own method for making realistic reproductions of absorption spectra. First he taped a piece of white paper on the table next to his spectroscope. On top of the paper, he taped a handmade stencil—a piece of thin, transparent plastic out of which he had cut a rectangle the same size as the paper. Then he applied some charcoal dust to the left side of the paper (representing the dark end of the spectrum).

For the next 30 to 60 minutes, depending on the complexity of the spectrum, he would hunch over the spectroscope, keenly observing the patterns of a particular gem. Every few moments he would turn to the stencil and use cotton swabs, erasers, and pencils to work the charcoal dust to resemble the spectrum, with its various gray to black areas, bands, and thin lines. In the beginning, he often was dissatisfied and would start all over again. Once he felt he had captured the image accurately, he placed it in a plastic sleeve and added it to a loose-leaf binder.

CROWNINGSHIELD WORKED WITH THE SINGLE-MINDEDNESS of a man possessed. Krashes recalled him coming in on cold Saturday mornings. "Even though the building's heat was turned off, he would be sitting there in his overcoat, delving into the spectra of gems, making those marvelous diagrams by hand, rubbing and inventing a smudging technique to show the various bands and lines in gemstones."

Tom Moses, a Crowningshield protégé who went on to become vice president of identification services at the Gem Trade Laboratory in the 1990s, remembered his mentor's legacy. "It is remarkable to see how closely he reproduced what a gemologist can actually see in a spectroscope. And it was fun to watch him. He was like an artist mixing his paints, dabbing here and there, and mixing again to get the right effect."

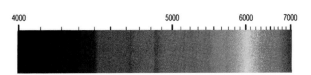

Although subsequent advances in technology made such precise handmade creations unnecessary, Crowningshield's images continued to be used and referred to for decades, in much the same way that naturalist John J. Audubon's famous 19th-century paintings of rare birds continued to be used even after the advent of photography.

Looking through the spectroscope, Crowningshield painstakingly reproduced by hand the absorption pattern of every transparent gem variety submitted to the New York lab. Shown here is his drawing for spessartite garnet.

BY THE MID-1950s, Crowningshield had created 113 different records, what David Federman of *Modern Jeweler* later described as "his own database of hand-drawn spectra . . . for just about every facetable gem used in jewelry."

At the end of the 1950s, Crowningshield sent his collection of hand-drawn spectra (which resembled black-and-white photographs when reproduced) to GIA headquarters in California. They were used in Liddicoat's *Handbook of Gem Identification* starting with the sixth edition in 1962. The book's chapter on spectroscopy was also rewritten based on Crowningshield's work.

Crowningshield and his lab colleagues used the spectroscope to identify not only a variety of natural gems, but also the expanding array of synthetic and treated stones flowing into the market. Indeed, the work of the GIA Gem Trade Laboratory in the 1950s increasingly focused on this growing area of concern. And it was in this arena that Crowningshield and his spectroscope would crack an important gem-detection case.

■ "THE MYSTERIOUS LINE": THE HUNT FOR 5920 Å

An unexpected result of splitting the atom was the growing influx of treated diamonds, especially yellow diamonds, into the market in the early 1950s. Treated diamonds were so abundant by the mid-1950s that Crowningshield wrote, "One of the problems presented to the jeweler of the Atomic Age [is] determining whether the color of a diamond is natural or produced by some type of atomic bombardment."

It was also GIA's problem. Its laboratory on both coasts was being pressured by jewelers and dealers to find a way to distinguish between natural- and treated-color diamonds. Many in the trade refused to handle yellow diamonds in particular due to uncertainty over possible treatment.

One of the major issues facing the gem trade in the 1950s was detection of treatment in irradiated yellow diamonds, such as those shown here.

THE INSTITUTE'S SEARCH FOR A WAY TO IDENTIFY treated diamonds began in 1953, only a couple of weeks before GIA introduced its new diamond grading system. That March, at the AGS Conclave, Krashes and Crowningshield examined what they called their "first really attractive yellow-treated diamonds." The diamond dealer who showed them the diamonds had treated them himself, he told them. Indeed, that was the only way they knew the gems were treated, because there weren't any visual clues. The implications to the gem and jewelry industry were clear, said Crowningshield: "We realized we had to find a way to detect this."

Crowningshield felt that the best tool—indeed the only suitable tool—would be the spectroscope. Diamonds that underwent a yellow color change by irradiation in a nuclear reactor, followed by heat treatment, were virtually indistinguishable from natural-color diamonds. But, he theorized, the process that changed their color so significantly might also cause a change in their absorption spectra—and perhaps that could be detected with a spectroscope.

OVER THE NEXT SEVERAL MONTHS, Crowningshield and his colleagues labored over the problem. It was a tedious, frustrating process. In early 1955, production of golden colors in diamonds by irradiation increased significantly. And the Gem Trade Lab still hadn't found a way to identify them because, except in some cyclotron-treated stones, there were no visible clues. The problem became so serious that the New York lab refused to issue reports on any colored diamonds unless "evidence of cyclotron treatment is present." Then, in January 1956, the answer was handed to them—literally.

"We received a round yellow diamond, about 19 carats," said Crowningshield. "It was the biggest one we had ever seen, and it offered the best opportunity to see if there was something about this diamond's color that was due to treatment."

Careful study by Crowningshield revealed a narrow, distinct absorption line at the 5920 Å point on the spectroscope. As far as he could determine, the band had never been recorded in the literature on the absorption characteristics of diamond. However, this diamond's size made it easy to see its lines. And this line definitely stood out. Here was the clue Crowningshield had been searching for.

"I was very excited," he recalled. "I wanted to show it to Bert right away, but he had just left for lunch." When Krashes returned a short time later, Crowningshield took him to the spectroscope to show him what he had found, but it was gone. The line had disappeared!

400 450 500 550 600 650 700

A major breakthrough in gem identification came in early 1956, when Crowningshield discovered the 5920 Å (592 nm) absorption line in irradiated yellow diamonds.

Crowningshield, startled for a moment, suddenly realized what had happened: Light from the viewing projector to which he had attached the spectroscope had heated the diamond, causing the line to disappear. It was another unexpected but valuable insight that would become part of the detection methodology.

He knew he had to cool the stone, but how? "Suddenly, I had an idea," said Crowningshield, retelling the tale years later. "I ran downstairs to a local candy shop on the corner which sold ice cream and bought a piece of dry ice." Then, he rushed back up the five flights of stairs to the lab, put the diamond on ice, looked, and the line was visible once more. The initial method was primitive, but the principle is still being used today, with more sophisticated options for cooling diamonds to extremely low temperatures.

The 5920 Å line was the clue that GIA and the trade needed to identify irradiated yellow diamonds. Ironically, while the 19-carat diamond flaunted its internal 5920 Å line, it also had "no visual evidence of treatment." So Crowningshield was forced to issue a report that said "no evidence was observed that, in the opinion and experience of the Laboratory, would prove the origin of the color of the diamond."

Rumors spread through the diamond district that GIA's lab had found a way to identify treated diamonds, but Crowningshield wasn't ready to make a public statement based on a single observation. "Before we announced anything, we had to be sure that what we had was foolproof," he explained later.

The Gem Trade Lab launched a 10-month research marathon, involving gem experts in America and Europe in a study of some 10,000 stones to track down what Crowningshield now called "the mysterious line." The project itself was another first for GIA: Never before in gemology had there been such an intensive test of a theory. It was good science, and it laid the foundation for the rigorous analysis common in today's gemology.

"Å" is the symbol for the angstrom unit (one ten-billionth of a meter), by which wavelengths of the visible spectrum were then reported. By the latter part of the century, the preferred international unit was nanometer (one billionth of a meter, or 10 Å), and this line was written as 592 nm.

GIA MADE ARRANGEMENTS TO EXAMINE as many known treated diamonds as possible. One dealer of treated diamonds, Theodore Moed of New York, was especially helpful, providing his entire stock of treated and untreated diamonds for GIA's examination. "With careful observation," wrote

SUDDENLY, SAID
LIDDICOAT, GIA'S
NEW YORK LAB "HAD
BECOME AN ENTITY TO
BE RECKONED WITH."

Crowningshield later, "we were able to find the mysterious 5920 line present in every yellow to gold-yellow treated stone," as well as some brown treated stones.

The next task was to evaluate natural yellow diamonds "of unquestioned history." That task was tougher, but they actually found quite a few, including those in the collections of the American Museum of Natural History, Tiffany & Co., and many others. The result: The line was absent from natural stones.

For scientific accuracy and precision, Crowningshield and his associates next tested hundreds of yellow non-gem rough of such poor quality it was unlikely anyone would have been tempted to treat it. Not one contained the mysterious line at 5920 Å.

Crowningshield published his findings in the Winter 1957–1958 issue of *Gems & Gemology*, in an article titled "Spectroscopic Recognition of Yellow Bombarded Diamonds and Bibliography of Diamond Treatment." Meanwhile, the GIA Gem Trade Laboratory began issuing reports on yellow diamonds stating that "it is the opinion of the laboratory that the presence of an absorption line at 5920 Å in the spectroscope is strongly indicative of color induced by atomic bombardment."

The impact on the trade was immediate and significant. The number of yellow diamonds sent to the lab for identification rose sharply. Auction houses and galleries put out the word that anyone who wanted them to handle canary-yellow diamonds loose or in jewelry had better first get a GIA diamond grading report.

Suddenly, said Liddicoat, GIA's New York lab "had become an entity to be reckoned with."

ONE INCIDENT IN 1958 MADE THE LAB a household word not only in New York's gem trade and jewelry salons, but also in living rooms across Eisenhower-era America. Like a fairy tale, it began with a beautiful princess—in this case, Princess Nina (British model Nina Dyer), wife of Prince Sadruddin Aga Khan. She had purchased $250,000 of jewelry containing three large yellow diamonds (including a 70-carat pendant) and a black pearl from renowned jeweler Harry Winston.

When she brought the jewelry to GIA's New York lab for verification, "we were flabbergasted," recalled Krashes. "It wasn't often that a princess visited GIA's lab!"

After thorough study, Crowningshield and Krashes found not only that the color in the diamonds was due to treatment, but also that the pearls were cultured and dyed black. Liddicoat, for his part, was "scared to death" by the finding. "What if Winston challenged the report and sued us?" he said later, only half kidding.

When the princess returned, Crowningshield and Krashes carefully explained the bad news to her. They pointed out that the luxury retailer couldn't have known the gems were treated, because that could only be determined with equipment such as the spectroscope. The princess returned the jewelry to Winston, who refunded her money.

That finding was "a big feather in our cap," said Krashes. "Subsequently, Winston and others started to send a lot of diamonds to us for grading and color-origin reports." The story was written up by popular gossip columnist Walter Winchell and even made it into *Time* magazine later that year.

IN SUBSEQUENT YEARS, CROWNINGSHIELD USED THE SPECTROSCOPE to make other discoveries. In the late 1950s, for example, he investigated one dealer's lament that expensive jadeite cabochons were being returned by his customers because the gems were fading badly. Tests were available to show whether the jade had been dyed, but they were destructive, so he couldn't use them on stones he wanted to purchase. A nondestructive way to detect dye was needed.

In his research, Crowningshield found a distinct change in the spectrum of jadeite that was caused by the dye, which made it easier to distinguish the treated material from natural-color jade. Dealers began having their jade shipments checked for dyed material, and by 1961 *Jewelers' Circular-Keystone* reported, "Complaints about fading jade have died away."

In just a few years after Hans Myhre's visit, Crowningshield's use of the spectroscope had transformed it from an interesting but rarely used instrument into an essential gemological tool.

■LEAVING THE IVORY TOWER

Meanwhile, long-overdue revisions to GIA's curriculum were in progress. One was GIA's first resident jewelry merchandising (store management) class, launched in 1952. Held on the University of Southern California campus, the two-week course (conducted jointly by GIA and USC School of Commerce instructors) taught practical business methods. The class was enthusiastically received, but it was simply too short to do more than cover the bare essentials of merchandising. The class was dropped, but not GIA's intent to teach jewelers useful, practical business methods.

Howard Wechsler/GIA

Bob Crowningshield's five decades of research using the spectroscope represented a monumental contribution to gem identification.

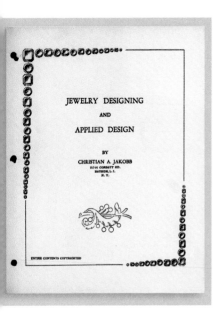

Christian Jakobb's jewelry design course was incorporated into GIA's curriculum in 1956, the Institute's first venture into design.

Another course added to the curriculum was GIA's first venture into jewelry design. Christian Jakobb was a famous New York jewelry designer who taught for many years at the New York Mechanics Institute. But by 1954, he was in his mid-70s and ready to retire. Wanting to perpetuate his jewelry design course, and believing that GIA was the most appropriate organization to do so, he asked the Institute to take it over.

GIA agreed, and in September 1956 the Christian Jakobb design course—later simply called jewelry design—was added to the correspondence-course curriculum. The program taught sketching and rendering finished designs, design interpretation, and the art of wax carving and modeling. All necessary materials and tools were provided. Although this course, too, wasn't as successful as GIA had hoped, it marked the beginning of the Institute's efforts to develop a satisfactory jewelry design program.

THE BIGGEST CHANGE IN THE INSTITUTE'S CURRICULUM proved to be a shift in its educational philosophy. The early courses composed by Shipley and his advisors were heavily scientific and theoretical. That was a necessity at a time when many jewelers were ignorant of gemology fundamentals. But by the mid-1950s, some of that material was simply too esoteric.

"Shipley had made every effort to make the early courses practical, but some material frightened students unnecessarily," noted Liddicoat. "There was a lot of ivory tower information which wasn't useful over the counter. So we tried to more effectively implement his vision by making them more relevant to the independent jeweler's daily business operations."

The new emphasis on practicality meant the entire curriculum had to be reviewed, rewritten, and restructured. To that end, GIA abandoned course numbers in favor of descriptive names such as Colored Stones.

Three other changes in particular reflected Liddicoat's determination to make information easier for students to learn and apply. One was the way students' knowledge was tested. Studies by educators showed not only that multiple-choice questions were preferable to essay-type ones, but also that in home-study programs the number of lessons completed per student increased substantially with multiple choice. So the Institute replaced most of the essay questions with multiple-choice questions.

A second change was to make the courses visually engaging. During this time, GIA introduced attractive illustrations throughout its course materials, which were now printed rather than mimeographed.

A third major change concerned the number of assignments in each course. GIA educators found that many students completed a correspondence lesson in a single sitting. This meant that students would find it easier to finish their diploma if they had fewer assignments, even if those assignments were longer. So in the late 1950s, the Institute reduced the total number of assignments from 139 to 119. The result: A higher percentage of students obtained their diplomas, with a shorter time to completion.

IN 1958, the restructured resident gemology courses—diamonds, colored stones, and gem identification—and the completely revised diamonds correspondence course were published. Meanwhile, GIA was expanding its one-week traveling classes, adding gem identification, jewelry design, and diamond setting. Liddicoat was pleased with the results of the decade of work on GIA's curriculum. "We had something now that was more down to earth and acceptable for a store owner to be willing to pay for the course for his employees," he said later. "That had a lot to do with [the Institute's] growth from that point on."

Thanks to the greater relevance and practicality of GIA's courses and traveling classes—as well as publicity in national magazines such as *Time* and *The Saturday Evening Post* and appearances by Institute officials and graduates on local and national TV shows—"almost every year has seen a new record in the number of civilian enrollments," reported *Jewelers' Circular-Keystone*. Just as important, more of those enrollees stayed with their studies to completion.

IT HAD BEEN ONLY 30 YEARS SINCE ROBERT SHIPLEY had founded the Institute and spurred the gemology movement, "no more than a twinkling of an eye [compared to] the five thousand years during which men have polished gems and fashioned jewelry," noted *Jewelers' Circular-Keystone* in a 1961 report assessing GIA's impact. Yet in that brief time, "man's scientific knowledge of gemstones advanced by giant steps," largely due to the Institute, which had "developed an ever-expanding body of scientific knowledge and applied it to an area where, for centuries, judgment depended largely upon intuition or inheritance."

Significantly, the GIA-trained individual who entered the retail jewelry business at the end of the 1950s no longer had to rely on "parental jewelry tradition," the article continued. He could compete "on equal terms with more venerable firms in the arena of gemological knowledge [and] build his own tradition, that of being a man who really knows jewels."

These developments were signposts to an era—only a few years away—of soaring growth and international influence for the Institute.

A NEW HOME

The San Vicente facility served as GIA headquarters from 1956 to 1976.

By the early 1950s, GIA's headquarters on Alexandria Avenue was simply too small, too cramped, and too inadequate to meet the Institute's needs, even with the drop-off in enrollments after the end of the GI Bill in 1951.

"We had totally outgrown the place," said Liddicoat. Some GIA governors recognized that the Institute needed something bigger and designed to meet its modern needs, not those of the 1930s. GIA was growing so quickly that in 1951, board member Clifford Josephson Jr. told a reporter that, at this rate, "someday we'll build a school to train youngsters in [this] business."

That same year, the GIA Board of Governors authorized construction of a new headquarters. Not until January 1954, however, did the board give the go-ahead to build a new home. By then, GIA's endowment fund, set up in 1942, had grown to more than $100,000. The board used $32,000 of it to buy a lot at 11940 San Vicente Boulevard in the Brentwood section of Los Angeles, and retained Richard Neutra to design the new headquarters. Neutra, one of the great architects of the 20th century, was a leading advocate of functionalism in architecture and developed a style known as "California Modern."

He began designing the building in late 1954, working closely with the staff. Construction began in February 1955, and in late September of that year GIA moved into its spacious new headquarters. (Planning and construction costs eventually totaled just under half a million dollars.) The San Vicente location was formally dedicated on February 27, 1956, in conjunction with the 26th annual meeting of the Institute's board of governors.

The new building, a functional, box-like design, provided larger facilities for every department and a large classroom that could be divided into two by drawing a folded door. The new West Coast GIA Gem Trade Laboratory had a complete X-ray room and a full complement of gem-testing instruments, as well as equipment for photographing gemstones and jewelry.

In back was a patio with a small reflecting pool next to a spiral staircase—a modernist 1950s touch—up to the second floor. At the top of the staircase was a round shield on the banister with the word "G E M," one letter each in the 9, 12, and 3 o'clock positions.

Plaques from the old Alexandria Avenue headquarters were rededicated in recognition of the achievements of Robert and Beatrice Shipley; Godfrey Eacret, GIA's first chairman and indispensable early supporter (for whom the lab was named in the 1940s); and Dr. Edward Wigglesworth, GIA's first president and director of its first Eastern laboratory.

Standing at the top of the staircase, left to right, are Kenneth Moore, Gale Johnson, Richard Liddicoat, and Lester Benson.

The building wasn't completely occupied by the Institute. Neutra's design included two ground-level retail storefronts that GIA rented out, until it needed them, just as Shipley had done 15 years earlier. Indeed, that retail rental space was "one of the ways we sold the board of governors on approving the new headquarters," explained Liddicoat decades later. "They actually insisted on it, so we could expand into the storefronts if we needed to."

GIA officials, including Liddicoat, were satisfied with the Institute's new home. "We thought it would care for our needs for some time to come," he said. "That was a mistake. It wasn't long before we outgrew that, too."

This photo, taken at the 1968 Conclave, shows many of the people who shaped the Institute during the 1960s. Standing, left to right: Bert Krashes, Joe Murphy, John Charter, Richard Liddicoat, Bob Earnest, Glenn Nord, Bob Crowningshield, Chuck Fryer, Ken Moore, and Gale Johnson. Seated: Steve Zack, Eunice Miles, and T. J. Barrows.

BEARING FRUIT

1960–1969

The decade of the 1960s was a turbulent time in the U.S.—demonstrations, an unpopular war, advances in civil rights, and a loosening of social restrictions.

But for the Gemological Institute of America, it was a time to nurture what it had planted in the 1950s. The Institute deepened its roots in the gem and jewelry industry and grew, using its one-week traveling classes to change how jewelers bought and sold. It signed up important retailers such as Zale Corp., added innovations in diamond education, created a full-time resident education program, and gained staff members who would lead the Institute through the final third of the 20th century.

■CHANGING FACES

While America mourned the shocking deaths of President John F. Kennedy and later Martin Luther King Jr. and Kennedy's brother Robert, GIA faced a different kind of loss, with the departure of valued veterans.

Lester Benson, the Institute's Renaissance man, died suddenly in 1961 at the age of 39. In less than 15 years, Benson—a G.G. and FGA with distinction—had made a significant impact on GIA and gemology as an instructor, researcher, inventor, and writer.

Not only was Benson a charismatic teacher, but he also helped develop GIA's diamond grading system, its first correspondence course in jewelry design, and effective ways to teach appraising. With fellow instructor Kenneth Moore, Benson created new gem-testing equipment in the 1950s. He had a "rare ability to mentally create an object, sketch it on paper, and then fashion the tools necessary to make it," noted an American Gem Society tribute.

As supervisor of GIA's research laboratory, Benson developed a number of tests used in gem labs around the world, including the "spot method" for determining refractive indices of polished materials with curved surfaces. An expert in gem identification and photomicrography, he also redesigned the lab's X-ray diffraction unit and adapted the spectrophotometer for gemological studies.

In the weeks following his death, the Institute was deluged by hundreds of letters of condolence from students, graduates, former associates, and industry leaders. "Gemology," wrote Liddicoat, was "robbed of one of its leaders."

When Lester Benson died suddenly in 1961, Liddicoat wrote, "Gemology was robbed of one of its leaders."

OTHER VETERAN STAFF MEMBERS RETIRED. One was a creator and sustainer of GIA, the woman whose handwritten notes attached to lessons had inspired hundreds of early students, the acknowledged "right hand" of Beatrice and Robert M. Shipley, and later Richard Liddicoat: the seemingly indispensable Dorothy Jasper Smith.

When she retired in 1963, Liddicoat summarized her contributions in a letter. "You made friends of hundreds of correspondence students. You enrolled them and shepherded them through the courses," he wrote. "You saw deadlines were met, first for Mr. Shipley, then for me. . . . Each day's enrollment delighted you. Each new success was your success."

Bea Shipley put it aptly. Through Dorothy Smith's decades of service and support to the Institute, she wrote, "You became 'Mrs. GIA.'"

BUT THERE WERE NEW FACES to fill the gaps left by the departing veterans. One was Gale Johnson, a Minnesota watchmaker and jeweler who received his G.G. in 1954. Johnson joined GIA in 1959, and for two years he was an instructor in the traveling classes.

But Johnson also had a strong interest in instrument design. (In addition to being a licensed watchmaker, he had been trained as an optical instrument technician and photographic technician during four years with the Marine Corps in the late 1940s.) After Benson's death, Johnson bought half interest in the instrument manufacturing company started by Benson and Ken Moore. Johnson and Moore renamed it Marcus McFall Inc.—their middle names—and began work on a new generation of instruments.

At that point the business was part-time, and they were the entire staff. But within a couple of years, it had grown into a full-time operation with a small crew; Moore was in charge of sales, while Johnson oversaw development and manufacturing. In 1964, they sold the company to GIA. Both men kept their respective positions in what was then GIA's instruments division (named GEM Instruments in 1977).

Research and design of an instrument, Johnson later explained to *Jewelers' Circular-Keystone*, involved "months of sweat." He and his fellow designers would "carry around a dozen problems at any one time," he said. "The problem generally is that we'd like to build a better instrument—a darker field, a smaller refractometer, or something to give better identification of some synthetic. You carry all these problems with you, and hopefully, every so often an answer comes up." Solutions might come from conversations with other staff members or simply skimming trade journals in machinery design. Often, Johnson added, creation of a new device didn't involve new ideas, but "just different ways of putting the pieces together."

Through the rest of the 1960s and '70s, Johnson and Moore led the division in creating or revising a number of important instruments. As gemology became even more established within the jewelry industry, the Institute was able to keep pace with the growing demand for microscopes, spectroscopes, refractometers, dichroscopes, polariscopes, and other products.

Gale Johnson joined the Institute in 1959 and (with Ken Moore) headed GIA's instruments division through the 1960s and '70s.

ANOTHER NEWCOMER was a former military counterintelligence agent, jeweler, and watchmaker named Glenn Nord. Nord was to have a significant impact on GIA, aggressively spreading its gemological teachings, assisting Liddicoat as an administrator, and eventually leading the Institute through one of its most difficult periods in the mid-1980s.

Although he studied economics at the University of North Dakota, there was "always something about gems that really interested me," Nord said, "ever since seventh grade when I first caught the fever, reading a story about gems that sparked my curiosity."

After he graduated from college, Nord went to the top jeweler in his hometown of Grand Forks, North Dakota. The jeweler advised him, "If you're interested in the jewelry business, you have to learn the watchmaking business." (Many post–World War II jewelers started as watchmakers.) So in 1949, Nord attended Elgin Watch College in Elgin, Illinois, graduating a year later.

But the Korean War interrupted his career. In 1950, Nord was assigned to the military intelligence corps, where he was trained in counterintelligence and sent to the Far East. Upon returning home in 1954, he returned to Elgin to brush up on his watchmaking skills and then entered the jewelry business.

While working in Beloit, Wisconsin, for "an exceptional retail jeweler" named Wyman Tracy, Nord learned of GIA. Encouraged by Tracy, he used his Korean War GI Bill benefits to enroll in the Institute's correspondence course. By Nord's own admission, he "floundered along for two or three years." Then, in 1958, he decided to get serious about his gemology training. He and his wife, Hannah, moved to Los Angeles, where he found a temporary job working for a retail jeweler. Nord completed the home study courses

Glenn Nord, who joined the Institute as an instructor in 1961, later served as its president from 1983 to 1986.

and took the two three-week resident classes then required for a Graduate Gemologist diploma, which he received in 1959.

AT GIA HEADQUARTERS, Nord met Richard Liddicoat. "I was impressed by him," recalled Nord. "He was very scholarly and softspoken, a terribly nice guy."

Nord apparently left his mark on Liddicoat, too. Two years later, in mid-1961, Liddicoat offered him a job as an instructor. Nord couldn't believe it. "I thought Dick had lost his mental balance," he joked.

Besides, Nord's own jewelry career was going well. Since getting his G.G., he had joined Morrison Adams Jewelers in San Diego. Encouraged by Fred Cannon of the Slaudt-Cannon Agency in Los Angeles—a manufacturers' representative and secretary-treasurer of the GIA Board of Governors since 1949—he even planned to open his own store.

Ironically, Cannon led to Nord's hiring at the Institute. "He was always singing Glenn's praises," recalled Liddicoat. At the 1961 executive meeting of the board of governors, Liddicoat announced he wanted to hire Nord to fill the vacancy created by Benson's death. "Glenn and I have plans," said Cannon. "If you want him, do it now."

So Liddicoat phoned Nord, who drove to Los Angeles to meet with him. Two things were quickly apparent in meeting with the Institute's executive director, Nord said later. First, the GIA job would mean a substantial cut in his income. But second, the job would be "like working in heaven, because this was the chance to *really* learn about gems and work with some very good people at the same time."

So despite plans for his own business, Glenn Nord accepted Liddicoat's offer. "It was the best thing I ever did," he said long afterward.

■CAMARADERIE AND TIGHT BUDGETS

When Nord joined GIA in October 1961, the Institute had only 22 employees—18 in Los Angeles and four in New York (less than half the number working for the Institute at the height of the GI Bill enrollments a decade earlier). Because of its small size, there was a real camaraderie among the staff, an attitude encouraged by Liddicoat.

"Everyone pitched in where and when needed," recalled Nord. "We all did everything. We taught classes, both resident and correspondence. We did lab research, and then we hit the road to bring the latest information to jewelers across the nation. The variety just made it that much more fun."

The same was true at the New York office where, throughout the '60s, "we were issuing reports on high-quality diamonds . . . doing colored stone identification, pearl research, and teaching classes [all] at the same time," said Bob Crowningshield, then director of the New York branch.

GIA on the air: (Left) Glenn Nord, appearing with Barbara Walters on NBC's "Today" show in August 1965. (Right) Bob Crowningshield, making a television appearance in the early 1960s.

And both the Los Angeles and New York staffs continued to burnish the Institute's image. Institute officials appeared on radio and TV, and were the subject of articles in national trade magazines. They lectured at AGS Conclaves and jewelers' conventions, and spoke to local trade, business, and civic groups. Lab members wrote articles for trade journals and entries for encyclopedias.

Still, this was no easy time for GIA. Despite growing success and acceptance, the Institute and its staff lived on a tight budget. It was financed primarily by tuition income, which had remained fairly stable for years. (In some cases, tuition had actually dropped.)

Gem instrument sales were a secondary source of income, but continuing resistance by some jewelers and suppliers to using such equipment, even well into the 1960s, kept that low. Revenues from the sale of GIA publications and laboratory services were still small.

In New York, lab membership and testing fees didn't even cover staff salaries, let alone the expensive equipment needed for gemological research. Indeed, clients were astonished at how little the Institute charged for its expertise. Famed jeweler Harry Winston even called the New York office to complain about the "outrageous" price of his diamond grading report. The $5 fee, he said, was simply *too low* for the type of work the laboratory did.

During the 1960s, the annual AGS Conclave was an especially important forum for the Institute in communicating to the jewelers of North America. Left to right: Crowningshield, Miles, Nord, Liddicoat, and Krashes conduct the GIA Panel at the 1965 Conclave in Chicago.

OTHER ACTIVITIES—especially the resident and traveling classes—became more important as revenue-makers, and GIA stepped up its marketing of them.

When Glenn Nord went on the road in early 1962, he took an especially zealous approach toward promoting GIA, holding his classes from noon to 7:30 p.m. so he could save his mornings for visiting local jewelers. While Krashes and Crowningshield handled road classes in the East, Nord covered the West and Midwest, spending 16 to 20 weeks a year teaching. "I would wrap up one class on Friday in Dallas, then drive to Oklahoma City or wherever for a new class on Monday," he recalled. "But I really enjoyed it. It never wore me out, and I built a lot of friendships."

Nord—like Krashes, Crowningshield, and most of GIA's later traveling instructors—made an extra effort to get to know the one-week students and make them feel at ease. For example, Nord would greet each person as he or she entered the class, and then reintroduce that person to the next one who walked in, recalled Liddicoat. "If he had a class of 24, by the time the 24th person came in, he knew them all by name—and that impressed them," said Liddicoat.

Nord was also a great salesman of GIA instruments, recalled Liddicoat. "He was great on the microscope and impressed on his students that they couldn't properly practice what they learned unless they had a microscope, too. He would come back from his road trips having sold *every one* of the microscopes he had taken with him."

■CHANGING AMERICA'S JEWELERS

By the early 1960s, "GIA's traveling classrooms," as *Jewelers' Circular-Keystone* dubbed them, were becoming part of the gemological landscape of the jewelry industry. In 1961, about 500 students attended one-week classes in New York, Los Angeles, and other cities and towns. By 1964, there were at least 650 students in one- to three-week classes scheduled throughout the year. At the end of the decade, close to a thousand were enrolled annually.

One reason for the growth was that these classes weren't limited to correspondence students. The Institute's unrestricted enrollment policy, noted Liddicoat, enabled its road classes to seed a wider field in the industry. Indeed, those courses—with training in diamond appraisal, gem identification, jewelry design, and later diamond setting—were "the means by which we really took GIA to the people," said Nord.

In doing so, GIA played a major role in changing how jewelers sold.

During the 1960s, GIA was active in promoting awareness of colored stones, including a newly discovered zoisite dubbed "tanzanite."

IN THE 1950S AND '60S, MOST SMALL-TOWN JEWELERS sold watches, clocks, gifts, tableware, and flatware, even electrical appliances, but they *didn't* carry 14K or 18K gold jewelry, or designer brands. That type of jewelry was found primarily in the major metropolitan areas. The same was true for colored gemstones. Small-town jewelers seldom sold more than the occasional ruby, sapphire, emerald, or cultured pearl, recalled Nord.

What most small-town jewelers *did* carry was usually gold-filled or gold-plated diamond jewelry. But most of the diamonds were well under a half-carat. Any time a jeweler sold a one-carat diamond, it was considered "a major, major sale," said Nord.

GIA—through its traveling classes, correspondence courses, and annual AGS Conclave programs—helped change that. It not only taught jewelers about gemstones and jewelry, but it also taught them *how to sell* bigger and better diamonds, colored stones, and gold, silver, and platinum jewelry. Indeed, said Nord years later, the Institute "could claim much of the credit" for changing jewelers' inventory and how they merchandised it.

Consider colored gems. In 1965, colored stone imports into the United States were just over $10 million. Meanwhile, GIA aggressively promoted them as a product that could boost jewelers' sales and image. By the late 1960s, those efforts began to bear fruit. At the 1969 Conclave in New York, Liddicoat, Nord, and Crowningshield spoke to a standing-room-only crowd of jewelers about the colored gem market, with an emphasis on pricing and new developments (including a zoisite from Tanzania that had recently been dubbed "tanzanite" by Tiffany & Co.). The gist of it all, said a report of the session, was that "diamonds still are tops, but colored gemstones are coming on fast."

Over the years, demand for colored gems from retailers and their customers continued to grow. "I really believe GIA was the leader, the innovator, the

149

one that started pushing colored stones in the 1960s and got people talking about them and asking their suppliers for the merchandise," Nord said.

Nevertheless, many suppliers and traveling jewelry salesmen still discouraged jewelers from taking GIA courses and using its instruments, worried that jewelers would know more than they wanted them to know about gemstones. Palo Alto, California, jeweler (and later GIA governor) Arthur Gleim, for example, recalled traveling jewelry salesmen who came to his store in the late 1950s and '60s: "If they saw your [GIA] 'scope, they said, 'Are you one of *those*?'"

Sallie Morton of San Jose, California, had a salesman tell her, "You're going to lose more sales than you'll ever gain. Take that thing and hide it in the back room!"

So, Nord said, he and his fellow instructors "had to really do a lot of foot-and legwork to get people involved." Nord himself learned that with his very first one-week traveling class in February 1962, in Houston, Texas. When he arrived at the hotel the night before, he found that only two jewelers had registered. "My heart rate quadrupled on the spot," he joked later.

Rather than retreat, however, Nord took the offensive. At nine o'clock the next morning, just three hours before the class was to start, Nord—as Shipley had 30 years before—went from store to store "selling" GIA. He literally followed the first two jewelers into their stores as they opened for business, preaching the value of the Institute's diamonds course. Within half an hour, he had signed up one of them. Then, in the next two hours, he visited a half dozen other jewelers, signing up two more.

WHEN SMALL-TOWN JEWELERS GOT INVOLVED in a GIA traveling class, the impact on their business could be significant. Consider the story of Bob Edgar of Ogallala, Nebraska, a farming town of 4,500. A watchmaker for 13 years, Edgar had recently bought his former boss's little jewelry shop when he enrolled in the early 1960s in a diamond class taught by Nord in nearby Grand Island, Nebraska.

Edgar wanted to build up his jewelry business, especially in diamonds. But Ogallala was not a big diamond jewelry market. Local residents who wanted to buy an important piece of jewelry usually drove to Omaha (300 miles away) or Denver (225 miles away). The largest diamond Edgar had ever sold was a half-carat.

The first day of class, Edgar was skeptical. "I hear from all my jewelry suppliers that I won't be able to sell any diamonds when I get done with this class, because I'll know too much," he told Nord. "But I'm not selling anyway, so I'll give it a try."

It was intensive training. After Nord's class ended at 7:30 p.m., he and his students would have dinner together. "We would talk about business until midnight or later because people really wanted to learn," said Nord. Edgar's chats with Nord, for example, covered how to sell bigger and better diamonds and various aspects of store operations, even decor.

Courtesy of Zale Corp.

The effect on Edgar and his business was immediate. Now able to explain the whys of diamond pricing and quality to his customers, he sold several one-carat diamonds within the first year after the class. He convinced more people to buy their diamond jewelry from him, rather than take their business to the big cities.

The biggest impact, Edgar told *Jewelers' Circular-Keystone* a couple of years later, was on *how* he sold his diamond jewelry. "When you have knowledge, you don't have to show how cheap you can sell," he said. "You make the sale by telling the customer about [the diamond's] quality."

A spur-of-the-moment visit from Nord led to Morris Zale's endorsement of GIA training. Zale Corp. became the first major retail jewelry chain to underwrite tuition costs for its employees.

Small-town jewelers weren't the only ones who needed to be convinced. So did larger retailers, including the country's growing number of regional and national chains. But when "managers found that trained employees became more effective in their selling efforts with knowledge to give them confidence, they gained interest in GIA training," said Liddicoat.

A major reason for that change in attitude was an incident that occurred one morning in Dallas, Texas, when history was made literally on the turn of a card—a business card, that is.

IT WAS THE EARLY '60s, and Glenn Nord was in Dallas to teach a one-week class. He decided on the spur of the moment to visit Morris Zale, chairman of the Zale Corp., America's largest retail jewelry chain.

"I went in without an appointment and gave my card to his secretary," recalled Nord. "I said I was only in town for a short time and would like to see Mr. Zale. She asked me to wait a moment and went into his office. She took the card in with her, but came back in a few moments and said he was too busy.

151

"I figured Mr. Zale just didn't want to be bothered. But I was determined to see that man. So I looked at the secretary and said, 'In that case, may I have my business card back?'

"She gave me a funny look, and then went back into his office. Through a crack in the door, I heard her say, 'He wants his card back.' It was very quiet for a moment. And then I heard Mr. Zale exclaim, 'He wants *what*? Bring him in here!'

"I didn't know what to expect, and I was pretty shaky going in," Nord continued, "but there was Mr. Zale at his desk, and he had a broad smile on his face."

In fact, Zale—well-known in the industry for his frugality and lack of ostentation—was impressed with Nord's forthrightness and thriftiness. He gave him an immediate hearing—"after he talked to me about my technique for seeing people," Nord chuckled.

Nord made good use of the opportunity. He talked with the veteran jeweler about GIA's courses, its instruments, and the possibility of holding training seminars at the Zale headquarters.

Morris Zale, like many other jewelry retailers, had thought the Institute's training was so technical and esoteric that his employees wouldn't be able to use it. But Nord explained that the courses had become more practical and relevant under Liddicoat. "I said how important such training was for them, and how it would improve their business."

At the end of the impromptu meeting, Morris Zale called in his training director, Tom Harms, and told Nord, "Give him your phone number. He'll be in touch, because we want to start training with you!"

Not long afterward, Nord spoke at a Zale Corp. managers' conference. At the meeting, Morris Zale announced that the company's managers and other employees would be allowed to purchase GIA microscopes for their work, a major step in view of the strong opposition that many in the industry still held against using gemological instruments in their jewelry stores.

But even more important was another announcement by Zale, based on an idea of Nord's. Rather than pay for Institute training up front, Nord had suggested, Zale should encourage his employees to enroll and pay for it themselves, then reimburse those who successfully completed the courses. (A number of independent jewelers were already doing this.) Zale liked the idea, and his corporation became the first major jewelry chain in the U.S. to underwrite the cost of GIA tuition for its employees.

With Zale's endorsement, more firms started to reimburse their employees for tuition charges or to actually enroll students as a regular expense item. By the early 1970s, corporate training programs were becoming a routine part of GIA's business.

■EVALUATING DIAMOND CUT: THE RAPID SIGHT SYSTEM AND PROPORTIONSCOPE

During the 1960s, the Institute expanded its offerings in diamond education and equipment. One of those additions was a new class on diamond setting. Glenn Nord had observed that many jewelers would rather carry loose diamonds than mounted inventory, but this meant that they always had to send out to have them set by a manufacturing jeweler.

"So we thought we could be of real service if we gave them a five-day class on how to handle diamonds efficiently," Nord said, covering tasks such as how to set a center stone in different mountings. GIA added the one-week class to its on-the-road curriculum in 1964. "We traveled all over with it, using a collapsible jeweler's bench we threw into the back of a station wagon," he recalled. The class was successful from the start.

"In the course of training, we saw a need to teach people how to handle jewelry, size rings, and things like that," said Nord. "That led to a five-day class in jewelry repair [in 1973], and that developed into the jewelry manufacturing arts course [in 1978]."

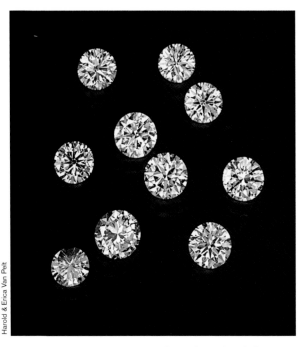

Harold & Erica Van Pelt

GIA's "rapid sight" system, introduced in 1962, provided a simple method for analyzing the make of large numbers of diamonds.

ONE OF THE INSTITUTE'S MOST IMPORTANT diamond initiatives of the '60s—certainly its most innovative—was the "rapid sight" method of estimating diamond-cut quality, which Liddicoat devised. The spark for this idea came not from the jewelry trade, but from a most unexpected place—a car company.

At the beginning of the 1960s, the Chevrolet division of General Motors launched a national incentives program to reward its top salespeople with diamond rings and other jewelry. Chevrolet contracted with the Gordon B. Miller

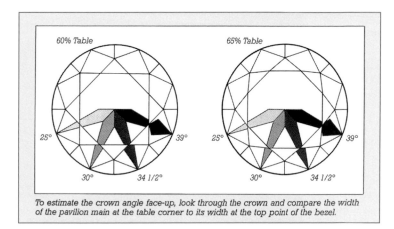

60% Table   65% Table

25°   39°   25°   39°

30°   34 1/2°   30°   34 1/2°

To estimate the crown angle face-up, look through the crown and compare the width of the pavilion main at the table corner to its width at the top point of the bezel.

Liddicoat led the way in developing the "rapid sight" diamond proportion grading system.

Co. in Cincinnati to manufacture the pieces. Because of the large quantity and variety of diamonds Miller would be buying—from thousands of one, two, or three pointers to many weighing a carat and a half—he had to be sure their quality was consistent, with no substandard gems. So he hired GIA to examine them on an ongoing basis.

"We had to look at *huge* numbers of diamonds, sometimes ten thousand small stones at a time," recalled Liddicoat. "It was boring work." But as he thought of ways to make it more interesting, he began to notice that "certain characteristics associated with particular sets of proportions and facet angles" stood out.

"After looking at so many 2 1/2 pointers, one after the other, it hit me that there was a relationship between the depth of the stone and the appearance of the table in the diamond's pavilion. I noticed, too, that those that looked dark had deep pavilions." He began checking his observations with his Leveridge gauge and pointed them out to those assisting him.

"He began seeing certain consistencies in reflections in the stones," said Nord. "Everything in a stone was reflected inside. Over time, we could analyze the make of the stone by these reflections."

It became apparent, Liddicoat said later, "that the pavilion and crown angles and proportions could be judged within a very narrow tolerance by examining the stone face-up, with 10× magnification. So by the time we got into the larger stones, we could very easily tell the depth of a diamond to less than one percent of its girdle diameter just by looking down on its table from above."

The result was a simple "go/no-go" grading system, based on GIA quality standards. In 1962 and '63, Liddicoat published two articles in *Gems & Gemology* in which he carefully detailed what he called the "rapid sight" system for estimating diamond-cutting quality. "The angles and proportions of a brilliant-cut diamond may be judged by eye alone," he wrote. "By noting the characteristics seen through the table, plus glancing at the stone in cross-section, it is possible to judge the depth, table diameter, and pavilion depth very closely."

With minimal practice, a jeweler or diamond dealer could use this new method to determine key proportion characteristics of a round brilliant diamond quickly and estimate the depth percentage of any round diamond within a very narrow tolerance. The Institute refined the system over the next few years, and in 1967 the "rapid sight" diamond proportion grading system was added to GIA's diamonds course.

SUPPORTING GIA'S DIAMOND TRAINING were two new pieces of equipment from its gem instruments division.

One was the GIA PhotoScope. Developed by Kenneth Moore and introduced in 1964, it placed a Polaroid Land camera on one eyepiece of a binocular microscope, with a light wire at the focal point of the other eyepiece attached to a sensor (a light cell) by the camera's lens. Light coming through the eyepiece went through the wire into the sensor. When there was enough light to correctly expose the picture, the cell automatically activated the shutter.

The GIA PhotoScope, which debuted in 1964, could be easily adapted to most binocular microscopes to take photomicrographs.

The PhotoScope was easy to use and could be adapted to almost any binocular microscope. It was a significant addition to photomicrography, useful not only to the jeweler in selling, appraising, preparing insurance reports, and gem identification, but also valuable in fields such as medicine and other disciplines that used binocular microscopy.

The other instrument, the GIA ProportionScope, provided fast measurement of make for round brilliant cut diamonds. The device, which debuted at the 1967 AGS Conclave, was a deceptively simple-looking metal box, $16^3/_4$ inches high, with a round glass screen and a niche two-thirds from the top that held a stone holder and a light. The jeweler placed a diamond in the stone holder, and its silhouette was projected onto the glass screen, on which a permanent cross-section image of an "ideal cut" brilliant had been imprinted for comparison.

The ProportionScope was based on a prototype developed in 1949 by GIA instructor Joe Phillips, and on subsequent innovations by Oklahoma jeweler John Holtzclaw, who built a proportion-grading instrument and showed it at the 1965 AGS Conclave. Several of Holtzclaw's features—including a movable screen and holes in a jaw of the stone holder to expose the culet— were used in GIA's ProportionScope.

The ProportionScope, introduced in 1967, provided a quick means of evaluating a diamond's proportions.

The device's potential impact on the diamond business was such that shortly after its debut, veteran gem expert Fred Pough wrote an article about it in *Jewelers' Circular-Keystone*. "The individual jeweler, long faced

In early 1960, GIA's Eastern branch moved to a new location on 580 Fifth Avenue, in the heart of New York's diamond district.

with the time-consuming job of measuring each submitted stone to make sure that it lies within an acceptable tolerance, has needed a rapid way of checking dimensions accurately," wrote Pough. And the GIA ProportionScope provided that.

In addition, for the first time, jewelers could *clearly* show their clients the differences between diamonds that were well proportioned and those that were not.

■ LIFE IN THE LAB

January 1960. The East Coast lab was, literally, on the move.

After 12 years in its original cramped fifth-floor office on East 47th Street, GIA's New York branch and Gem Trade Laboratory moved a block away to new, air-conditioned quarters on the sixth floor of 580 Fifth Avenue, at the northwest corner with 47th Street. This would be the first of three moves for GIA New York in the decade, reflecting the Institute's own growth and change.

In some respects, it was also a symbolic move. First, it brought the Institute into the heart of New York's diamond district, to a building that also housed a number of jewelry firms. And, in a gesture that indicated the growing importance of the laboratory to the New York gem trade, 25 percent of the cost of the move was contributed by the lab's 35 member firms.

The new facility was twice the size of the first one. It featured a larger laboratory for diamond grading and gem identification and a much-needed classroom. Indeed, after years of makeshift classes and hotel meeting rooms, it seemed to Krashes to be "a *huge* classroom." GIA education kept gaining attention and enrollments from retailers and gem dealers. "There really were no comparable diamond courses elsewhere," noted Crowningshield. And as more signed up, the Institute's grading system and terminology "was gradually absorbed by the trade," he added.

By the late 1960s, said Liddicoat, "practically every father of a young man entering the business expected him to take our diamonds course."

Not all of GIA's East Coast students, though, came from the gem and jewelry trade. One was Albert S. Pacetta, New York City's commissioner of markets, whose duties included cracking down on vendors of phony gemstones to consumers. In 1965, Pacetta enrolled himself and six of his inspectors, who formed the core of a special squad that investigated suspicious jewelry dealings.

Courtesy of the New York City Municipal Archives

Albert Pacetta is sworn in as New York's commissioner of markets by Mayor John Wagner in January 1962. Pacetta enrolled himself and six of his inspectors in GIA courses in 1965 to better investigate fraudulent jewelry dealing.

Other government organizations and officials consulted the Institute and relied on its testing services. They included the U.S. Customs Service, the Better Business Bureau, the Federal Bureau of Investigation (FBI), the New York Bureau of Frauds, the New York Bureau of Weights and Measures, and the Federal Trade Commission. A number of banks and insurance companies also sought GIA's counsel.

WORK IN THE LABORATORY STEADILY INCREASED. By the start of the 1960s, the New York lab alone was examining more than 100,000 diamonds, colored stones, and pearls annually. At that time, however, there was a definite division of labor. In Los Angeles, work focused on grading and evaluating diamonds for GIA classes and some outside clients, and on assembling master sets for jewelers to use in color grading their own diamonds. The East Coast laboratory emphasized detection, grading, and identification services.

Throughout the 1960s, the laboratory on both coasts graded an increasing number of diamonds, most of them destined for sale as investments in Europe, the Middle East, and the Far East. "It was during the '60s that we really began to roll as far as diamond grading was concerned," said Bert Krashes. "People saw the value of the GIA report in buying and selling diamonds."

AS THE NUMBER OF DIAMONDS SEEN in the lab grew, so did the technical competence of its graders and leaders. "Sitting together side by side for hours grading is when Crowningshield and I were able to establish to our

Lester Benson undertook a major study of black natural and cultured pearls. His research helped distinguish between natural-color black pearls (as shown here) and those that had been dyed.

Harold & Erica Van Pelt

satisfaction what a VVS$_2$ or a VVS$_1$ really was," said Krashes. "With thousands of stones coming in, we got a much better sense of diamonds and became a lot more proficient."

The Los Angeles lab also made strides in the '60s. Following the discovery at the end of the 1950s that naturally blue diamonds are electro-conductive, GIA researcher Lester Benson—in collaboration with the De Beers Research Laboratory in South Africa—built a simple conductometer to separate natural- from treated-color blue diamonds.

Another problem was in determining the origin of black pearls, partly due to a proprietary technique that was being performed in Europe, most commonly known as the "French method." The pearls took on a range of colors—some black with iridescence, and others with a brown or coppery appearance. GIA had long known that pearls soaked in silver nitrate and darkened by exposure to sunlight could be identified by a pattern left on X-radiographs. But by the end of the 1950s, there were additional dyes that darkened pearls and did *not* leave an X-ray pattern.

Looking for a universal means of detection, Benson in 1960 examined black natural and cultured pearls that had been treated with a variety of dyes. Then he studied the shells of various mollusks in which natural-color black pearls were found and tested the black portions of those shells. Benson discovered that with exposure to ultraviolet radiation the black portion of the shell interior produced a reddish glow. A similar fluorescence was found in almost all natural-color black pearls.

Next, he swab-tested known dyed pearls with a very weak acid solution, and found that those with surface treatments stained the cotton swabs slightly. Those pearls that showed evidence of surface dye also did not fluoresce the reddish color seen in their natural-color counterparts.

Together these tests made it possible to distinguish between natural-color black pearls and those that had been dyed. Indeed, they were so reliable that by 1960, the GIA laboratory began issuing reports for black pearls specifying the origin of their color.

During the '60s, the lab also continued its research into synthetic gem materials, such as new synthetic emeralds, alexandrites, and rubies. In this, the Institute was supported by the industry. As early as 1961, firms planning to introduce new gem simulants or synthetics sent samples to GIA for preliminary testing and reporting.

By 1965, the Gem Trade Laboratory had developed a number of tests used by jewelers and other gem laboratories worldwide. In the words of Crowningshield, "One discovery or development seemed to lead to another, and there was always something new coming through the door."

ONE GIA RESEARCH PROJECT of the era that elicited much interest—and even put the Institute in court—was identification of coated diamonds. Surface treatments of off-color diamonds had been used for decades, but they were crude applications and easily detectable. In the 1950s, though, less-visible coatings were developed that "raised the color grade of certain diamonds to near colorlessness by disguising their true light-yellow or brown color," Eunice Miles wrote. They were convincing enough to concern the Jewelers Vigilance Committee, the Diamond Manufacturers Association, and the Federal Trade Commission, which in 1957 issued Rule 36, making it an unfair trade practice to sell an artificially colored gemstone without disclosing that it was treated.

But that wasn't enough to stop the problem. A wave of treated diamonds entered the trade in the early 1960s, especially in New York. In one case, a purchaser paid $30,000 for a diamond, only to see its value fall to $12,000 after it was boiled in concentrated sulfuric acid and the previously undetected coating was removed. The practice became so prevalent that it caught the attention of the New York state legislature, which made selling coated diamonds without disclosure a misdemeanor. But what was really needed was an effective way of detecting treatment.

One day, Eunice Miles had a Newtonian realization. As she walked by a car, she noticed an imperfection in its paint job. She immediately thought of the surface of a diamond, which because of its physical nature is more resistant to coatings. So a treated diamond, she reasoned, would also probably show evidence of imperfections in the coating.

Shane McClure/GIA

Eunice Miles, shown browsing the New York office's gem display in 1960, undertook an important two-year investigation into coated diamonds and the methods for detecting them. The diamond shown in this photomicrograph was coated blue so it would appear less yellow.

Chuck Fryer, hired in 1966, was one of the finest gemologists to ever work for GIA. Fryer eventually became head of GIA's West Coast Gem Trade Laboratory.

Miles began a two-year investigation of diamond-coating techniques and methods of detection. She consulted scientists at important industrial research laboratories about substances used in industry and ways of detecting them, and then undertook an exhaustive series of experiments with various substances and methods of application. With the microscope, she looked for clues to the treatment, using magnification from 10× to 1000×.

In late 1962, Miles published her results in a *Gems & Gemology* article titled "Diamond Coating Techniques and Methods of Detection." It featured her research data, illustrations of coatings on diamonds, and her recommendations for "development of acuity in visual perception of them." Concerned that more unscrupulous dealers would use these techniques, neither Miles nor GIA ever revealed exactly what the coatings were or how they were applied.

Miles was cited in the U.S. Department of Mines 1963 annual report for advancing diamond research with her work in detecting coated diamonds. Later, the FBI used her data to arrest a major dealer in coated diamonds.

BY 1966, THE GROWING WORKLOAD in Los Angeles—especially in the lab—required an additional staff member. That person would be Charles W. "Chuck" Fryer, one of the best gemologists to ever walk through the doors of GIA. Ironically, though, it took three years for Fryer to be hired—until a "fixed" gem test made it inevitable.

Fryer came from the construction trade. He was a glazier, one who cuts glass and sets it in window frames. But he also cut faceted gemstones, a hobby since boyhood. When Fryer left military service in 1952, a friend urged him to take lessons with former Institute instructor Charlie Parsons in San Diego. It was through Parsons that he learned about the Institute and signed up for correspondence courses, using his Korean War GI Bill benefits.

Fryer sailed through the lessons—until he came to the requirement for the two three-week resident classes (one on diamond grading and one on gem identification) in Los Angeles for the Graduate Gemologist diploma. "I couldn't afford to take six weeks off from work to live in L.A. and have no income," Fryer said. So, he kept putting it off.

"Eventually," Fryer explained, "my wife said, 'Bite the bullet and do it.' So I did." He moved to Los Angeles for the classes and passed his final exams in 1963. For good measure, he also took his final exam for the British FGA, which he passed with distinction that same year.

Gaining both titles sparked an epiphany for Fryer. "I decided I would really like doing this!" he said. And there was another influential factor: "I also realized how fortunate I was to have been in the glass business for so long and never have suffered a cut. So I decided to quit while I was ahead."

GIA's Glenn Nord had first met Fryer in San Diego when Fryer cut some gems for him. "I knew Chuck was an exceptional gemologist and a superior gem cutter," said Nord. At Nord's suggestion, Fryer called Liddicoat to see if there was room for him on the staff. But the Institute had just hired jeweler Bob Earnest, who would soon oversee its growing resident class program. "Not right now," Liddicoat told him.

Undeterred, Fryer quit his job in construction and was hired to manage R & B Artcraft, a San Diego business that sold jewelers' supplies, lapidary equipment, and gemstones. Over the next three years, Fryer also helped found the San Diego Gemological Society, where he taught gemology and took part in local gem shows. And he still found time to attend morning classes at San Diego City College.

In 1966, Nord contacted Fryer to cut some gems as part of a GIA project. But instead of sending them to Los Angeles, Fryer brought them to the Institute personally, and again talked to Liddicoat about a possible job. Liddicoat said, "Well, let's have you take the 20-gemstone identification test and see how you do."

What Fryer didn't know was that the test was a practical joke, rigged to be so hard that he couldn't *possibly* pass it. "It was the only time we 'fixed' an exam," said Liddicoat with a smile. "Chuck was so good we just had to have some fun. So Glenn and I made up an exam for him, putting in stones that absolutely shouldn't have been there. It was a most miserable exam; neither Glenn nor I could have passed it." Instead of "A list" stones commonly encountered by jewelers in normal business, they put in "B list" stones that were rare and unlikely to ever be seen by a jeweler. These included a 1 1/2 carat brown diamond and a treated green diamond (neither of which Fryer had seen before), as well as a sinhalite, a rare stone with properties very similar to peridot, an "A list" gem.

WHAT FRYER DIDN'T KNOW WAS THAT THE TEST WAS A PRACTICAL JOKE, RIGGED TO BE SO HARD THAT HE COULDN'T *POSSIBLY* PASS IT.

To challenge Fryer, Nord and Liddicoat placed a rare sinhalite in his 20-stone exam.

Judy Colbert/GIA

Liddicoat and Nord presented the test to Fryer, then sat back, arms folded, ready to tell him the joke when he failed to identify all 20 stones.

"I didn't know I was being set up," Fryer said later. "All I knew was that this test was supposed to have only 'A' stones, and I kept thinking, 'These don't all look like 'A' stones to me!'"

The final obstacle was the sinhalite. Fryer spent a long time on it, trying to decide whether or not it was a peridot. But he noticed in his examination with a spectroscope that there was one extra line in the absorption spectrum. Also, like sinhalite, it had a strong negative sign. Fryer identified it correctly.

The joke was on Liddicoat and Nord: Fryer had identified every stone and passed with a perfect score. After that, there was no question about hiring him. Fryer was soon named supervisor of GIA's Gem Trade Laboratory in Los Angeles. A grand title, but in reality he and a secretary were the entire lab staff. And there was much to do.

Fryer was directly involved in the Institute's quality analysis of diamonds. His lab work included identification of, and the first reports on, tanzanite in 1967. In fact, all the gemstones that came to the Los Angeles lab for identification went through Fryer. By the early 1970s, that number had risen to several thousand a year.

MEANWHILE, BACK IN NEW YORK, the informality of the early '60s was evaporating. By the late '60s, diamond grading reports had become more formalized, and so had the grading process.

"All this business meant we needed a system for taking in stones and grading them," Krashes recalled. It was already Institute policy that any gem had to be examined by two graders. But detailed records also became the norm, and a third diamond grader and sometimes more were called in to arbitrate disagreements on color or clarity to ensure consistency. "Like an assembly line, each stone went through the same rigid grading and recording process," said Krashes.

As the 1970s dawned, staff gemologists were almost completely occupied with diamond grading, and GIA could claim that "over 90 percent of grading reports on fine diamonds above one carat" were issued by its Gem Trade Laboratory.

◾A FULL-TIME RESIDENT PROGRAM

In 1962, GIA began its first full-time resident classes in Los Angeles, which covered the entire course and led to the Graduate Gemologist diploma. By 1965, it was offering a combined correspondence and resident program in L.A. A year later, the resident programs were attracting enough people to merit their own supervisor. The man Liddicoat chose was an amiable, experienced jeweler named Robert A. "Bob" Earnest.

Born and raised in Springfield, Missouri (not far from Monett, the childhood home of GIA founder Robert M. Shipley), Earnest grew up in the family jewelry business. In the early 1950s, he learned of the Institute through a supplier who urged him to take the correspondence course. Finally, in 1956, he came to Los Angeles, enrolled in the resident classes, and earned his G.G.

Bob Earnest joined GIA in 1963 as an instructor and later headed the Institute's West Coast resident program for two decades.

Earnest was working for San Francisco jeweler Robert Lindemann in 1962 when he saw a classified ad for a GIA instructor in *Jewelers' Circular-Keystone*. Intrigued, he called the Institute, went to Los Angeles, and passed the hiring exams. He soon received a letter from Liddicoat offering him a job.

"I told my boss I was going to GIA," recalled Earnest later, "and what did he do but make me vice president!" So Earnest called Liddicoat to turn down the job, but in early 1963, after several months in his new post, he decided it was not for him and called Liddicoat again. Liddicoat told him, "Come on down."

Earnest was put in charge of GIA's colored stones and gem identification correspondence courses. He also helped teach the one-week diamond appraisal, gem identification, and diamond setting classes, and even did pearl X-ray work in the Los Angeles lab. Then, in 1966, Liddicoat asked him to supervise the Institute's on-site resident studies. It was a post Earnest would hold for the next two decades.

As program supervisor, Earnest was a jack-of-all-trades—welcoming students, providing their books and study materials, setting up classrooms, arranging for instructors and guest lecturers, overseeing exams, and finding housing, especially for the growing number of international students. "We didn't have dormitories," he recalled years later, "but there was a lot of housing around the Institute, mostly apartment buildings whose owners were happy to rent rooms to students."

"BY THE EARLY '70s, WE WERE HOLDING CLASSES IN SIX DIFFERENT LOCATIONS AT THE SAME TIME," SAID EARNEST, "IN BUILDINGS AROUND THE CORNER, IN A CHURCH, EVEN IN A GREEK RESTAURANT."

Over the next few years, noted Earnest, two separate faculties—one for correspondence courses and the other for resident instruction—began to develop. Earnest also arranged for a number of guest lecturers, such as Morris Hanauer of the American Gem & Pearl Co. and gemstone importer George Houston.

The resident classes were held 9 a.m. to 4 p.m. five days a week, but the curriculum itself kept getting longer as "more materials to study, more stones to test, more work projects, more lectures, and more reading assignments were added," said Earnest. By 1971, it had become a five-month program, and in 1973, it expanded again, to 26 weeks. Meanwhile, additional classes—such as jewelry design, wax carving, and other subjects—were added at the end of the '60s.

Class sizes kept growing, too. By the end of the 1960s, the program had grown to 15–20 students per class, up from 5–10 at the beginning of the decade, with a new class starting every month.

SOME INTERESTING DEMOGRAPHICS spurred that rapid growth. The '60s were a turbulent period in the U.S., a time when many young people began "looking critically at most of the industries they felt damaged the economy and used too much energy," Liddicoat explained in 1981. But they found that the jewelry industry "dealt in beauty and was an avenue of self-expression that didn't do any harm to . . . anyone."

Attitudes toward higher education were also changing. "There was a time," Liddicoat noted, "when the bachelor of arts degree was a necessity for any kids whose family could afford to send them to university. That kind of changed with the '60s generation. Many were more interested in training programs that could get them where they wanted to be more rapidly." So the Institute was approached "by many young people with no association with jewelers who chose a career in the jewelry industry [and who] appreciated GIA's hands-on approach to things," Liddicoat added.

But the first full-time resident students weren't all young people. A number of them in the late '60s and into the '70s, said Earnest, were "more mature—often doctors, lawyers, and other professionals seeking a second career."

Nor were they all Americans. Interest from abroad propelled much of the resident program's growth from the start. By the late '60s, close to 50 percent of all resident students came from abroad, many of them from Japan.

As the number of full-time international students grew, so did problems with language comprehension. To address the situation, Earnest negotiated an agreement with the worldwide English Language Schools (ELS). Those who wanted to study at the Institute first had to attain proficiency in English at an ELS school in their home countries. Once they came to the U.S., they took a final crash course in English so they would be able to handle the reading demands of the gemology courses.

In the late 1960s, as the demand for resident training kept growing, GIA had to find more room. The Institute took back the space at its headquarters that it had rented to two retail stores, and even leased three classrooms nearby. "By the early '70s, we were holding classes in six different locations at the same time," said Earnest, "in buildings around the corner, in a church, even in a Greek restaurant."

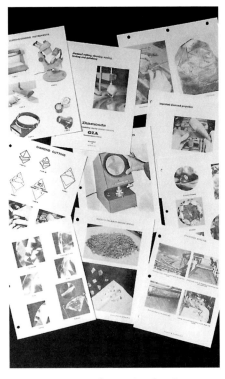

A sampling of GIA course materials from the 1960s.

By 1975, the resident program was turning out more than 200 Graduate Gemologists annually. Making this expansion even more impressive was the fact that it occurred with virtually no publicity by GIA. "Its growth has been entirely on a word of mouth basis," reported *Gems & Gemology* in early 1970.

AS THE DECADE DREW TO A CLOSE, the Institute could look back on a period of steady growth and prosperity amid the political and social turmoil of the 1960s. GIA education continued to permeate the gem and jewelry industry, with the widespread popularity of the one-week traveling classes, the endorsement of America's largest retail jewelry chain, and the development of a full-time resident program. The GIA Gem Trade Laboratory thrived on the strength of its diamond grading reports, now in their second decade, while the gem instruments division kept pace with innovative products for jewelers. And in Glenn Nord, Chuck Fryer, and Bob Earnest, a new generation of leaders joined the Institute. All of these developments set the stage for the 1970s boom years at GIA.

In 1976, GIA moved into a new headquarters at 1660 Stewart Street in Santa Monica, California.

BOOM TIMES

1970–1980

GIA enjoyed unprecedented growth in the 1970s. In education, correspondence-course enrollments soared. The resident gemology program boasted a year-long waiting list by mid-decade. New courses, equipment, and programs were added, and classes were taught abroad for the first time.

Meanwhile, trade and consumer demand swelled for the Institute's grading and lab services, leading to expansion of the Gem Trade Laboratory on both coasts. Staff size increased tenfold. A crowded-to-the-corners Institute was forced to move yet again to larger headquarters.

It was an amazing decade, one in which GIA was transformed from a small, family-like firm into an international training and research center. Much later, many credited this enormous growth to the global diamond investment boom of the late 1970s. Although the diamond boom certainly did affect the Institute, GIA's remarkable expansion actually began in the early 1970s, a time of instability and consumer uncertainty in the U.S.

■ANOTHER NEW HOME

By the early 1970s, due largely to its increasingly popular resident classes, GIA's operations were spread across West Los Angeles. Clearly, this couldn't continue. In 1972, the board of governors approved a search for a new headquarters site. It had to be in what Institute officials called "a suitable environment," with nearby apartment buildings and public transportation for resident students.

In late 1973, GIA paid $500,000 for a two-and-a-half acre lot at Stewart Street and Pennsylvania Avenue in Santa Monica, just a couple of miles from its San Vicente headquarters. The award-winning firm of Parkin Architects was commissioned to design a new home that would be more than three times the size of the old one.

Ground was broken in July 1975, and a year later, on August 2, 1976, GIA moved into its fifth headquarters in 45 years, a state-of-the-art blond brick and smoked glass facility. For the first time in almost a decade, all of its operations—education, the West Coast lab, instruments, and research—were combined under one roof.

■THE DIAMOND INVESTMENT ERA

The diamond was GIA's lodestone for attracting business through most of the late 20th century. During the late 1970s, in particular, the gem's popularity

A one-carat D-Flawless diamond that brought $1,600 in 1971 sold for $7,800 in 1977, and $62,000 at the market's peak in 1980.

as a "safe" investment during inflationary times sparked overwhelming demand for Gem Trade Laboratory services.

Concerned about domestic and global economic and political problems, investors—both professionals and laypeople—sought security in tangible assets such as gold, artwork, or gems as hedges against inflation. Diamonds especially, with their tradition of steadily rising value, became a target for speculators. As a result, diamond investment firms sprang up throughout the U.S. Using high-powered promotional packages and seminars, these firms touted diamonds, especially those one carat and larger, as investment opportunities.

Diamond prices soared—a one-carat D-Flawless that brought $1,600 in 1971 sold for $7,800 in 1977—and so did public speculation. Lay investors, who often lacked expertise or capital, were bombarded by promotions promising fantastic increases in gem worth. In reality, such gains applied only to the highest-quality stones, and were primarily a result of speculative buying.

Jewelers, especially those who were trained gemologists, were often approached for their professional opinions on the investment quality of particular stones. And as a result of investors' frenzied gem purchases, the volume of diamonds available in the marketplace dwindled. "The traditional retail jeweler, who had spent a lifetime building a reputation of integrity as a diamond merchant, saw much of his business for better-quality stones slip away," wrote GIA's Bill Boyajian in a *Gems & Gemology* retrospective article a decade later.

DIAMOND PRICES SOARED, AND SO DID PUBLIC SPECULATION.

Diamond prices continued to rise. That same one-carat D-Flawless rose to $15,000 in 1978, then to $22,500 by 1979 and finally to $62,000 at its peak in 1980. By the late '70s, diamond dealers merely had to hold goods for a few weeks—and eventually just a few days—to make money on them. "We could make a profit simply by arriving at our office," one Israeli dealer told trade journalist Russell Shor. By the end of the decade, 20 percent of all half-carat diamonds worldwide were in investors' hands, and global investments in diamonds totaled about $1 billion—half of that in the U.S. alone.

THE DIAMOND INVESTMENT FRENZY meant rapid change for GIA. Enrollments shot up, requiring more instructors and support staff. Many of the new students were investment consultants, buyers, salespeople, and graders—people with no previous diamond experience who needed Institute courses to understand their product. They also needed equipment, so GIA's instrument sales skyrocketed, too.

The greatest impact, though, was felt in the Gem Trade Laboratory. Consumers and investment houses that had little or no prior experience with diamonds clamored for an impartial authority with an impeccable reputation to verify the quality of their investment diamonds. They didn't have to look far.

Even by the mid-1970s, almost no entity other than the GIA Gem Trade Laboratory was grading diamonds in an unbiased, scientific manner. "We were the only game in town," said Liddicoat later, "the only lab with no axe to grind."

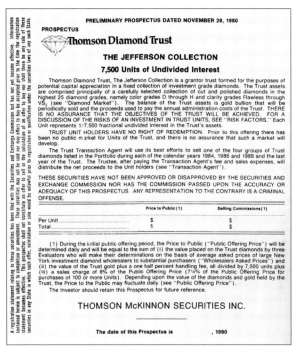

A prospectus for the Thomson Diamond Trust, one of the many diamond investment firms that sprang up in the late 1970s.

Its laboratory on both coasts examined about 200,000 diamonds, colored stones, and pearls a year (including a significant share of the large diamonds sold in the U.S.). The grading reports the GIA laboratory issued were rapidly becoming the authoritative word on diamond quality. Those reports had a threefold value. They gave an unbiased opinion on the relative quality of a stone. They provided a "fingerprint" for identification in case of loss. And if a stone was later damaged, the report was proof of its condition at the time it was examined.

The GIA report was just what diamond investors needed to legitimize their stones and their businesses, and it became part and parcel of the boom. Liddicoat's grading system was now used as a marketing tool for these investment activities. The Institute, however, was uneasy about being linked with some of the players in this business and unhappy with some of the ways its name and grading system were being used. As early as 1972, for example, it blocked a firm called West Coast Commodity Exchange from setting up the world's first diamond futures market by basing its certificates "on the standards of GIA." Nonetheless, Liddicoat told *Jewelers' Circular-Keystone* in 1978, "Whether we like it or not, the [grading report] of a fine diamond of a carat or more has become a merchandising tool for dealers."

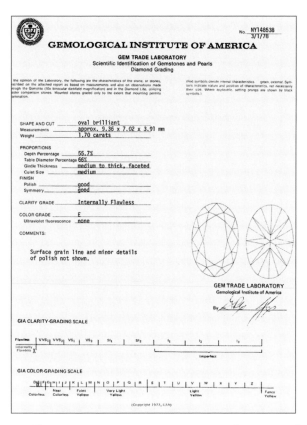

GEMOLOGICAL INSTITUTE OF AMERICA

No. NY148538
3/1/78

GEM TRADE LABORATORY
Scientific Identification of Gemstones and Pearls
Diamond Grading

SHAPE AND CUT ___ oval brilliant
Measurements ___ approx. 9.36 x 7.02 x 3.91 mm
Weight ___ 1.70 carats

PROPORTIONS
Depth Percentage ___ 55.7%
Table Diameter Percentage 66%
Girdle Thickness ___ medium to thick, faceted
Culet Size ___ medium
FINISH
Polish ___ good
Symmetry ___ good

CLARITY GRADE ___ Internally Flawless

COLOR GRADE ___ E
Ultraviolet fluorescence ___ none

COMMENTS:

Surface grain line and minor details
of polish not shown.

GEM TRADE LABORATORY
Gemological Institute of America

By

GIA CLARITY-GRADING SCALE

GIA COLOR-GRADING SCALE

(Copyright 1977, GIA)

The diamond investment boom of the late 1970s fueled the widespread use of the GIA grading report.

Investment house promotional materials regularly used GIA terminology and cited its grading system. As demand for diamond documentation rose in the late 1970s, the trade commonly called the grading reports "diamond certificates" or "certs." And some even dubbed them "the fifth C" (for certificate) of diamond selling.

Indeed, by decade's end, the borrowing of GIA terminology and the use of its grading reports became so pervasive in the global gem market that *New York Diamonds* magazine later wrote that "it was virtually impossible for a dealer to sell a stone without the [GIA] certificate." The GIA diamond report had become the universal language for diamond investors. Whether in Antwerp, Hong Kong, Johannesburg, or Oshkosh, Wisconsin, when people referred to a D-Flawless diamond, almost everyone—the dealer, the jeweler, the consumer, or the investment adviser—understood what it was.

With the increasing demand for diamond reports, a number of other gem labs entered the scene, including several in New York, Antwerp, and Tokyo. Some investment houses in North America simply began issuing their own certificates.

Even so, by the end of the '70s, the GIA report remained the industry standard. Most of the other labs borrowed the Institute's terms for their certificates. And despite the growing competition, the industry still perceived GIA reports to be the most influential of all. In fact, the *Goldsmith* stated in 1980, a GIA report alone could boost a gem's value "by 10 percent" over that of a comparable gem graded by another lab.

AS DEMAND FOR LAB SERVICES SURGED, GIA DEVELOPED a cadre of gemologists who focused solely on grading or identification. In 1976, the GIA Gem Trade Laboratory graded more diamonds and identified more colored gems than ever before. The following year, it saw an *85 percent* increase.

In New York, impatient clients clamoring for reports crowded GIA's offices. Clients who had been issued numbered tickets lined the hallways waiting for their turn, until the lab resembled a bakery at rush hour. In response to the crisis, the laboratory set quotas. The New York lab limited clients to stones one carat or larger. As the flood of work swelled, limits were set on how many diamonds each dealer could bring in, first at five stones a day and later five a week. (To cope, some clients hired other dealers to take their stones to GIA for them.) In a further attempt to meet the demands of the industry, GIA opened a second New York lab in the same building at 580 Fifth Avenue to handle smaller diamonds. And to reduce backlog, GIA New York encouraged clients to send smaller stones to the West Coast lab and began redirecting business there itself.

During this growth spurt, in 1978, Bob Crowning-shield and Bert Krashes were appointed GIA vice presidents. Crowningshield, the longtime director of the Eastern office, continued to hold those reins while Krashes directed the second New York laboratory location. Later, management of the gem identification functions of the laboratory in New York and California was assigned to Crowningshield, with Krashes overseeing diamond grading on both coasts.

GIA's most radical measure in response to the flood of work, however, was to change the way it hired graders. Since the 1940s, the Institute had recruit-ed employees from among its best graduates. But as the need for instructors and graders exploded, this pool of graduates began to dry up, especially in New York, which had a smaller student base.

So Krashes decided to try what Liddicoat called "a very interesting gam-bit." Aware that many college graduates were having a hard time finding jobs in 1977, he began advertising in the *New York Times* for young people with college degrees to be Gem Trade Lab diamond graders. No prior experience in grading—or even in the jewelry trade—was needed. From dozens of applicants per ad, prospects were selected and screened through group interviews, polygraph and psychological tests, and a two-day dia-mond grading class designed to spot those individuals with a natural feel for diamonds. In the end, the best—about 10 percent of the applicants—were hired.

"It was amazing," Liddicoat told *Jewelers' Circular-Keystone* in 1981. "We found many superior people this way, which made it possible to expand our laboratories effectively [into the 1980s]." Indeed, the idea proved so successful that GIA continued using it into the 21st century.

In 1978, at the height of the diamond investment boom, Gem Trade Laboratory veterans Bob Crowningshield and Bert Krashes were named vice presidents of GIA.

BECAUSE MORE NEW YORK DEALERS WERE SENDING their smaller stones to GIA's West Coast lab, the Santa Monica lab doubled the size of its technical and clerical staff between 1976 and 1978. At the same time, calls for a Los Angeles lab from the city's cutters, gem dealers, and jewelers were growing louder. "They found it inconvenient to mail the gems to us or to drive to Santa Monica," said West Coast lab supervisor Chuck Fryer.

For these reasons, and because of the emergence of Los Angeles as a major jewelry center, GIA's officials and board agreed with Liddicoat that a more convenient laboratory in the city was needed. In early 1976, GIA opened another lab, its third, at 606 South Olive Street in downtown Los Angeles. It was directed by Peter Yantzer, a 1972 GIA graduate who had been an instructor and a staff gemologist on both coasts. The lab had a staff of three (including Yantzer) and over 1,000 square feet of office space.

Within months, trade members in Los Angeles and New York had discovered the new lab, and they deluged it with work. "The overflow of goods from New York grew at a tremendous rate, and we went though a frantic growth spurt in a year and a half," said Yantzer. In 1978, the Los Angeles lab expanded to a facility five times the size of the original.

THE HEAVY WORKLOAD CREATED HEADACHES as well as opportunities. Although GIA's grading system was based on specific principles and the process was tightly controlled, many aspects of grading were still subjective. Graders were only human, and two people looking at the same diamond might give it slightly different grades. And the price of the diamond was largely a matter of the grade it received. Clients of the New York lab who wanted to see if they could bump up the grade on a diamond would often courier their stones to the West Coast lab or even catch a flight and submit them in person. The possibility of a difference in grade made these expensive trips worthwhile.

Soon, so many diamonds were going west after receiving a report in New York that GIA had to crack down. The job of catching "repeaters" was given to Gary Roskin, then a staff gemologist and grader at the Los Angeles lab. "It was like being Sherlock Holmes," he recalled. "We checked every stone that came in [using computer data] to see if it matched any already graded in New York," especially larger stones of 3 carats or more. "If we found stones had already been graded, we gave them back. There was no charge—but also no report."

DURING THIS SAME PERIOD, the Santa Monica lab was also growing. As 1979 came to a close, Santa Monica had 56 graders and was running two shifts. With the mushrooming workload and the need for Fryer's talents in

Education, Yantzer assumed supervision of the Santa Monica lab and Sally Ehmke was named director of the Los Angeles lab.

At the decade's end, thanks to investment fever, GIA's Gem Trade Laboratory was doing record business.

▪ POPULATION EXPLOSION

Political turmoil, inflation, and economic uncertainties beset the United States as the 1970s began. With inflation rising, President Richard Nixon took the U.S. dollar off the gold standard in 1971. That move pushed gold prices sky high (from $35 an ounce in 1970 to $825 by 1980) and lured investors, but it also shook consumer confidence in America's paper currency. Meanwhile, prices climbed sharply for basics, especially food, oil, and gasoline.

Yet none of this seemed to affect the Institute. Annual correspondence-course enrollments ballooned to 8,000 by the mid-'70s and reached 18,000 by the end of the decade. In the full-time resident gemology program, new classes started every month and filled rapidly. The Institute's staff kept pace with the rising enrollments and new programs. In 1970, GIA employed 50 people; by mid-decade there were 125.

Pete Yantzer enrolled in 1972, one of a growing number of GIA students with no jewelry industry background. Yantzer was appointed director of the new Los Angeles lab in 1976.

Why did the Institute experience this remarkable growth precisely at a time when the U.S. economy was struggling? One factor was the changing profile of its students. For most of its first four decades, the Institute's typical student was a middle-aged man with a high school education and up to 15 years in the jewelry business. But in the 1970s, the average student was in his late 30s—and the average age continued dropping for another decade—with a year of college training and, often, no background in the jewelry trade.

Pete Yantzer, for example, was fresh out of the Air Force in 1972. He was married and had attended college for one year. He found a tight job market and didn't relish going back to college for another three years.

"I needed a profession where I could get a good job quickly," he recalled. A friend's father, a jeweler, suggested, "Go to GIA, become a gemologist and get a job in the jewelry industry." Using his veteran's benefits, he enrolled in the resident program and was hired as a staff gemologist on graduation.

Bill Boyajian enrolled at GIA in early 1975, just after graduating from college. A year later, Boyajian was teaching resident gemology. He eventually rose to the Institute's presidency in 1986.

ANOTHER NEWCOMER TO GEMOLOGY WAS BILL BOYAJIAN, the 23-year-old son of a drilling contractor from Fresno, California. To pay for his college expenses, Boyajian dug ditches and worked part-time in a liquor store. One of his customers was a well-dressed man who managed the jewelry department of a local department store. Impressed by Boyajian's efficiency, the customer offered him a job. Boyajian had no prior interest in the jewelry industry, but he accepted the offer—and quickly found, to his own surprise, "I loved gemstones and jewelry, and really enjoyed selling and sharing items with the people who came in. A new world opened up to me. I knew this was where I wanted to be."

"If you really want a career in jewelry," said his new boss, "then go to GIA and become a Graduate Gemologist." Boyajian asked other jewelers in town, and they all told him the same thing.

Just to be sure, though, he traveled to Los Angeles during a break in his Army National Guard service in the summer of 1974 and took a tour of the Institute. He liked what he saw. "There was something in the air there, a combination of academics, business, and romance," he recalled. "Here was a school whose entire focus was on gemology, on training future gemologists to serve in the jewelry industry, and on helping them land jobs in the trade."

In February 1975, three weeks after graduating from Fresno State University, he began his studies at GIA. The direction of Boyajian's career was established on his very first day at GIA, minutes after he entered the main building. The first person he met was the manager of the resident program, Bob Earnest, who immediately introduced him to a lean, well-dressed gentleman with briefcase in hand. "Meet your diamond class instructor, Jim Lucey," he said.

As he took a seat in his first diamond class, Boyajian "looked around the room and saw people from all over world. I listened to my instructor, one of the more knowledgeable and inspirational people I had met in my life, and thought, 'Wow, what a place this GIA is, and what an industry!'

"In that first class on that first day, I knew then what I was going to do—I wanted to be like that man and teach that class!"

Boyajian applied for a job with GIA a month before completing his G.G. and started work on August 25, 1975. Over the next eight months, Boyajian was given a variety of jobs, which included working in the West Coast laboratory, cataloging gemstones, and traveling with the extension classes. Then, in 1976, the goal he set that first day came true. Boyajian began teaching resident gemology classes, becoming one of the program's core instructors for the next three years.

ON THE EAST COAST, GIA's New York resident classes were filling up just as quickly. "Gemology no longer attracts just jewelers and sons and daughters of jewelers," noted veteran GIA New York gemologist Eunice Miles in 1974. "Many high school students from non-jeweler families are considering gemology as a career, [while others are] incorporating gemology courses into their [college] major requirements when they can prove they are related."

Encouraged by Eunice Miles, Tom Yonelunas enrolled at the New York campus in early 1976. Yonelunas was named head of the GIA Gem Trade Laboratory in 1988.

One of those was a young New Yorker named Tom Yonelunas, who was studying marine geology at the State University of New York at Stony Brook. In the hot summer of 1974, while investigating graduate courses in California, he realized that oceanography was not for him. After he returned to New York, he voiced his doubts to some friends. An acquaintance overheard him and mentioned that he knew someone studying in the city at a place called the Gemological Institute of America. "Why don't you try there?" he asked.

Yonelunas recalled the casual suggestion a year later while sitting in a mineralogy class at the university. He looked up GIA's New York address and made an appointment to visit. There he had the good fortune to be met by Eunice Miles, who was a confidante and job counselor of sorts to many students.

Within an hour, "her enthusiasm for gemology infected me as it had so many others," said Yonelunas. "She instilled in me a great fascination with gems and inspired me to seriously consider studying gemology as a career."

Yonelunas focused on mineralogy his senior year and concentrated on courses compatible with gemology. He kept in touch with Miles, "a very natural and warm personality, who was very generous with her time and exceptionally supportive." She put him in touch with people in the trade who gave him rough gem materials for his studies. After graduating from SUNY, Yonelunas enrolled in January 1976 in the new resident course at GIA New York.

The program wasn't as structured as in California, or as it would be in later years. "You could proceed at your own pace," recalled Yonelunas, who finished the six-month course in four. On the advice of his instructor, he began working in the lab, weighing and measuring diamonds, while still in the resident program. When he graduated with his G.G., Yonelunas was immediately recruited to work for GIA. He became the eighth gemologist in the New York lab.

WHILE MORE YOUNG PEOPLE OUTSIDE THE JEWELRY INDUSTRY were coming into it by way of GIA, more of those born into the business were staying. That was evident at American Gem Society Conclaves by the end of the decade, where one in six of those attending were young people.

It was a significant turnaround. Before, young people wanting to learn the jewelry business spent years in the store learning watchmaking or jewelry repair. "But GIA helped change that by saying, 'You can study gemology [and] come in [to the retail jewelry trade] that way,'" said former AGS president Sallie Morton in 1981. "So, young people who are not mechanically oriented have a chance to come into the business without feeling they have to learn to fix watches."

Complementing that was the changing attitude of many parents about their children following them into the jewelry business. "I can remember a day when fathers said, 'No, I don't want my son in the business with me. Let him be something successful like a doctor or a lawyer,'" recalled Morton. "They really didn't believe their children could be successful in the jewelry business!" But in the 1970s that belief changed, thanks to the professional pride and confidence GIA training helped instill. By the end of the decade, Morton said, parents in the trade felt that "this is a business they sincerely want their children to come into."

IN THE 1970S, MORE YOUNG WOMEN BEGAN TO SEE GEMOLOGICAL TRAINING AS THE PATH TO A SATISFYING CAREER.

SOMETHING ELSE IN THE GIA STUDENT PROFILE was changing, too: gender. In the Institute's first decades, there were few female students. As late as 1970, only 7 percent were female. Starting in the '70s, along with America's growing feminist awareness, more young women saw gemological training as the path to a satisfying career, while those already in the business used it to improve their professional skills and standing. By decade's end, 45 percent of the Institute's students were women, and the number of female instructors was growing, too. One was Janice Mack.

The daughter of a 1950s Graduate Gemologist, Mack was raised in a family that owned six jewelry stores in eastern Oregon and sent nine of its 12 children into the business. She grew up in her father's store, doing everything from wrapping gifts to bench work, as well as jewelry sales. In her first year of college, Mack decided to try GIA. In 1972, she applied for the Arthur F. Gleim Jr. Scholarship, GIA's first correspondence-course scholarship (established in memory of the son of GIA's chairman who died in Vietnam). Mack was one of the first recipients.

In 1974, she went to Los Angeles for the two one-week classes required for her Graduate Gemologist title. "I blasted through those stones and loved it," Mack said. Impressed with this enthusiastic young gemologist, her father's old teacher and friend Richard Liddicoat asked her to work for the Institute. She immediately agreed.

Janice Mack, whose father studied under Liddicoat in the 1950s, was one of GIA's most popular traveling instructors in the 1970s.

Mack began as an instructor, and by the late 1970s she was a popular teacher of GIA extension classes. Mack created the Doorstep program (which brought tutors and equipment to local correspondence-course students), helped devise the penlight method of gem identification, and worked on GIA's colored stone grading system. In 1984, Mack was named Woman Gemologist of the Year by the Association of Women Gemologists.

AS NOTED EARLIER, from the late 1960s onward, close to 50 percent of resident students came from abroad. Indeed, during the 1970s, GIA classes often resembled United Nations conferences, with students hailing from such diverse nations as Japan, Thailand, France, Germany, Taiwan, Israel, and Brazil, as well as the United States.

Many of these students represented the best of the world's jewelry and gem firms. One 1970 class, for example, included Yuzo Yamamoto, a jewelry buyer with Japan's famous Takashimaya department stores; Iwao Yamamoto (no relation), of Yamakatsu, an important Japanese cultured pearl firm; Jhanwar Kothari, who came from a long line of jewelers in India; Cortio Ocampo, whose family ran a jewelry store in the Philippines; and Massimo Bedetti, whose family jewelry store in Rome catered to such famous clients as Sophia Loren.

Most international students were young and, like their U.S. counterparts, they had enrolled because the Institute offered a quick and reliable way to enter the profession or improve their jewelry skills. "I want to accumulate knowledge quickly," said Yuzo Yamamoto in 1970. "In Japan, there is only one way to learn about jewels—long experience." GIA's training was much faster and "very good," he said.

HOME STUDY COURSES
Offered by Gemological Institute of America

- DIAMOND COURSE*
- COLORED STONE COURSE*
- GEM IDENTIFICATION COURSE*
- PEARL COURSE
- JEWELRY DESIGNING COURSE
- CREATIVE DISPLAY COURSE
- JEWELRY RETAILING COURSE

APPROVED FOR VETERANS

Rising consumer awareness pushed GIA enrollments during the 1970s, as consumers became more knowledgeable and began looking for a G.G. diploma on the jeweler's wall.

MEANWHILE, OTHER IMPORTANT TRENDS in the '70s were pushing more U.S. jewelers to enroll themselves and their staffs in GIA's courses. One was the increasing savvy of the consumer. As consumers became more sophisticated about the jewelry they purchased and more concerned about getting their money's worth—thanks to consumer rights advocates like Ralph Nader—they began asking jewelers questions about matters they had taken for granted in the past, and they expected those jewelers to be professionally trained.

"The rising tide of consumerism favors the merchant who can answer consumers' questions knowledgeably," Liddicoat wrote in 1974, and for that reason, the jeweler-gemologist was "uniquely qualified." By the end of the decade, consumers were looking for a GIA diploma on the jeweler's wall, and jewelers knew it.

At the same time, growing competition from department stores, discount houses, mass merchandisers, and off-price retailers prompted more jewelers to realize that gemological training gave them an edge in sales and service as well as purchasing.

GIA's deepening influence within the industry also contributed to burgeoning enrollments. In the '60s, the diamond nomenclature it had created was seldom encountered outside its curriculum or alumni, even on orders to gem dealers. But within a decade, the terminology was so widespread that jewelers and gem suppliers were compelled to take GIA courses in order to speak the same language as their colleagues and customers, *New York Diamonds* magazine reflected in 1988.

The Institute's reputation for excellence, then, had spanned the gaps of age, gender, and nationality. By the decade's end, as Mike Allbritton, then manager of the one-week extension courses, noted at the time, "If you want to get anywhere in the industry, the logical starting place is GIA."

■GOING GLOBAL

In the early 1970s, GIA began taking its training beyond North America. It started with an Israeli diamond dealer who was curious to know if the Institute's teaching had anything to offer Israel's expanding diamond industry.

ELAZER SHALEV, an official of the Israeli Diamond Institute, came to the U.S. in the late 1960s for the one-week diamond and gem identification classes. He was quickly convinced that GIA should take this education to Israel's diamond cutters and colored-stone dealers as soon as possible.

Shalev persuaded top officers in the Israeli Diamond Institute to contact GIA, which agreed to a pilot program. In the spring of 1970, Liddicoat sent Glenn Nord to Israel. It was the first time GIA offered its classes overseas, and the first step in what would become a global outreach to tens of thousands of students.

It was an intensive project for Nord. During a six-week period, he taught nine classes on three different subjects—diamonds, gem identification, and colored stones—in the Diamond Exchange Building in Ramat Gan, the heart of Israel's diamond trade. Shalev served as Nord's Hebrew interpreter and also asked students from each class to interpret for those who couldn't speak either Hebrew or English. "I would teach in English, Shalev would translate it into Hebrew, and then a student would translate that into Russian if there were Russian Jews in the class," recalled Nord with a smile. "It might sound like a circus, but it was very efficient!"

Most of the students were diamond cutters, but not all. One was the head of the Technion (the Israel Institute of Technology) in Haifa, who oversaw diamond research and developed the country's first automatic diamond-cutting machine. "He came to see what was going on," said Nord, "and stayed on as a student."

Unlike GIA's early days in New York, where it struggled for recognition from the trade, the Institute's training was openly welcomed in Ramat Gan. The students were avid learners, but they didn't docilely accept what they were told. "One statement would get 15 questions, and you had to be prepared to prove everything to them," said Nord. "For our 'rapid sight' estimating system for cut, for example, I had to have everything set up with mirrors so they could see for themselves what I was saying."

The training's impact was immediately apparent. Sitting at lunch in the bourse (the diamond trading center in Ramat Gan) after just a couple days of teaching, Nord would suddenly hear English phrases like "black center" or "girdle reflector" peppered among the Hebrew. "There was no doubt about it," said Nord later. "They were immediately using GIA terms to discuss and explain what they were learning."

Nord and Liddicoat, photographed at the ancient site of Capernaum on the Sea of Galilee, took GIA education beyond North America with a diamond class in Israel in 1970.

GIA'S TRAINING HELPED IMPROVE DIAMOND CUTTING IN ISRAEL.

GIA's teaching did more than change Israeli terminology: It also helped improve diamond cutting in Israel. Prior to the Institute's classes, the cutting done in Israel was adequate, but crude by U.S. standards. After the Ramat Gan sessions, though, manufacturers started to look at cutting quite differently. Said Nord, "We helped a great deal in upgrading that, producing better brilliance, better 'fire' in their diamonds."

GIA's teaching was so effective that in 1971, Israel's diamond-cutting industry asked the Institute to set up a branch in Ramat Gan. GIA declined. It still had a small staff, and its hands were full teaching the U.S. jewelry industry. However, the Institute did continue to send Nord to give classes in 1972, 1973, and 1974. After that, GIA-trained members of the Israeli industry began to offer gemology classes.

GIA TRAINING ALSO STARTED TO TAKE HOLD IN JAPAN in the early 1970s, thanks to a retired Japanese military officer and a tenacious young woman, both intent on bringing gemological education to the land of the rising sun.

The retired officer, Kenzo Yamamoto, had moved to San Francisco in 1949 at the invitation of the U.S. Army, where he worked as a civilian specializing in Russian and Chinese mineral resources. Yamamoto's years of mineral studies in the U.S. sparked an interest in gemology, and in 1967 he enrolled in GIA's correspondence course. Yamamoto's instructor, Glenn Nord, was "impressed with his command of both English and gemology." Nord later became "good friends with this remarkable gentleman who [was] very astute and diligent, a very gentle and kind man well versed even then in gemology."

Yamamoto obtained his G.G. in 1968 at the age of 67 ("I may well be the oldest G.G. in Japan," he joked afterward). He retired from his San Francisco job, returned home to Japan, and set to the task of bringing gemology to his native country. It was a major endeavor. There were only seven trained gemologists then in all of Japan, and very few gem labs.

Yamamoto contacted Taichiro Imai, then president of the Gemological Association of Japan, and sang the praises of GIA. Imai was so impressed with Yamamoto that he hired him as a consultant. The old Army officer worked with Imai's group for 18 months, but he continued to talk to other jewelers about the Institute and its training and grading services.

MEANWHILE, IN THE LATE 1960S, a young Japanese woman named Yoshiko Doi was studying business at Santa Monica City College. While there, Doi met a fellow Japanese student who mentioned he was also studying gemology in

GIA's resident program. Doi had never heard of the Institute but was curious to find out what they were teaching, so she stopped by. A staff member gave her a tour, as well as a special sales pitch: If Doi enrolled, she would be the first Japanese woman to take GIA resident courses. She was intrigued. "It was a completely new field to me, a new industry that seemed exciting and full of potential—and it sounded like fun," said Doi later.

Using money she had saved for a trip to Europe, she enrolled in GIA's resident course. Despite no prior interest in gemology or jewelry, she was fascinated by what she learned.

Just after Doi completed her G.G., Liddicoat asked her to join GIA and assist the growing number of Japanese students with any problems involving language or cultural differences. She signed on in February 1969. "Besides being an excellent gemologist, Yoshiko was a natural choice as an informal liaison between the two cultures," Liddicoat said. Considering the problems that many had with the English language, Liddicoat added, "it just seemed logical to ask her to translate our courses."

This was another milestone for GIA: the first time its training materials had been translated into a foreign language. Still, it was harder than anyone expected. Since Doi had no prior background in jewelry and had learned about gemology in English, she struggled to find the correct Japanese terminology.

By late 1970, though, Doi wanted to return to Japan. Like Yamamoto, she also wanted to bring gemological training to her homeland. Before leaving the U.S., she discussed the idea of a GIA program in Japan with Liddicoat. He suggested that they start with one-week gem classes sponsored by a leading company or organization in the Japanese jewelry industry. That was easier said than done.

IN 1971, SHORTLY AFTER SHE LEFT SANTA MONICA, Doi began visiting Tokyo jewelry trade groups, retailers, and gem dealers, touting the advantages of gemological training and GIA courses. While a few people knew of the courses of the Gemmological Association of Great Britain, almost none had heard of GIA. Indeed, she joked later, a few mistakenly thought that she was promoting the "CIA." But the response from those in the trade, all of whom were men, was no joke: She was repeatedly rebuffed.

In a culture that respected experience, male leadership, and the wisdom of age, she was a young woman, with neither a jewelry trade background nor a family in the business, promoting an unknown education program. "It

"IT WAS A COMPLETELY NEW FIELD TO ME," SAID DOI. "A NEW INDUSTRY THAT SEEMED EXCITING AND FULL OF POTENTIAL."

Kenzo Yamamoto (left) and Yoshiko Doi established the Association of Japan Gem Trust (AGT), an affiliate with exclusive rights to administer the Institute's courses in Japan. Doi, a former GIA staff member who had returned to Japan, translated the courses and managed AGT.

was very negative," she recalled much later. "No one felt they could trust me."

No one wanted to help her set up a GIA education program—except Yamamoto. At GIA's suggestion, Doi contacted him. Together, they set up a nonprofit organization called the Association of Japan Gem Trust (AGT), which would operate like GIA and provide gemological training in liaison with the Institute. As first a consultant to AGT and later its president, Yamamoto provided the senior male authority figure AGT needed. Doi brought educational and managerial expertise.

On November 1, 1971, with GIA's endorsement, AGT opened in Tokyo with seven employees. They began by teaching Doi's translation of the Institute's one-week extension course in diamonds. Soon, AGT added the Graduate Gemologist correspondence courses, which Doi also translated. Her goal, she said, was to "see a G.G. diploma hanging in the store of every jeweler in Japan."

A few months later, in 1972, AGT opened a small laboratory in its Tokyo headquarters. Its primary purposes were to provide income for the young organization and to promote the GIA diamond grading system. Although at the time there were a few gem labs in Japan, they specialized in colored stones. None offered a grading service for diamonds.

There was little interest initially in AGT's diamond grading reports, but in less than a decade GIA terms took deep root in Japanese society, aided in part by the worldwide diamond investment boom of the late 1970s. By 1981, the popularity of grading reports in Japan was such that nearly every center stone of 20 points or larger came with one.

IN EARLY 1972, AT AGT'S INVITATION, the Institute sent Nord to Japan twice to teach one-week classes in diamond evaluation and gem identification. His class on diamonds especially was "a shock to many students," Doi said, "but the material excited them." (Diamond jewelry in Japan was so uncommon in the late 1960s that less than 10 percent of brides-to-be received a diamond engagement ring.) The GIA training received a tremendous response from the Japanese industry.

With no publicity beyond word of mouth, enrollments began to take off. Helping propel interest in AGT's home study program was the fact that correspondence courses—in everything from accounting to housekeeping—were quite popular in Japan and available from both colleges and technical schools. In addition, AGT had arrived at a fortuitous moment. Japan's post-war rebuilding efforts were beginning to bear fruit, and its economy was starting to explode. The country's diamond market was also being transformed. De Beers had turned its attention to Asia's growing consumer market, launching marketing campaigns that promoted diamond jewelry to Japanese consumers, especially women. By 1976, with an ease and speed that astonished even the most optimistic diamond dealer, Japan had become the world's second-largest consumer market for diamond jewelry—exceeded only by the U.S.

The nonprofit Association of Japan Gem Trust (AGT) opened in Tokyo in 1971. Often, instructors (here, Mike Allbritton) were sent from GIA to teach the one-week classes.

AGT's educational and lab operations, including its grading reports, grew steadily during the 1970s. In 1976, just five years after opening, AGT moved to larger quarters in Tokyo and opened a second office and lab in Osaka. Still, it wasn't easy going for AGT in those first years. There were centuries-old prejudices to overcome. Many in the trade were still very conservative and believed that if young people wanted to be trained as jewelers, they should go through years of apprenticeship.

And yet, said Doi, looking back 20 years later, enrollments kept rising because "many young people appreciated the very practical information of the GIA course material and actual hands-on practice they could get. The casual, nonstressful class atmosphere was something they had never experienced, and it appealed to them."

■PASSING THE TORCH

In December 1973, following what had begun as routine medical tests, Glenn Nord's doctor told him he had an inoperable brain aneurysm. He could die within the year, the doctor said. The news shocked Nord and forced him to do something that he never thought he would do: leave the Institute.

In 1974, a brain aneurysm forced Glenn Nord to do something he never thought he would do: leave the Institute.

"Leaving GIA was very emotional for me," Nord recalled. His closest friends were there. He loved gemology, he loved spreading gemological training, and Liddicoat depended on him to help run the Institute. Nord, GIA's de facto executive vice president, "knew the Institute inside and out," one staffer recalled.

But now the medical diagnosis left him no choice. He had a family to provide for, and while GIA staff made reasonable salaries, Nord noted, "they weren't enough to enable you to save a lot of money at the bank." During Nord's career with the Institute, several companies had tried to recruit him. He began quietly checking into those job opportunities. Within weeks he was hired as vice president of sales for the Joseph Goldfinger Group, headquartered in Tel Aviv and probably the world's most famous diamond dealer at the time. Indeed, the Goldfinger firm was so anxious to get Nord that it set up its U.S. wholesaling unit (GSI Gem Corp.) in both Los Angeles and New York, simply because Nord didn't want to move his family away from Los Angeles.

The toughest part of leaving GIA was telling Liddicoat, his friend and mentor. In fact, it took him three weeks after he was hired by Goldfinger to do it. "Each morning I'd say, 'I'm going to tell Dick today.' Then I would get to his office, stand outside the door and say to myself, 'I'll tell him tomorrow,'" Nord said. "This went on day after day for weeks! Finally, I knew I had to do it. I got up the nerve, walked in, sat down, and told him my plans."

Liddicoat listened, astonished. "It was traumatic," he recalled. "Glenn was my right arm, an all-around guy who could teach and work in various positions at GIA. He was incredible."

Nord finished his teaching duties that spring of 1974 and left in June. He wouldn't let his GIA colleagues give him a big send-off or any going-away gifts. "Doing that would have been like saying goodbye for good," Nord recalled. "And I didn't want to say goodbye to GIA. I said I would still come by." In fact, Nord would eventually come back.

ALTHOUGH NORD'S DEPARTURE was a great loss for GIA, the Institute hired a number of exceptional people that decade who helped keep the organization moving forward. Like Bill Boyajian and Tom Yonelunas, this new vanguard of instructors and gemologists came from a variety of backgrounds.

Some were young sons and daughters of jewelers. Among these were Janice Mack, the popular traveling instructor; John Cubitto, an experienced craftsman who taught gem classes in New York and served as staff photographer; and Michael Waitzman, who oversaw the move to GIA's new headquarters in Santa Monica and eventually became manager of GIA's Gem Media department.

Other newcomers were industry veterans. These included Dennis Foltz, who supervised GIA's home study program and went on to become vice president of Education in the 1990s; Rick Shalberg, who started the resident jewelry manufacturing arts department; and David Morrow, who created GIA's first resident retail store management course. J. Michael Allbritton, a watchmaker and jewelry designer from Hattiesburg, Mississippi, succeeded Nord as supervisor of the on-the-road gemology classes. W. Douglas Parker, a third-generation jeweler from Greenville, South Carolina, began in the lab in 1974 and then started teaching one-week classes. By 1981, he was supervisor of all extension programs in GIA's New York facilities. The oldest "rookie" hired in the '70s was Burt Streeter, a longtime supporter of GIA and AGS. Streeter, who retired in 1972 after a 50-year career in jewelry supply and retail, was enlisted by Liddicoat to teach at the Institute and help revise some of the courses. Even after he retired again in 1984, Streeter continued as a special adviser on retailing.

Still others came from outside the industry, pulled to GIA by the attraction of gemology. Dr. Robert Gaal, after working around the globe in geology and mineralogy, with a stint as curator at the Natural History Museum of Los Angeles County, enrolled at the Institute in the mid-1970s. Gaal was subsequently hired to serve as a research scientist and associate editor of *Gems & Gemology*. An instructor for years, former computer programmer Archie Curtis used his data processing skills to computerize the Gem Trade Lab's diamond grading reports. By 1981, he was director of administration. Paul Holt, a former law student, began his career with GIA doing lab work and teaching classes. In 1977, he was named director of the resident education program in New York.

Veteran instructor Archie Curtis (top) rose to director of administration in 1981. Mike Waitzman (bottom) eventually became manager of GIA's Gem Media department.

WHILE EACH OF THE AFOREMENTIONED staff members made significant contributions, others hired in the 1970s would have a more lasting impact, with more than 25 years of service to the Institute. The West Coast Gem Trade Lab in particular benefited from an influx of talent during the 1970s. Karin Hurwit, a native of Germany, arrived in 1972 and became a key figure in

Clockwise from top left: Karin Hurwit, Sally Ehmke, Susan Johnson, and Susan Adams were among the new faces at GIA in the 1970s.

gem identification into the 21st century. Sally Ehmke, who had a B.A. in geography, joined the Institute in 1976 and in 1979 was appointed director of the Los Angeles lab. In 1991 she was named director of operations for the West Coast lab, a position she still held more than 10 years later. Several more who would lead the West Coast Lab into the 21st century soon followed, including Sheryl Cashmore, Michael Clary, twin brothers Alan and Dino DeGhionno, Angelique Giaimo, Bruce Lanzl, Shane McClure, and Phil Yantzer (the younger brother of Pete Yantzer).

The New York laboratory was benefiting from a similar influx of young talent, who would ultimately be with GIA for the next two decades. Among these were Richard Abella, Joe Chiaravalle, Vincent Cracco, Ivy Cutler, Bill Farley, David Fowler, Dan Gillen, John King, and Bruce Moriarty.

In Education, Susan Adams was hired in 1969 and went on to direct the jewelry manufacturing arts program and later extension education before retiring in 2002. Raymond Page, a former U.S. Air Force officer, joined in 1971 as a diamond instructor and became supervisor of the resident diamonds program in 1975. Page later became the Institute's accreditation officer, a post he held into the 21st century. Susan B. Johnson, hired to support Glenn Nord in 1974, rose to a number of key positions during the next three decades. Carl Chilstrom, a 1978 hire, became one of GIA's top resident instructors into the 21st century.

Ray Page, a diamond instructor for many years, occupied the new position of accreditation officer as the Institute grew.

The Institute's instructor exemplar of the '70s and '80s, though, may have been James R. Lucey, whom Liddicoat once called "an educator in the truest sense, [with] a love of gemology, expertise in many technical aspects, and [a] gift for teaching."

THE SON OF AN IOWA JEWELER, Jim Lucey paid his way through college selling engagement rings to fraternity brothers. After a stint in Vietnam with the Air Force, Lucey came to GIA in 1972 for its resident gemology course. He applied for a job when he received his G.G. and was immediately hired as an instructor in the course he had just left. "It was supposed to be a round trip," he joked later, "but it turned out to be one-way!"

Lucey was a tall, handsome man with a precisely trimmed mustache and what one student called "an outstanding smile." He was always impeccably dressed—colleagues called him "Sir James of Lucey," a title he good-naturedly accepted. He was organized, precise (for his first classroom, he took great pains to ensure his desk, chair, and file cabinet perfectly matched the decor), and concerned with doing things "the right way."

Lucey prided himself on his knowledge of gemology and on presenting it in ways that captured his students' interest and compelled them to learn its details, too. He drew liberally on his experience in the family store. "In any session of the diamonds course," he told *In Focus* in the early 1980s, "literally dozens of incidents come to me, and I use them to point out methods for handling customers and creative problem solving."

But being serious about education didn't mean being dull. Lucey was also known for his sense of humor. One Lucey tactic for a dozing class was to

"Sir James of Lucey": Charismatic and impeccably dressed, James Lucey was one of GIA's most popular instructors of the 1970s and '80s.

suddenly "drop" a diamond. With students down on their hands and knees looking for it, Lucey would send one to find a teacher who could bring a "diamond magnet" to retrieve the lost stone more quickly.

In the 1980s, Lucey applied his successful teaching methods to additional forums. He taught weekend gem seminars at museums around the country with Bill Boyajian. "He put on a clinic every time he stood at the podium," said Boyajian. "His great sense of humor and infectious storytelling were marvelous. Every line was always appropriate and beautifully delivered. His charm was mesmerizing."

Lucey's death in 1994 prompted an outpouring of condolences from colleagues, jewelers, gem dealers, and industry leaders whom he had educated, influenced, and inspired. They spoke of his "impeccable integrity," "enthusiasm about gemology," "willingness to share his knowledge," and "eagerness to help the industry."

In such ways, Lucey both typified GIA instructors and set an example for others to follow.

■THE INCREDIBLE EXPANDING CURRICULUM

By the mid-1970s, GIA's curriculum was, in Liddicoat's words, "spreading into an incredible number of areas." Twenty years earlier, the Institute had created the diamond grading system, which boosted enrollment and led to the creation of GIA grading reports. Now in the 1970s, the Institute added more types of professional education—from pearls to store management—and improved the technology it used to train the industry. Following are some of them.

PEARLS

Pearl identification provided a major part of the lab's activity in the early years, and that only intensified when the Institute acquired the Gem Trade Laboratory in New York in 1949. Indeed, natural and cultured pearls provided much of the the lab's business until GIA's diamond grading system took hold in the 1950s.

It wasn't until the late 1960s, however, that work began on a pearl course, which was finally unveiled in 1970. It focused on spherical saltwater cultured pearls from Japan and the South Seas (with tips on lighting and display). Hoping to do for pearls what it had done for diamonds, GIA's course also taught students a new pearl grading system based on color, luster, quality, and value and loaned them cultured pearls to practice grading and appraising. The course was revised twice in the 1970s by Jill Fisher, a San Francisco antiques dealer who joined GIA in 1969. With other members of the Jewelers Vigilance Committee's pearl commission, she also helped revise the FTC's proposed pearl guidelines for the jewelry industry. Fisher was an avid pearl enthusiast and became a prominent lecturer on the subject.

GIA's pearl course, unveiled in 1970, was taught and revised by Jill Fisher during that decade.

JEWELRY ARTS

In 1972, the same year GIA first sent its one-week gemology classes to Japan, Nebraska bench jeweler Rick Shalberg was hired to develop a one-week class in jewelry repair. A self-taught craftsman, he began his jewelry career repairing watches for fellow servicemen in Italy during World War II. After the war, he operated his own jewelry stores in Nebraska for two decades. At the time Shalberg joined the Institute, the best training programs in jewelry arts and crafts were the three- and four-year apprenticeships available in Europe. Shalberg wanted to design a program that would get to the point and deal with the essential projects that a bench jeweler faced in his everyday duties. He also wanted a class that could be taken on the road, so he developed practical one-week classes in jewelry arts that were taught around the country.

In September 1978, GIA also launched the pilot of a six-month resident jewelry manufacturing arts program. It was immediately popular. In response, two sessions of the six-month program were offered in 1979, and five the following year. In the mid-1980s, yet another classroom was outfitted with jeweler's benches, tools, and equipment so the Institute could begin offering eight six-month programs, starting in 1987.

Shalberg ran the jewelry manufacturing arts department, assisted by Susan Adams, until he retired in 1985 and Adams took over as manager.

Rick Shalberg developed GIA's traveling class in jewelry repair and went on to introduce the six-month jewelry arts program in 1978.

RETAIL STORE MANAGEMENT

Competitive pressures on jewelers in the late 1970s led GIA to add training programs to strengthen their retailing and business skills. "Too many of our graduates were going back into the field without adequate practical

Veteran jeweler
David Morrow created
GIA's six-month resident
course in retail
management, which
was launched in
January 1980.

business knowledge," noted Liddicoat. "If all they want are jobs in some busy jeweler's back-room writing appraisals, that's fine. But if they are to be complete jewelers, they need complete training." Three programs were added in the late 1970s to provide that. One, introduced in 1978, was a 23-lesson home study course focusing on jewelry retailing, written and supervised by Burt Streeter. The popularity of the course led to a two-week resident program in 1983.

Another program was needed to teach essential business skills. Many jewelry store owners who declared they would teach their kids "all they need to know about the business" often didn't. "Years go by, and parents really don't do it [or] are unwilling to let go of the reins," noted Liddicoat.

To create and supervise a practical program on store management, Liddicoat turned to a successful jeweler named David Morrow, then executive vice president of Hardy & Hayes, his family's business in Pittsburgh, Pennsylvania. Morrow had also taught at the University of Pittsburgh and written many articles on management for trade magazines.

Morrow developed a six-month resident course on retail jewelry store management, which debuted in Santa Monica in January 1980. Its goal was to create effective store managers and employees by giving them the skills and knowledge a retail store manager routinely needed in all phases of store operations, such as inventory control, buying, or personnel administration. The program was dropped from the Institute's curriculum when Morrow left in 1986, but revived in 2001 with the GIA School of Business. Like Morrow's earlier program, the school was designed to teach jewelry business, using case studies, guest speakers, and group projects.

BY THE LATE 1970s, GIA had grown so rapidly that it became difficult for the Institute's staff to give full attention to the mushrooming home study and resident programs and ensure that course materials were updated. The answer to that dilemma was a burly ex-Marine with a walrus mustache named Dennis Foltz.

Born in Wyoming, Foltz had been a jeweler in California for 13 years when he joined GIA in 1976 as an instructor in the resident diamonds course. A year later, he was named supervisor of home study courses. Foltz quickly realized that the purpose of home study had changed since the days of Shipley, in large part because of the changing profile of the people taking the courses. Many now took them for vocational training rather than job enrichment. "Therefore, the courses have taken on a new meaning and require a different slant," he wrote in 1978. "We must fully examine terms that would be taken for granted by members of the trade [and recognize the] trend in the industry to greater product knowledge."

That same year, Foltz initiated the first major revision of a GIA home study course since the early 1960s—a rewrite of the diamond grading lessons, the heart of the Institute's diamond course and its training. The rewrite was so extensive, said *Jewelers' Circular-Keystone* afterward, that it amounted to "major surgery." A number of areas (such as procedures for clarity and color grading and evaluating fancy diamonds) were more thoroughly covered. They were also made more relevant to current trade conditions and adaptable to future market developments. The revision, which was unveiled in mid-1979, combined input from key GIA personnel and industry authorities.

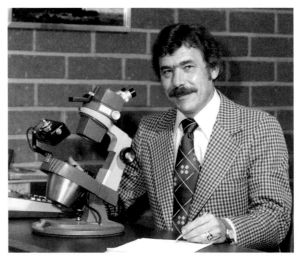

Ex-Marine Dennis Foltz became supervisor of the home study program in 1977 and undertook a major revision of the courses.

■EXTENSION CLASSES

The GIA staffers who were probably best known in the 1970s were the self-styled "Road Warriors," teachers of GIA's traveling one-week extension classes. By the mid-1970s, these instructors had developed into a well-organized team.

The concept behind the extension classes, Mike Allbritton once explained, was that "if you can't bring the students to the Institute, bring the Institute to the students."

By the late 1970s, demand for the on-the-road classes had become so strong in some cities that the two-person teams had to schedule what Janice Mack called "daily doubles." One class began in the morning and ended in the early afternoon. A second class began in the late afternoon and ended at night. The one-week instructors were also popular speakers at the annual AGS Conclaves, two standouts being Doug Hucker and Mark Ebert.

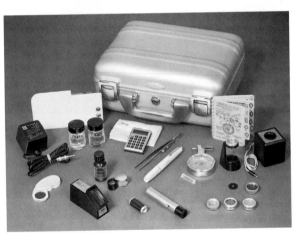

Like Janice Mack, Mike Allbritton was a popular traveling instructor of the 1970s. Mack and Allbritton's penlight technique (above left), introduced in 1976, is still widely used in gem identification. More portable instruments were provided in the GIA MiniLab, introduced in 1977.

THE TRAVELING CLASSES WERE SUCCESSFUL not only in educating jewelers, but also in coming up with some clever developments. One was the "penlight technique" developed by Mack and Allbritton, and still used by many gemologists and gem dealers around the world. It began almost as an afterthought.

"We kept the classroom dark during gem identification classes because of the overhead projector and the tensor lamps on the table," recalled Mack. "So we started carrying small penlights as we walked around."

Intrigued by what the pocket-size penlights enabled them to see, the instructors began experimenting with the technique, using it to pick out doublets and triplets, as well as gas bubbles within stones, and sometimes to see whether a stone was natural or synthetic. Mack and Allbritton introduced the technique at the 1976 Conclave and developed it into a hands-on workshop. It was a useful tool for "off-the-cuff" analysis and rapid identification.

After developing the penlight technique, Mack and Allbritton began to think about the advantages of portable gemological instruments. They talked with Gale Johnson, vice president of instrument manufacturing, about producing a mini-refractometer "and it just kept evolving," according to Mack. "We asked for a tiny little polariscope, then a little hand spectroscope."

The end result, unveiled in 1977, was the MiniLab, a compact aluminum briefcase with all the necessary tools a jeweler needed to examine and identify most gems. It was, said Ken Moore, vice president of instrument sales, "ideal for professional jewelers to take on buying trips or when calling on customers for gem identification."

As enrollments in GIA's home study programs and its road classes soared in the late 1970s, Mack realized there was another educational opportunity the traveling program could offer. "All these students were signing up, and here were our extension program classrooms empty in the mornings and on weekends, with thousands of pounds of equipment sitting there unused," she said. "I thought, why not invite local home study students to come use the equipment and stones when we were in their cities?"

Since GIA's earliest days, getting correspondence students to finish their courses promptly—or at all—had been a challenge. This was a way, Mack thought, to move people through their diamond and gem lessons quicker and accelerate course completion. In 1980, the innovative Doorstep program was officially launched. It was, in effect, a home study course tutorial that traveled in conjunction with the on-the-road classes. Anyone enrolled in a correspondence course could take it as often as they liked and get hands-on practice with diamond grading and gem identification, as well as review classes.

The Doorstep program was one more variation on GIA's ongoing efforts to bring its training and equipment as close to its students as possible. By 1982, Doorstep sessions were held in 39 cities, including Hong Kong. The concept continued into the 21st century as the Student Lab.

▪THE COLOR OF RESEARCH

Diamonds weren't the only gems commanding attention from GIA in the 1970s. Colored stones such as ruby, emerald, and sapphire were now on the agenda, too. The Institute actively promoted colored stones as a product that could boost a jeweler's sales and image. Demand for colored gems from retailers and consumers rose in the 1970s and 1980s, and by the mid-'90s colored stone imports had grown to about $500 million. "I'm not saying GIA is solely responsible for that," said Liddicoat in 1997, "but we played a very big part by introducing the beauty and salability of colored stones to our students."

With the rising popularity of colored stones, increasingly sophisticated technologies for manufacturing synthetic gemstones and artificially enhancing the color of natural gems became a matter of growing concern to the Institute.

"Not only are we seeing realistic synthetic versions of alexandrite, ruby, opal, turquoise, and lapis," reported Mike Waitzman, then supervisor of the resident colored stone and gem identification program, to *Guilds* magazine in 1975, "we are also finding that artificial color enhancement of stones is much more difficult to detect."

That worried Liddicoat. Gemological research had been an important part of the Institute's activities since its early years. However, the focus on diamonds and the growing demand for GIA's grading services increasingly pushed research to the background. The Gem Trade Lab continued to issue reports on synthetics and other gem discoveries, of course. (It was the first to report in 1971 on faceted synthetic diamonds created by General Electric,

Harold & Erica Van Pelt

Diamonds weren't the only gems commanding attention from GIA in the 1970s. Demand for colored stones also rose during the decade.

South African geologist Dr. Vince Manson joined GIA in 1976 to head the Institute's first formal research department.

and it also reported on synthetic alexandrite and turquoise, among other gem simulants.) But the rising mountain of diamond work meant that the scientific scrutiny and equipment needed to identify and understand new synthetics, new gemstones, and even the very nature of gem color itself was lagging. As an internationally respected educational facility—people in the trade already called GIA the industry's own college—the Institute needed a separate department dedicated to original research.

AT THAT MOMENT IN GIA'S HISTORY, Liddicoat crossed paths with an eloquent geologist, Dr. D. Vincent Manson, whose love of gemstones and research made him the right person to create the Institute's first state-of-the-art research facility.

Manson, born and raised in South Africa, was the son of a 1920s "Diamond Rush" miner-turned-farmer. "I grew up with a love of nature, diamonds, and other gems," he recalled. "I was always on field trips digging for gems." By college, this fascination with geology and gemstones was evolving into a career. "Gems are the end result of natural geologic processes," Manson would say later. "They are our Rosetta stone for understanding and reading the history written in rocks." He dedicated his professional life to deciphering that history.

Manson first learned of the Institute as a research assistant in the De Beers Diamond Research Laboratory in Johannesburg during his university years. The laboratory owned a DiamondLite with GIA's name on it. The instrument, he was told, was "made by a company in America that focuses on diamonds."

Manson came to the United States in the 1960s to earn his doctorate in geology from Columbia University. In 1965, he began an 11-year stint as curator of gems and minerals at the American Museum of Natural History. He did major research on diamond inclusions, but also found time to serve as associate editor of *Natural History* magazine, help filmmaker David Wolper produce "The Time of Man," and supervise the addition of a new gem hall at the museum.

While at the museum, Manson made his first contacts with GIA. He visited its New York office and lab, where he met Crowningshield, Krashes, and Miles. At a museum exhibit on opals in the early '70s, he met Richard

Liddicoat. "He was a soft-spoken but insightful gentleman, with an easy smile," Manson recalled later. "He listened to what you said, but the range of his knowledge was extraordinary. It didn't matter if the issues involved science, industry, or business, he was equally at home in all areas and comfortable talking about them."

Their next meeting was at a 1973 international conference sponsored by De Beers at the Kimberley Mines in South Africa, where Manson presented a paper on inclusions in diamonds. Liddicoat was in the audience and invited Manson to visit GIA, which he did the following year. At the 1975 Conclave in Minneapolis, he and Liddicoat met again.

"Come and work with us," urged Liddicoat. Manson was preparing the installation of a major exhibition hall at the museum and declined. "Then come and visit us again," said Liddicoat. In early 1976, after the Tucson Gem and Mineral Show, Manson did. He also visited the new headquarters then under construction and talked with Liddicoat about creating something the Institute hadn't had since its early years under Bob Shipley Jr.: a formal research department.

That trip clinched matters. "I loved what I saw," said Manson, who resigned as soon as he had finished the exhibition hall and in August 1976 joined GIA as director of research.

The timing was good. The flow of new synthetic and imitation gems into the market justified the creation of a research lab to track them, and the prosperity from the investment boom enabled the Institute to buy the needed equipment. Just as important, GIA had reached the point, said Manson later, where "it had to generate original research to fulfill its role as an educational institution," to justify its position as gemology's university.

"GIA is like a stool with three legs—education, instrumentation, and lab functions," Manson said in 1997. "They support each other and need each other. Ignoring any one of them distorts GIA's perspective."

MANSON BEGAN WORK ON THE NEW RESEARCH FACILITY in August 1976, the same week that GIA moved into its new Santa Monica headquarters. He and his two-person staff spent the next 20 months—and a capital budget of $150,000—setting up a research laboratory, the sole purpose of which was to expand knowledge of the nature of gem materials.

One key research tool was a scanning electron microscope (SEM), with magnification up to 150,000×. With an energy-dispersive X-ray fluorescence (EDXRF) system attached, it could also make nondestructive qualitative chemical

Carol Stockton of GIA Research looks at an image on a scanning electron microscope (SEM), GIA's first high-tech instrument. SEM was capable of high-magnification imaging as well as (with EDXRF) qualitative chemical analysis.

analyses of gem samples. A spectrophotometer was used to record the spectra of hundreds of gemstones to better understand their causes of color.

The new GIA Research department was the first to study plastic-impregnated opal, the mineralogical composition of the opaque green gem material maw-sit-sit, and the chemical and physical properties of a variety of unusual gem garnets from East Africa. With the UV-visible spectrophotometer, they helped distinguish natural-color from treated-color (irradiated) diamonds.

"Our entire purpose at the research lab is to understand the nature of gems," said Manson in the late '70s. "We operate on the frontier of what can be done in gem research."

One of the most important functions of the lab was creation of a database of gemological information. As early as 1979, data on more than 9,000 gem samples had already been cataloged. The data helped GIA researchers gain a better understanding of the complex world of natural, treated, imitation, and synthetic gem materials. It was an extension of the attitude that the Institute's pioneering gemologists—Shipley Jr., Liddicoat, Crowningshield, Benson, Fryer, and others—had brought to their gemological studies.

"They were acute observers of nature who could see what was superficial and what was intrinsic," said Manson, "and when they exchanged their observations with each other and with their students, they were not just saying what they had seen, but expanding the way we saw and understood things."

The research lab scrutinized how gem color is affected by a variety of factors. It studied new synthetics and differences between natural gems and simulants in order to spot fakes. Its study of the range of color in individual gem species and chemical analyses of gemstones also led to identification of a number of coloring agents. The knowledge acquired through this research enabled GIA to develop new gem-testing techniques that helped both the Institute and jewelers spot new imitations, synthetics, and treatments. "The research lab's work," Manson told *Jewelers' Circular-Keystone* in 1978, was "a bridge between trade problems and scientific inquiry."

It also helped further a longtime GIA goal: development of a quality-grading system for colored stones, much as the Institute had done for diamonds in the 1950s. Pursuit of that goal would occupy GIA with varying degrees of success over the next 20 years.

A final visit: Robert Shipley toured the new Santa Monica head-quarters on February 18, 1977, just three days before his 90th birthday. Shipley was accompanied by his nephew Al Woodill.

■A LAST VISIT

A tall old man with a lion's mane of white hair, piercing blue eyes, and a bristling white mustache strode through the entrance of GIA's new head-quarters in 1977. Nattily dressed in a white linen suit and polka dot bow tie, he looked like a retired banker or college professor making a visit. But as he toured GIA headquarters with Richard Liddicoat, people stopped and looked at him. Older ones smiled and waved; younger ones simply stared at the man who was to them a legend.

AFTER A QUARTER
CENTURY, ROBERT M.
SHIPLEY HAD FINALLY
COME HOME.

Like a tourist from a faraway country, he seemed out of place. Yet he belonged there. GIA's founder had returned: After a quarter century, Robert M. Shipley had finally come home.

THE SHIPLEYS ENJOYED THEIR RETIREMENT. They traveled a good deal, but also enjoyed their home in South Laguna Beach, California. Shipley indulged in hobbies—gardening, high-fidelity equipment and recording, and collecting works of art and classical music records—while Bea focused on her work with the Girl Scouts in addition to cooking and entertaining.

In the late 1960s, Shipley began attending AGS Conclaves again, and he wrote some booklets and manuals for the Society. In 1969, AGS named its highest honor the Shipley Award.

Just as he was starting to enjoy professional recognition once again, Shipley suffered a devastating loss when Bea passed away in the summer of 1973, at the age of 85. Married for 43 years, both had overcome divorce and adversity to become gemological pioneers during the 1930s. Beatrice Shipley was remembered as the businesswoman who managed and financed the early operations of GIA and AGS.

A few years later, with the opening of GIA's Santa Monica headquarters coinciding with his own birthday, the right moment came for Shipley to see the fruits of his vision and hard work. On February 18, 1977, just three days before he turned 90, Robert Shipley toured GIA's gleaming new home at Liddicoat's invitation. He was "quite overwhelmed and delighted with what GIA had become," recalled Liddicoat. They went upstairs to the student lounge where students, staff, and board members hosted an informal reception in Shipley's honor, complete with birthday cake. But it was as much a welcome home as it was a birthday party.

A round of applause broke out for this man who had done so much to reshape the global gem and jewelry industry. GIA board member George Kaplan remembered the moment vividly. "He was magnificent as he strode into the lounge in his white suit," Kaplan said. "He looked eight feet tall."

Even at 90, he still had the charisma, the twinkling eye, the enthusiasm and wit, and the knowledge that had inspired jewelers in the 1930s. Shipley charmed his audience with a lively account of GIA's early days, when gemology was almost unknown and he drove across America, selling lessons store to store. He spoke of the support of his wife Bea and his son Robert Jr., of pioneers such as Eacret and Wigglesworth, and of an earnest young gemologist named Liddicoat.

And then, echoing words he used when he retired from the Institute in 1952, he urged GIA's staff to not only teach students ethics and gemology, but also to give them "more than just the means to make money."

"Give them something to make their lives happier and their surroundings more beautiful. Give them something to live by."

As Shipley sat down again, staff members, governors, and old friends gathered around to wish him happy birthday and to reminisce. And students brought their workbooks for him to autograph. Shipley was the center of attention, respected and beloved.

A year later, Robert M. Shipley, the founder of the Gemological Institute of America, passed away. He died in his sleep on April 18, 1978, at the age of 91, in a convalescent home in Ventura, California. His death was mourned by industry members throughout the world. A final tribute came two decades later, in December 1999, when *Jewelers' Circular-Keystone* named Shipley its "Person of the Century."

■A BANNER DECADE

"As we say goodbye to the 1970s, it has been a banner decade for the Gemological Institute of America," wrote Richard Liddicoat in his year-end holiday letter to GIA students in December 1979. And indeed it had been. The Institute had never enjoyed such growth, expansion, and financial success—nor would it again for some time. Spurred by the diamond investment boom, the '70s had been what Bill Boyajian would later call "a non-stop, go-go era."

Enrollments in GIA courses and classes in the U.S. and abroad had mushroomed, with 18,000 in correspondence courses alone by 1980. The Institute's staff encompassed some of the finest researchers, educators, and gemologists in the industry. It had established its first affiliate abroad, in Japan. And it had added many new and revised courses geared to the changing jewelry market.

The era also saw a transformation in GIA's finances. The Institute began the decade with annual revenues of about $3 million, mostly from correspondence courses, with about 50 employees on both coasts. By 1980, it had become a $23 million operation that employed some 500 people (100 of them diamond graders in Los Angeles and Santa Monica alone). Indeed, there was so much growth in so short a time that T. J. Barrows, then head of education administration, joked at decade's end that GIA's "greatest need now is an organizational chart!"

"GIVE THEM SOMETHING TO MAKE THEIR LIVES HAPPIER, AND THEIR SURROUNDINGS MORE BEAUTIFUL," URGED SHIPLEY. "GIVE THEM SOMETHING TO LIVE BY."

Richard Liddicoat examines a slice of liddicoatite, the gem species of tourmaline named in his honor in 1977.

Charles Carmona

In fact, the Institute's casual administrative style was quickly becoming more formalized to cope with mounting demands on its operations and staff, especially on president Richard Liddicoat. A pivotal figure in those years was Jill Fisher, the pearl instructor who in 1978 was named assistant to the president. For the next few years, she was, in effect, the doorkeeper to his office, controller of his agenda, and his representative when he was away. Fisher also oversaw hiring until the early 1980s, when GIA brought in its first official personnel manager, David George.

The turn of the decade saw other new posts added to the GIA organizational chart. The Institute hired its first financial controller in 1979. In 1980, Dr. Peter Keller, curator of mineralogy and geology at the Natural History Museum of Los Angeles County, was hired for the new post of director of education. It was a job created not only to coordinate educational functions but also to relieve some of the pressure from Liddicoat.

It was in the 1970s that the Institute solidified its international reputation, and its officials and staff members became gemology's respected mentors and leaders. In the early 1970s, for example, Bert Krashes was named an honorary vice president of the Canadian Gemmological Association, while Bob Crowningshield was hailed as "one of the world's leading gemologists" by *Jewelers' Circular-Keystone*.

A growing list of honors recognized Richard Liddicoat's contributions to the industry. In 1976, he received the AGS Robert M. Shipley Award and was named honorary vice president of the Gemmological Society of Australia. Another very special honor was the designation of a new gem mineral liddicoatite. In 1977, Dr. Pete J. Dunn and his colleagues at the Smithsonian Institution named this calcium-lithium-aluminum member of the tourmaline group for Liddicoat in "recognition of his many contributions to gemological knowledge and education, as well as the leadership and dedication he has given to the field of gemology."

"Inasmuch as this tourmaline mineral occurs as a beautiful gemstone, it is doubly fitting that it was named for a world-renowned gemologist," reported *Pacific Goldsmith* in 1978.

■LOOKING TO MOVE—AGAIN

Even before the first microscope was carried into the Institute's new headquarters in August of 1976, the facility was already too small. Rocketing enrollments for the resident classes, by then with a 12-month waiting list, raised the question of the new building's adequacy while construction was still underway. To cope, GIA added another 3,600 square feet to the second floor, increasing total size to over 50,000 square feet, and bought an adjacent lot for later expansion.

It still wasn't enough. Enrollments continued to surge, requiring more instructors and more people to handle administrative functions. The addition of resident JMA and retail management programs tightened the squeeze for classroom space.

By 1978, the complex designed to house GIA's operations for years to come was already overcrowded. So the Institute gave over its new headquarters to resident classes, correspondence-course instruction, the library and the audio-visual section, and the Gem Trade Lab and research departments. Everything else went into space GIA leased in two nearby buildings. A new bookstore and cafeteria (or "Faceteria," as it was nicknamed by Liddicoat) soon were added in those rented facilities.

Even so, by 1980 GIA was so large and crowded that its officials were again predicting that the Institute might have to move soon—this time to true campus acreage.

CHAPTER 9

Members of the GIA Alumni Association, formed in 1982, gather in front of the Santa Monica headquarters. By the end of the 1980s, the association boasted some 4,000 members worldwide.

CELEBRATING AN ERA

1980–1982

It had been half a century since Robert M. Shipley Sr. opened a little office in down-town Los Angeles in 1931 and called it "The Gemological Institute of America." The seed planted there had grown through both hard times and prosperity into an impressive global organization.

By 1981, GIA had hundreds of students in residence in Santa Monica and New York, with a lengthy backlog of applicants. Thousands more were enrolled in GIA's home study programs. The Institute offered classes in Europe and Asia, and it had an affiliate branch in Japan. Its diamond grading system, research, and instruments were transforming the international gem and jewelry industry, as they had America's.

Four events in the early 1980s marked this important half-century milestone and served to celebrate the Institute's future direction: the revamping of Gems & Gemology, *the creation of the GIA Alumni Association, the introduction of a colored stone grading system, and the first International Gemological Symposium.*

■A NEW *"G&G"*

From the start, GIA founder Robert Shipley wanted to produce a publication dedicated to gemology. That began with *Gemology*, a four-page newsletter that appeared in January 1931, just after the first classes started in downtown Los Angeles. It was the first such gemological publication. (Jewelry trade magazines didn't yet cover gemology, and *The Gemmologist*, the official journal of the Gemmological Association of Great Britain, did not appear until August 1931.) Yet *Gemology*, the newsletter, was short-lived. Probably due to lack of time and staff in those first years, there were no subsequent issues.

But Shipley didn't abandon his idea. One goal of the new Institute, he wrote in the early 1930s, would be "a quarterly 'house organ' . . . containing stories and photographs of diamonds and gems and selling copy." In January 1934, the Institute published its true "house organ," called *Gems & Gemology*, aimed at serving the "gem-merchant" and GIA students. It contained no non-GIA advertising and was subscription-supported.

Gems & Gemology—or *G&G*—would become the journal Shipley envisioned, but it faced an uncertain identity in its first decade. The journal originally was dubbed (on the second page, in small print) the "official organ of the American Gem Society." Identification with AGS affected the publication's

Gems & Gemology, the Institute's flagship publication, first appeared in 1934 (left). Richard Liddicoat, whose first *G&G* byline appeared in 1941 (right), was one of many distinguished gemologists to write research articles for the journal over the years.

content. In its early issues, *Gems & Gemology* presented not only gemological information but also material of general interest to retail jewelers. The idea was to attract more jewelers to the journal and, through it, to GIA's courses and membership in AGS.

With the Summer 1943 issue, *Gems & Gemology* finally became "the quarterly official organ of the Gemological Institute of America." And in 1947—the same year GIA and AGS formally split—the board of governors designated *Gems & Gemology* GIA's official journal.

GEMS & GEMOLOGY WAS INFLUENTIAL from its earliest years. Regular installments of a "Gemological Encyclopedia" and a "Gemological Glossary" during its first decade educated readers in gemology basics. Early articles detailed the beginnings of the gemological movement, such as the reports on the first gemological Conclaves, Robert Shipley Jr.'s groundbreaking articles on using stereoscopic magnification and darkfield illumination to study gems, and Edward Gübelin's pioneering studies on gemstone inclusions.

Basil Anderson and Robert Crowningshield contributed articles on gem spectroscopy, and George Kaplan discussed diamond cutting. Over the years, other researchers such as Dr. Edward Kraus, Dr. Karl Schlossmacher, Dr. Sydney Ball, Robert Webster, and Lester Benson contributed regularly. Later, Dr. Kurt Nassau provided seminal work on gem treatments. *Gems & Gemology* was also the first gemology journal to report on new materials such as taaffeite, tanzanite, and tsavorite, as well as new sources for known gems, such as the first discoveries of diamonds in Siberia.

Shipley himself was a frequent contributor to *Gems & Gemology* in the 1930s and 1940s. Richard Liddicoat also wrote articles for more than five decades. His first bylined article, "A Solution to Diamond Color Grading Problems," appeared in the Fall 1941 issue.

FOR ITS FIRST 68 YEARS, *Gems & Gemology* had only two editors-in-chief: Shipley, until his retirement in 1952, and Liddicoat. A succession of associate editors did most of the hands-on work. The first were Robert Shipley Jr.; Anna Beckley, GIA's first research librarian and a contributor to its early courses and publications; Liddicoat, during the two years before he went into World War II military service; and Virginia Hinton, the first female jeweler to become a Certified Gemologist.

After the war, editorial duties were handled by Kay Swindler, GIA's first public relations spokesperson. Swindler was succeeded by Jeanne Martin (through the 1950s into the 1960s), Lawrence Copeland (through the 1960s), and Dr. Robert Gaal and John Koivula (during the 1970s). But despite their hard work, none had the impact on *Gems & Gemology* that a veteran journalist named Alice Smith Keller did. Indeed, it's no exaggeration to say that the history of *Gems & Gemology* can be divided neatly into two parts— Before Keller and After Keller.

Keller came to GIA with an impressive resumé in journal editing, including the *Journal of Marketing* and four major medical publications produced by Houghton-Mifflin Company. She first became familiar with the gem and mineral world and met many of its leading figures when her then-husband, Peter Keller, was curator of gems and minerals at the Natural History Museum of Los Angeles County. Shortly after Peter joined the Institute in 1980 as director of education, the careers of Alice Keller and *Gems & Gemology* converged.

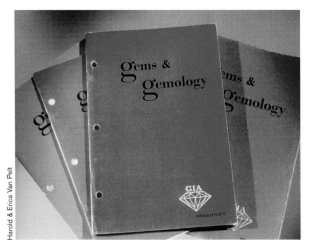

Harold & Erica Van Pelt

A collection of *G&G*s from the 1970s. Cover design notwithstanding, the journal's basic format remained unchanged from 1934 until 1981.

THE GEMOLOGICAL INSTITUTE OF AMERICA had metamorphosed in the decades leading to 1980, but the same could not be said for its flagship publication. *G&G*'s look, style, format, and size—$5^1/_2 \times 8^1/_2$ inches and usually no more than 32 pages—hadn't changed significantly since 1934. Color was used sparingly. And its limited readership made it something of a trade secret. Although there were tens of thousands of Institute graduates by 1980, *Gems & Gemology* itself had fewer than 1,500 paid subscribers!

In 1980, with GIA's 50th anniversary approaching, Liddicoat and the board of governors decided that the venerable periodical cried out for a complete makeover. The Institute had to have an academic journal that matched its reputation. "GIA is acutely aware of the greater need and desire of this industry and others involved in the field to be well-informed about new materials, new technologies and other developments in gemology," wrote Liddicoat.

THE HISTORY OF *GEMS & GEMOLOGY* CAN BE DIVIDED NEATLY INTO TWO PARTS—BEFORE KELLER AND AFTER KELLER.

Alice Keller became managing editor of *Gems & Gemology* in 1980 and revamped the journal in time for the Spring 1981 issue. In 2002, she was named editor-in-chief.

Peter Keller and research director Vince Manson, a friend of the Kellers for several years, thought they had the perfect candidate for the project: Alice Keller. Shortly after the board's decision, they sat her down in the Keller living room and asked, "Can you do it?"

She scanned what *G&G* had done and considered her extensive experience with professional journals, including work with four-color reproduction. It was "very compatible," she said later, with what *G&G* needed. As for gemology, Keller already had a good knowledge of gems and minerals and was familiar with many of the leaders in the community. "I knew these people. I had entertained them. I had gone to trade shows with them. I had bought minerals from them." So she said yes.

ALICE KELLER JOINED *GEMS & GEMOLOGY* in August 1980, with the support of Liddicoat and then–associate editor John Koivula, a respected gemological researcher. Koivula was "not only gracious but positively enthusiastic" about turning the job over to her, she recalled. Koivula stayed on as a contributing editor.

Keller had only six months to redesign the journal, which had to be ready in early 1981. Wasting no time, she began making changes. The first involved the journal's size and color. GIA's board "wanted the journal to have a presence, but it is difficult to have one with such a small format," she said dryly. "You just don't have the same impact."

Then Keller turned her attention to the journal's color photography. Although its first color prints (of Australian opals) appeared in the Winter 1946 issue, color in the journal was rare over the next quarter-century. In 1980, recognizing the integral role of color in representing gem materials, Keller revamped *Gems & Gemology* into an appropriate forum for gemological photography. She also did something no previous *G&G* editor had ever done: She sought out good examples of gems or jewelry mentioned in the articles and had them photographed for the journal. Prominent photographers over the next two decades included Tino Hammid, Robert Weldon, Maha Tannous, Shane McClure and, in particular, Harold and Erica Van Pelt.

As its signature, every issue featured an artistic cover shot. Most of the stunning covers published over the next 20 years were shot by the Los Angeles–based Van Pelts, probably the world's finest mineral and gem photographers. "I always considered myself blessed to have the Van Pelts, who expertly combine technical knowledge and artistic sensitivity," Keller said.

THE WINTER 1994 COVER EXEMPLIFIED the technical demands that confronted Keller and the Van Pelts in producing the journal's renowned gem photography. It also demonstrated the attention to production detail that set *G&G* apart from most other academic journals.

The issue's feature story was the GIA Gem Trade Laboratory's newly enhanced color grading system for colored diamonds. "We wanted to overwhelm our readers with the variety of colors in which diamonds occur," said Keller, and needed a cover photo that was "well-composed, attractive, and technically accurate."

She immediately turned to the Van Pelts. "They understood the need for accuracy," Keller asserted, "and are passionate about the materials they deal with."

Los Angeles photographers Harold and Erica Van Pelt have created almost every *G&G* cover since 1981.

The final cover photo showed 31 diamonds of different colors and sizes, including a large blue in the center, spilling across a light blue background. Many readers assumed that the "$17 million cover," as Keller called it (the estimated value at that time of the diamonds pictured), was simply a collage of individual photos. In fact, it was the end result of one of the most technically demanding projects in *G&G*'s history.

First, article co-authors John King and Tom Moses, plus others on the New York laboratory staff, spent weeks persuading the various owners of the diamonds to loan the stones. The actual photo shoot at the New York lab took a day and a half. The Van Pelts made precise and intricate adjustments of lighting and placements to represent the dramatic range of colors in which diamonds occur naturally as accurately as possible. The setup alone took three and a half hours, "with Erica nudging each stone into position with a toothpick," King recalled later.

Then, to ensure accurate reproduction and color consistency, King—who was instrumental in defining the color grading system—flew to Santa Monica for the entire color separation process and later joined Keller on press in Maryland to supervise the printing. "It was not only our most challenging assignment ever," said Keller later, "but also the most daunting and, to that point, one of *G&G*'s most important projects."

The effort was worth it, based on the reactions to the issue. "We put the actual color grades for each of the diamonds illustrated inside the issue,"

The Van Pelts' photographic wizardry was never more evident than in the remarkable Winter 1994 cover of *G&G*.

Geologist and gemologist Brendan Laurs was named editor of *Gems & Gemology* in 2002.

Keller said. "People told us they would sit there, put their own diamonds of similar color grades next to ones in the photo to compare, and say, 'That's pretty close!'"

In addition, the photos themselves were a first. Few people—even those who owned the stones used in the article—had ever seen "this many colors and such great value" together and all at once.

"But without a solid Van Pelt photograph to start with, we could never have done it," said Keller. "They are technical wizards."

MEANWHILE, KELLER APPLIED HER OWN WIZARDRY to other areas of the publication, thoroughly overhauling *G&G* editorial policies and sections of the journal.

The peer review system was significantly improved. Every paper submitted was read by at least three members of *G&G*'s much-expanded editorial review board, which was composed of prominent members of GIA and the wider gemological and academic community, to ensure accuracy and usefulness. Those papers slated for publication were also read by Liddicoat, *G&G*'s longtime editor-in-chief, and at least one of its associate editors. Keller herself did the final editing.

Existing sections, such as Gem Trade Lab Notes and Gemological Abstracts, were reorganized and expanded. With the Spring 1981 issue, Dona Dirlam took over Gemological Abstracts and Chuck Fryer became editor of the Gem Trade Lab Notes. A new section, Gem News, was added to provide gemological news briefs from around the world.

At the same time, Keller was developing a strong support staff and a network of top gemologists and researchers from GIA and around the world. One important addition to the masthead in the early 1980s was Carol Stockton, *G&G*'s technical editor. Stockton, whose background included both jewelry retailing and gemological research, was critical to ensuring the accuracy and soundness of the articles published. From the mid-1990s on, geologist and gemologist Brendan Laurs assumed many of the journal's technical and editorial responsibilities.

THE FIRST ISSUE OF THE NEW *GEMS & GEMOLOGY* premiered in April 1981, 50 years after GIA was founded by Shipley and 47 years after the first *Gems & Gemology* appeared. Inside was a written promise from editor-in-chief Richard Liddicoat that the new *G&G* would "become the most comprehensive periodical in the field of gemology."

The impact and appeal of the revitalized journal was apparent almost immediately. Subscriptions doubled within months, and by 1990 it had more than 10,000 subscribers. The quality and quantity of articles submitted for publication grew significantly, too. *G&G* encouraged that with the 1982 launch of its annual Most Valuable Article Award, later renamed the Dr. Edward J. Gübelin Most Valuable Article Award.

The quality of the journal's color reproduction was repeatedly recognized over the next two decades by awards from printing industry organizations, and its leadership among professional journals was honored by numerous "Gold Circle" awards from the American Society of Association Executives in the categories of journals and scientific/educational feature writing.

Amanda Luke/GIA

Alice Keller with the collection of more than 80 *G&G* covers that decorate her office.

Most important, *Gems & Gemology* was soon recognized as the industry's leading source of current gemological information. Over the next two decades, *G&G* published the seminal research on synthetic diamonds, diamond treatments such as fracture filling and high pressure/high temperature processing, synthetic moissanite, Mong Hsu rubies, Paraíba tourmalines, and Chinese freshwater cultured pearls, among many other topics.

By the 1990s, *Gems & Gemology* enjoyed a well-deserved international reputation as the "premier professional journal in gemology," according to Bill Boyajian. It had become, as the American Gem Trade Association noted in 1998 when it honored Alice Keller for her contributions to gemology, the "reference tool that the trade cannot live without."

■ALUMNI UNITED

By the start of the 1980s, GIA had produced tens of thousands of gemologists in America and abroad. Yet it had never established an alumni association, something that would offer graduates a lifelong connection with other alumni and the Institute. Manager of resident education Bob Earnest, who

The GIA Alumni Association was formed in 1982, with Institute veteran Bob Earnest as its executive director. Here Richard Liddicoat and Earnest display an Alumni Association certificate.

began as an instructor in 1963, was the original advocate of a formal alumni network.

"The concept of an alumni association had been blossoming for years," recalled Earnest. "In fact, for about 10 or 15 years, students had been asking for some kind of organization where they could keep in touch with each other after they graduated."

With each graduating class, the need for such an organization grew. But during the 1970s, other priorities—the Institute's rapid growth, an expanding curriculum, a new headquarters in Santa Monica— were always standing in the way. Still, Earnest continued his campaign for an alumni network.

In the fall of 1982, the Institute answered his long-awaited dream and established the Gemological Institute of America Alumni Association (GIA AA), naming Earnest the executive director. Its goals were to create an extensive communications network among Association members involved in gemology, to keep alumni informed of new developments in gemology, to promote goodwill among the membership, and to participate in fundraising activities for the benefit of GIA.

Membership privileges included access to a worldwide alumni directory, a semi-annual magazine titled *In Focus* (which covered gemological events, alumni activities, and research updates from the Institute), a newsletter, special pricing on GIA materials and books, and travel opportunities both domestic and abroad.

"We look forward to bringing together graduates of GIA and other gemological institutions in an organization that will serve the worldwide professional gemological community," said Liddicoat at the time.

WITHIN WEEKS, APPLICATIONS WERE STREAMING IN from graduates. Fifteen hundred alumni joined in the first six months. By the end of 1983, there were over 3,000 members, with a growing number of alumni chapters in the United States. At the end of the decade, there were 50 chapters worldwide, and some 4,000 members.

Much more than just a social channel for graduates, the Alumni Association also became an important foundation for ongoing gemological education. Local chapters provided opportunities to exchange ideas and information through lectures, videotapes, and workshops. They created forums for local and statewide communication among jewelers and gem enthusiasts, and meetings on topics ranging from photomicrography to store security.

In addition, Earnest led periodic tours to important gem centers around the world, complete with sightseeing, technical visits, and seminars. A two-week spring 1987 tour to gem localities in South America included meetings with Bogotá gem dealers, opportunities to buy Isla Margarita pearls in Caracas, and a visit to the mines of Ouro Preto, Brazil.

Earnest continued expanding the association's membership and leading alumni tour groups— five continents in all—until his retirement in 1988.

A group of students joins Earnest in browsing through an issue of *In Focus*, the Alumni Association's publication.

■MASTERS OF COLOR

At the start of the 1980s, GIA launched two colored stone projects—one a machine, the other a grading system—that seemed to hold great promise. Both were in response to the demand for colored gemstones, which grew sharply in the United States between the mid-1960s and mid-1980s. Even adjusting for inflation, import values of rubies and sapphires increased more than 15 times, and emeralds more than 19 times. Some of this growth was spurred by GIA's promotion of colored gems in its training and educational workshops. Also, the soaring prices for diamonds that accompanied the 1970s investment boom created a lack of merchandise in the lower (under $1,000) price ranges, a vacancy that colored stones could readily fill.

Unlike diamonds, though, there was no precise, consistent, trade-accepted terminology to describe colored stones, or a widely accepted grading system. "The jeweler was always dependent on the word of the 'experts.' He had to take things on faith," noted research director Dr. Vince Manson.

"Clearly," said Jim Lucey, then an instructor in colored stone grading, "if the burgeoning colored stone market was to be satisfactorily catered to, industry-wide standards and a consensus on terminology would have to be established."

By the late 1970s, then, retailers were asking GIA to do just that—develop a grading system and a course that would teach them to evaluate the characteristics of colored gemstones and help them make better-informed gem buying and selling decisions.

But the Institute had anticipated them by several years. As early as 1973, GIA was considering a short class in colored stone grading. And in the mid-1970s, colored stones came under the scrutiny of the new research laboratory. Then a man named Tom Ritzi offered the Institute what seemed to be the answer to its prayers for a simple and effective way to grade colored gemstones.

FOURTH-GENERATION JEWELER THOMAS RITZI, of Ritzi & Sons in Orlando, Florida, was, by his own admission, "fed up" with trying to grade and appraise colored gems using the ambiguous language then available, and with trying to describe to suppliers the kinds of colored stones he wanted. So in 1977, the University of Florida gemology program graduate set out to invent an apparatus that would reproduce an image of any colored gem just by turning "a few dials."

The device he put together, which he dubbed the RitziScope, was in effect a color simulator that reproduced the overall hue, tone, and "brilliance" of a stone. The lightweight machine, made of balsa wood, used a three-gun color filter system similar to what color televisions then used. It had two dials, one for red and the other for green and blue, to create adjustable color images of gems on a small screen. The viewer could then compare the color of the actual gem with that on the device.

Ritzi also developed a system whereby he could match colored stones on his devices to a numerical "color reading grade." He tested the new device in his two Florida stores and found it a great selling tool. Ritzi believed his invention could benefit other jewelers. They would only have to provide a set of color coordinates to get the right gems from their suppliers, rather than rely on memory or inadequate descriptions. However, Ritzi lacked the resources to develop and manufacture this device, and in mid-1978 he sold his patent rights to GIA.

The Institute's officials were delighted. GIA's diamond grading system had transformed its relationship with the diamond industry, and executives such as Liddicoat and Manson hoped to develop a system that would have a similar impact on the colored gem industry. Just months after acquiring Ritzi's device, they rushed a prototype of what they were already calling a "revolutionary instrument"—then titled the ColorScope—to the 1979 AGS Conclave in Washington, D.C.

"Using the ColorScope, it is now as easy to talk about the greens of an emerald or the reds of a ruby as it is the whiteness of a diamond," said Manson. Indeed, color itself would be reduced to alphanumeric notations that GIA envisioned would become colored gems' standard terminology and grading.

The device debuted on the market a year later, in April 1980, as the ColorMaster. Ritzi's balsa wood model had become a heavier metal machine, using fluorescent and incandescent illumination. It retained the three-gun color system, but used three dials for mixing colors (one each for blue, red, and green), based on the tri-stimulus color system, a standard set by the International Commission on Illumination (CIE) in 1931. A fourth knob allowed the user to darken or lighten images.

Seven color-modifying filters let the user calibrate innumerable colored light mixtures, which appeared as a transparent fashioned gem on a small screen— a three-dimensional representation of the actual gem. The user could then compare the gem's color to that of its ColorMaster representation.

Each color value on the device had an identifying number. Those numbers, plus the filters' letter designations (A through G), became the identifying terms of any colored stone—and the hoped-for basis for a new color language between gem dealers and buyers. Ideally, ColorMaster coordinates could be dialed on any ColorMaster and result in the same gem color.

AT THE SAME TIME, Liddicoat asked GIA extension instructor Janice Mack to head a project to develop a teachable colored stone grading system that could be used with the ColorMaster.

The project soon involved more than 80 people, including a dozen gemologists working on it full-time. It drew not only on GIA's extensive color research but also on the Munsell Color System (the color standard accepted by the U.S. Bureau of Standards and thousands of manufacturers in industries other than jewelry), the German Institute of Standards (DIN), and the color language developed in 1931 by the CIE.

"We took existing color science and created a system specifically for colored stones," said Mack. That wasn't always easy. First, they had to determine how to describe a stone's color by defining its hue, tone, and saturation. Then, they had to correlate the description to a ColorMaster notation that represented the color space in the Munsell system, in order to produce an image on the ColorMaster screen to serve as a master stone for that color. Gem traders were repeatedly surveyed on their preferred colors for each

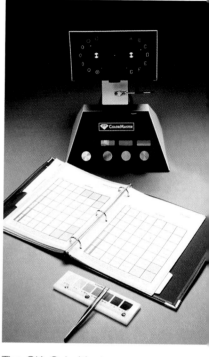

The GIA ColorMaster, which debuted on the market in April 1980, was designed to provide a standard for grading colored gemstones. The resulting coordinates could be communicated to anyone else using the instrument, without having to rely on vague descriptions or color memory.

The ColorMaster project marked GIA's first steps toward a colored stone grading system.

gemstone type. Those color preferences were computerized and charted, and each color description for a given gemstone was assigned a numerical grade.

By 1982, they had compressed the analyses, field research, and Munsell color spaces into what Manson called "a coherent, coordinated plan."

THE FUNDAMENTALS OF THE NEW GRADING SYSTEM were previewed by Mack in February 1982 at the Institute's first International Gemological Symposium and then officially presented two months later at the AGS Conclave in New Orleans. In the fall of 1982, Mack gave pilot classes in the new system to GIA personnel.

While it wasn't absolutely necessary to have a ColorMaster to use the new colored stone grading system, it was helpful to verify a grader's color descriptions and ensure greater accuracy. Indeed, the system and the device seemed interdependent. The ColorMaster had approximately 1,000 master notations (later increased to 2,000).

Manson believed strongly in the ColorMaster's potential, and from the project's inception he had predicted heavy demand for it (and for the GIA colored-stone reports that were to have been based on it). Yet less than 100 were sold in the first year, and sales never picked up, to the surprise and frustration of Institute officials. By 1982, just two years after it went on the market, the jewelry industry had grown wary of the ColorMaster. Why? The collapse of the gem investment industry during that period may have cooled buyer enthusiasm, but there were also serious criticisms of the ColorMaster as a product.

A core problem was the sensitive machine's inability to guarantee reproducibility. Some machines gave differing results for the same ColorMaster notations. In addition, the machines couldn't reproduce all colors, especially highly saturated blues and greens, or be used for all gemstones, such as jade and opal. GIA officials were not pleased. GEM Instruments had invested heavily in refining and producing the ColorMaster. Now, with the gem investment industry deflating and instrument sales dropping, the Institute couldn't afford to have an expensive gemological white elephant on its hands.

While GIA continued to offer the ColorMaster and training in colored stone grading for years, the ColorMaster was dropped as a product for sale in the mid-1990s.

■ A GLOBAL SYMPOSIUM

In the beginning, it was just a crazy dream. The idea, though ambitious, was simple enough. To mark the Institute's 50th anniversary and the advances in gemology in that half century, Vince Manson suggested, let's bring together the thinkers, the experts, the movers and shakers of the international gemological fraternity, and the grassroots jeweler-gemologists for a grand "state of gemology" meeting. Let them rub shoulders and exchange ideas.

In the late 1970s, when Manson first proposed the idea, nothing like it had been done on such a scale in the gem and jewelry industry. Yet it was an appropriate way to mark this GIA milestone and a logical extension of what Shipley himself had intended for the first American Gem Society Conclaves in the 1930s.

Such symposia were common in the scientific and academic worlds, where scholars and students come together to share position papers, theories, and developments in their fields. As the trade's leading educational, scientific, and research institution, said Manson, it was not only appropriate but also necessary for GIA—"the university of the industry"—to sponsor such an event.

"Vince didn't have to do a hard sell on it," recalled Liddicoat. "We all felt it was an idea whose time had come." And Manson was the person to chair it.

ON FEBRUARY 12, 1982, MORE THAN 500 PEOPLE from 35 countries gathered at the Century Plaza Hotel in Los Angeles for GIA's first International Gemological Symposium to discuss "Gemology: Past, Present and Future." They included gemological pioneers and leaders such as Liddicoat, Crowningshield, Krashes, Hans Bagge, Edward Tiffany, and George Kaplan. There were international authorities such as Switzerland's Dr. Edward Gübelin, the leading expert on gemstone inclusions; Germany's Dr. Hermann Bank, head of the German Gemmological Association; Kenya's Campbell Bridges, exploration geologist and discoverer of tsavorite garnet; America's Carroll Chatham, a pioneer in gem synthesis; and John Latendresse, principal supplier of American freshwater pearls. Hundreds of jewelers and gem dealers attended.

"VINCE DIDN'T HAVE TO DO A HARD SELL ON SYMPOSIUM," RECALLED LIDDICOAT. "WE ALL FELT IT WAS AN IDEA WHOSE TIME HAD COME."

215

"GEMOLOGY HAS
COME OF AGE,"
RICHARD LIDDICOAT
ANNOUNCED AT THE
FIRST INTERNATIONAL
GEMOLOGICAL
SYMPOSIUM.

Over the next three-and-a-half days, some 60 experts on diamonds, colored stones, synthetics and simulants, pearls, and gem identification delivered papers or sat on panels about production, mining, pearl culturing, synthetics, treatments, gem sources, and other aspects of gemology and the industry. There were also social events, including a gala dinner, and an open house at GIA headquarters.

The Symposium's multi-track format let attendees choose what they wanted to hear from a smorgasbord of gemological presentations. Four categories, or "tracks," of talks were offered concurrently in the morning and afternoon in different rooms. For those who were interested in presentations being given at the same time, audiotapes of each session were available at a nominal cost.

Looking back at the tracks of that first Symposium gives insight into the gemological issues that were important at the time. Indeed, the talks comprised what the Symposium's *Proceedings* volume later called a "State of the Science message for gemology." Liddicoat gave an eloquent and comprehensive overview of the development of gemological training and instruments in GIA's first half-century, and there were sessions on "selling gemology to the public." But the heart of the symposium was its focus on hot technical issues: treatments, gem sources (especially Africa), synthetics and simulants, pearls, and inclusions.

THE SYMPOSIUM WON ENTHUSIASTIC REVIEWS from participants. It certainly achieved the goal Manson had envisioned—to bring retailers, gem dealers, and management together with key players in the industry, the people who shape its future, the "international gemological fraternity" as he called it, in a "state of gemology meeting."

The first Symposium did something else, too: It showed how far GIA, its training and influence—indeed gemology itself—had come since Robert Shipley had mailed his first lesson. The Institute had grown into an internationally respected institution of professional learning and research. It had played a major role in creating that international fraternity of gemology. Its programs, training, and instruments had transformed and uplifted the domestic and international jewelry industry. A mere invitation from GIA was now enough to bring together hundreds of the industry's best and brightest.

"Gemology has come of age," Liddicoat announced proudly to the Symposium attendees, and so had the Institute. Indeed, the Symposium itself, said Manson in hindsight years later, was "a kind of summing up" of GIA's essence. It also marked "the end of an era for GIA"—and the start of what would be some of its most challenging years.

GIA celebrated its 50th anniversary with an International Gemological Symposium in February 1982, shown here in a photo collage. Hundreds of jewelers and gemologists from around the world attended the Symposium, which offered a smorgasbord of academic presentations and social events.

An August 1982 *Time* article reflected the dire state of the industry—and the Institute—in the wake of the diamond invest-ment collapse.

Economy & Business

A Gem That Lost Its Luster

The precious stone looks better in a ring than on a balance sheet

The official opening two weeks ago of the Jwaneng diamond mine in Bo-tswana, near the southern tip of Africa, should have been an occasion for celebra-tion. After all, Harry Oppenheimer, 73, the chairman of De Beers, the cartel that controls the production and sale of most of the world's diamonds, has called the site "the most important primary deposit found anywhere in the world since the dis-covery at Kimberley more than a century ago." The rich ore of the Jwaneng mine is expected to produce 3 million carats of precious stones in 1982, and eventually 4.5 million carats annually, nearly one-quarter of De Beers' total output.

This year, however, many of the diamonds laboriously ex-tracted from the arid Botswana earth will not be sold. They will instead be added to the growing De Beers stockpile of gems. The reason is that there is a world-wide glut of the precious gems. The vaults of diamond wholesal-ers are overflowing with rough as well as cut and polished stones, and the market for investment-grade diamonds has virtually collapsed. A rare one-carat D-flawless-grade stone that brought $62,000 at the peak of the market in 1980 is now worth only $15,000 or less, a decline of more than 75%. De Beers' sales arm, the Central Selling Orga-nization, saw profits tumble 46% in 1981, and Oppenheimer says that an upturn is not yet in sight.

In an effort to put some sparkle back into the diamond million." For less affluent buyers, De Beers is urging American parents to give their teen-age daughters small, heart-shaped di-amond jewelry "for those special occasions . . . as only a parent can."

While the price of diamond jewelry has remained relatively stable, the market for investment diamonds has collapsed be-cause of speculation run amuck. In the late 1970s, dealers in Tel Aviv, one of the world's diamond-cutting centers, began buying bushels of stones on credit after the

which in its six
250,000 stones.
promise that the
the stones and we
had ever lost any

Diamonds tu
vestment, largely
sell. Experts co
the exact charact
which means tha
vary widely. Mor
resale market for
stones at retail,
that they can be s
diamond dealers
price, which is i

DIAMONDS *WERE* A GIRL'S BEST FRIEND
Average price of a one-carat D-flawless

$60,000
$50,000
$40,000
$30,000
$20,000

1978 1979 1980 1981 1982

TIME Chart by Nigel Holmes   Source: The Diamond Registry

vestmen
Then I
price an
ond mor

As
and coll
diamond
gan in
started t
rates sho
ments li
more va
gold and
attractiv
price inc
selling f
oz., well
peak of $
coins is
it was a y

Inter
Corp. fi
under th
February

TRANSITIONS

1983–1986

Nothing lasts forever.

The lucrative bubble that was the diamond investment boom of the late 1970s collapsed, triggering losses throughout the industry, including at the Gemological Institute of America. Every segment of the Institute—education, laboratory services, instruments—was affected. And the losses weren't just monetary.

Though many didn't realize it at the time, the health—and possibly the continued existence—of GIA was at stake.

Yet the Institute would emerge stronger, in better financial shape, more resilient, and with a higher public profile than before, thanks to the man—Glenn Nord—brought in to revive GIA. It adopted a fresh approach to education, revamped operations, and established financial stability. But the Institute that took off in 1986 was very different from the one that needed help in 1983—because of the difficult measures taken.

■THE BUBBLE BURSTS

While GIA's success on the world stage was being applauded, it was a different matter behind the scenes. Things were changing in the early 1980s, and not for the better.

The Institute's staff and students had always seemed like family, a word used often by staff members during its first 40 years. "It was a very small organization, and everyone took care of one another," said former accounting manager Jan Fryer. "It really felt like a family operation."

"There was the camaraderie and closeness of a family," agreed Glenn Nord, recalling his years there in the 1960s and early '70s. "We all did double duty, everything except mop the floor." That wasn't just because of the small size of the Institute. The style set by Liddicoat himself was influential. He neither pressured nor demanded, but led by example, taking care to hire good people and then let them do their jobs. "One of Mr. Liddicoat's gifts was that he was always open to trying something new. GIA grew, and developed the people that it did in the '70s and '80s, because he allowed people to express ideas and then run with them," said former instructor Janice Mack.

But families change, and the Institute family was unavoidably affected by the impact of the diamond investment boom on its courses, laboratory, instruments, and staff. By the end of the 1970s, GIA's intimacy was disappearing

By 1982, the price of a one-carat D-Flawless round brilliant diamond had plummeted to $15,000, from $62,000 only two years earlier.

on both coasts. The Institute had grown from a tiny, close-knit group to a big organization. It was no longer a "family" business.

OTHER THINGS WERE CHANGING, TOO. By 1980, the diamond investment boom was a bubble about to burst. Industry leaders became Jeremiahs, warning of impending disaster. One was Moshe Schnitzer, president of the World Federation of Diamond Bourses, who told the WFDB Congress in Johannesburg that the investment sale of diamonds was "a powerful time bomb which may ruin not only those directly involved, but inflict damage upon our whole trade."

"You knew the bubble had to burst sometime," said Bill Boyajian, then supervisor of the colored stone resident education program. "And when it burst, we knew it would also burst at GIA."

The overheated investment market was already poised for collapse when De Beers began trying to cool it off in the late 1970s. Between March and July of 1978, its Central Selling Organisation raised surcharges on sightholders a total of 90 percent. Between August and September 1979, it imposed price increases totaling 43 percent. In February 1980, it raised prices another 12 percent. That, and rising interest rates, pushed up the cost of diamonds at every purchasing level. By spring 1980, a one-carat D-Flawless round brilliant was valued at about $62,000. "A ridiculous price," Crowningshield scoffed later. "We knew when *that* happened, it was all over." Soon after, diamond prices finally exceeded consumer demand.

"YOU KNEW THE BUBBLE HAD TO BURST SOMETIME," SAID BOYAJIAN.

U.S. consumer spending fell as the economy sank into recession. By June 1980, spending was at near-record lows. Jewelry retailers and dealers didn't restock. Diamond manufacturing came to a virtual standstill. The price of rough was so high that cutters could expect to lose 10 to 20 percent on polished stones because of the continuing drop in the value of finished goods.

By the end of 1980, diamond investors were scrambling for the exits. By September 1981, the price of the benchmark one-carat D-Flawless diamond had plummeted to $30,000; it was around $15,000 only 12 months later. By then, *Modern Jeweler* reported that investment promoters were frantically offering retailers diamonds at 25 to 35 percent below market value. The once-powerful investment market had collapsed.

It was one of the worst recessions in the modern history of the diamond trade. Between 1980 and 1984, hundreds of diamond companies went bankrupt, and thousands of others shut down after paying off debts. The impact of the "Crash of 1980" was soberly illustrated during the 1984 WFDB Congress in Antwerp, when all members rose for a moment of silence—the first since the end of World War II—to honor absent colleagues whose businesses had been closed or harmed by the crash.

BUT THE DEALERS WEREN'T THE ONLY ONES AFFECTED. The crash touched virtually every area of GIA's operations. The good times—spiraling enrollments, lab safes overflowing with diamonds, unprecedented instrument sales—ended abruptly. By early 1981, the diamond grading business had fallen apart and taken the associated revenue with it. Gary Roskin, then the assistant director of the Los Angeles lab, recalled, "We looked up one day [in early 1981] and realized we had 56 graders on two shifts sitting there with nothing to do." In September 1981, GIA closed its Santa Monica diamond grading lab, laid off half the staff, and consolidated operations with the L.A. lab. The decline in grading income continued, and by early 1983 only about 15 graders were left on the West Coast.

Meanwhile, instrument sales took a major hit, costing the Institute millions of dollars in revenue. The high volume of home study, resident, and extension class students—many of whom were involved in the investment boom—also dropped significantly by 1982. In effect, GEM Instruments lost its two biggest "customers": GIA Education and the GIA Gem Trade Laboratory.

THE SUDDEN CHANGES IN THE DIAMOND INVESTMENT MARKET, the shrinking revenues, and the declining enrollments worried many at the Institute, especially its officials. "Everyone was getting frightened about what would happen," Richard Liddicoat recalled later. The board of governors, especially, was "disturbed about the red ink and told me they wanted to let quite a few people go."

Liddicoat was less concerned. GIA had survived other tight financial situations, including a collapse in the junk bond market in the early 1970s that wiped out half of its investments. "The financial problems [in the early 1980s] didn't seem to call for a U-turn, just a slowdown," he said later.

The board disagreed. They told Liddicoat in early 1982 to start laying people off immediately. That gave him little choice, but he resolved to keep the cuts

THE BOARD OF GOVERNORS, ESPECIALLY, WAS "DISTURBED ABOUT THE RED INK," SAID LIDDICOAT.

as superficial as possible. He wanted to let a few people go and then wait until the July board meeting to discuss how much deeper to cut. He knew he was taking a chance. "I was treading water," he said later. But the board demanded more cutbacks, and Liddicoat—who had let very few people go in his four decades at GIA—began the unpleasant task of reducing GIA's 500-person staff.

All departments were affected. When research director Vincent Manson left on a month-long trip to Africa in 1982, he had a staff of 10. When he returned, only four people remained. Bill Boyajian recalled that by June 1983, the staff thought things couldn't possibly get any worse.

"And then," he said, "Dick Liddicoat had his heart attack."

■ "MR. GIA"

GIA without Liddicoat's leadership? The idea was impossible to conceive. He was Shipley's "heir." He had overseen the reopening of GIA's East Coast branch and the acquisition of its Gem Trade Laboratory. He had led the Institute's rescue from financial collapse in the early 1950s, developed its internationally accepted diamond grading system, and revamped Shipley's courses to make them more relevant to the modern jeweler.

He had inspired thousands of gemology careers. His handpicked staff, chosen from the best and brightest of GIA's graduates—"Liddicoat's brain trust," some called it—had expanded the Institute into a globally respected gemological education and research facility.

He seemed to be everywhere, indispensable. Even Liddicoat himself joked in the late 1970s that he was so involved in day-to-day operations he was like "part of the woodwork." He was the world's most famous gemological educator, revered and beloved. "He was Mr. GIA," said George Kaplan, then chairman of the board of governors. "An institution," said his friend and former colleague Glenn Nord. "I couldn't imagine GIA without him."

But the strain of reducing costs and operations had placed Liddicoat under extreme pressure. What seemed to distress him most was letting go of the very people he had hired. In spring 1983, the board asked him to prepare a plan to further reduce the Institute's operations and personnel. For this man who had strived to create a professional family as well as a world-class educational institution, a man whom students and staff looked on as a father figure, it was too much. It broke his heart—literally.

On Saturday, June 19, 1983, while working in his office, Liddicoat was stricken with a heart attack. He was 65.

WHEN WORD OF LIDDICOAT'S ILLNESS reached the students and staff of GIA, they were shocked and concerned for his health—and that of the Institute. Liddicoat's sudden vulnerability had exposed a serious weakness in GIA itself: There was no predetermined successor. Though the board had been after him for years to mentor a possible replacement, none of the department heads had been groomed to step in—temporarily or otherwise—if Liddicoat became incapacitated. Adding to the uncertainty was that no one knew how the governors—then a remote body to most students and staff—would handle the situation.

In June 1983, Liddicoat, then 65, suffered a heart attack while working in his office. Concern for his health forced Liddicoat to step down as president.

The governors, for their part, thought the Institute was facing disaster. The gem and jewelry industry was still in recession. GIA's longtime leader was in a hospital. Revenues were shrinking sharply, as were the sources of those revenues. "GIA's financial picture had become ominous very quickly," said Kaplan.

The Institute's governors were then meeting formally only once a year, though its executive committee met more often if immediate decisions were needed or an emergency arose. This was definitely an emergency. The executive committee—Kaplan and five other governors—met on June 25 in New York City. Could Liddicoat's health stand the stress of the drastic personnel cuts that had to be made once he recovered? And what about the problems that had to be dealt with now?

"We wrestled with what had to be done," said Kaplan. "If Dick was incapacitated, then we had to put someone in as soon as possible who could do the emergency surgery [on GIA] that was necessary." Several possible candidates were considered. Someone suggested Kaplan, who declined. Then board member and banker Paul Bailey asked, "How about Glenn Nord?"

Glenn Nord, Liddicoat's right-hand man in the late 1960s and early '70s, had left for health reasons in 1974 to become vice president of the International Goldfinger Group, and became a leading figure in the international diamond trade. In 1981 he retired, and in January 1983 he joined the board of governors.

Nord's intimate familiarity with the Institute, his solid gemological credentials, and his strong business background seemed just what GIA needed. As Kaplan recalled, "We all jumped up [at the suggestion] and said, 'Absolutely!'" Nord, they all agreed, would lead GIA through the profound challenges it faced.

George Kaplan, then chairman of GIA's board of governors, reacted quickly after Liddicoat's heart attack. With the Institute facing financial turmoil, Kaplan asked Glenn Nord to return as president.

KAPLAN PHONED NORD AT HIS HOME IN CALIFORNIA and asked him to come to New York to discuss short-term plans while Liddicoat was in the hospital. But he didn't tell him what the board was planning.

Nord flew out the next morning. The emergency executive session began with a discussion of GIA's tight financial situation, the tremendous strain it put on Liddicoat, the crisis facing the Institute, and above all the need for someone to do something about it.

There was a brief pause. Then Kaplan said, "Glenn, why don't you take over as president?"

Nord was stunned. His number one concern was the health of his close friend Liddicoat, who was still in the hospital. But Nord also had another concern: his own health. The inoperable brain aneurysm that had forced him to leave GIA in 1974 was a daily reminder of his own mortality. He still went to bed every night not knowing if he would wake up the next day.

"That was on my mind," he said dryly years later. "I knew there would be pressures with the new job that could affect it."

So, Nord told them, "I really, *really* don't want to do this."

He and the board members argued back and forth as he tried to find another solution—but for the board, there was no other option. Said Kaplan, "The clear, unanimous view was that he was the man for the job. It was clear to everyone—except Glenn."

Finally, Kaplan spoke bluntly. Liddicoat was seriously ill, and the problems could not wait for his recovery. GIA's financial situation was critical. Its very survival was at risk. Something had to be done now.

Nord gave in. He reluctantly agreed to become acting president and chief executive officer. He set two conditions. First, his appointment had to be temporary, only for six months. He told the board, "I can't do this for any length of time. I have a health condition myself, so if you want me to do this, you have to find someone to take my place." ("It's a blessing that we didn't really know how delicate Glenn's health was," said Kaplan later. "His accepting the job was an action of the greatest courage and dedication.") Second, Nord said that he, not someone else, would tell Liddicoat. He didn't want his mentor and friend to hear about his replacement secondhand.

The board agreed to both conditions, and reached one additional conclusion: Liddicoat should not resume his duties as president once he had recovered. ("They were afraid I was working myself into an early grave," Liddicoat said later.) On July 31, the board of governors formally confirmed Nord's appointment as acting president and CEO, and Liddicoat's as chairman of the board, with Kaplan as executive chairman.

Once he recovered, Liddicoat was again actively involved with the Institute, if in a different capacity. While he resumed his editorial work with GIA publications, especially *Gems & Gemology*, in his new post he was the liaison between the board and the Institute, the board's chief advisor about GIA. He also chaired GIA's planning and research committees. In addition, he traveled and lectured extensively for the Institute.

But Liddicoat's hand was no longer gripping the wheel. The educator who had prided himself on his independence as the Institute's head now had to relinquish that role. With surprising speed, the Liddicoat era—the period during which GIA had established itself as the industry's international leader in professional education, research, and gem testing—had come to an end.

The Nord era, just as abruptly, had begun.

GIA'S SURGEON

As far as Glenn Nord was concerned, his appointment as acting president wasn't a return to GIA because, in his heart, he had never really left.

But the Institute had grown and changed so much in the decade he had been away that most of the staff members knew little about Nord. Only the veteran staffers knew him well. Bert Krashes told the trade press that Nord "knows the internal workings [of GIA], has experience in the trade that it serves, and has a proven record as a businessman and administrator."

Yet this proven businessman didn't relish the charge he had been given. As Vince Manson observed, "When he came back here as president, it was like a surgeon coming to do this terrible surgery on his own child in order to save the child's life. Glenn did what he had to for GIA, no matter how difficult it was for us—or for him."

SHORTLY AFTER THE GOVERNORS' JUNE 27 MEETING, Nord moved into an office at the Santa Monica campus. Significantly, it wasn't Liddicoat's office in the main building, though as acting president he probably could have taken it. It was a little office across the street in the Richlar Building, which GIA was leasing. The building also housed GEM Instruments, accounting, the bookstore, and the cafeteria. It remained his office during most of his tenure as president. Doing that, as Gary Roskin put it, "was his way of saying that he was there to get us through this, and not take over."

WITH SURPRISING SPEED, THE LIDDICOAT ERA HAD COME TO AN END. THE NORD ERA, JUST AS ABRUPTLY, HAD BEGUN.

"WE WERE STARVING FOR STUDENTS [AND DID] ANYTHING WE COULD TO GENERATE ENROLLMENTS," SAID BOYAJIAN.

Nord spent his first days as president studying the finances, going over everything from pencils to paper clips. What he saw wasn't good. "There had been a tremendous amount of money coming in [during the diamond investment period], and then the money wasn't there anymore," said Nord in a 1985 interview with *The Goldsmith*. "We were out on a limb. We had to cut space, cut people, cut expenses everywhere."

GIA still had several hundred people on staff, even though lab business on both coasts had dropped sharply in the previous 18 months. And income was plummeting. In 1981, the Institute had about $23 million in revenues. By 1982 that was down to $18 million, and GIA was in trouble. Enrollments had dropped significantly. "It was devastating," recalled Bill Boyajian. "We were starving for students [and did] anything we could to generate enrollments. It was a very difficult time."

Worst of all, the Institute's courses—the foundation of GIA and the core of its training—needed extensive revision and revamping to help the industry cope with the challenges and demands of the 1980s. "There were a lot of things we had to do to survive," said Nord later. "We had to develop new courses, products and gemological instruments, cut our staff, *and* increase business—and do it all at the same time." And quickly.

AN INFORMED STAFF was essential to Nord's management style. So one of his first acts, after reviewing the finances, was to let employees know what he planned to do, how it affected them and their departments, and what he expected. He held the first meeting with the Institute's top managers, about half a dozen people, and—as he put it—immediately "got down to the nitty-gritty."

He told them how the Institute would be run from then on: "Things will be done properly and on time." It was a tough conversation. As one person at that meeting recalled, "He didn't present himself to us as a savior, but as a businessperson who said this [Institute] has to be run more efficiently."

Nord was wise enough to also spend time listening to his new staff. He wanted to hear where they thought problems lay. He held many meetings with them in the weeks and months that followed. "It was a constant thing as we improved procedures," said Nord.

Within days of his arrival, Nord started tightening the organization and making tough calls. He made most of the actual decisions on where and how much to cut, in concert with GIA's department heads.

The first task he faced was reducing the large staff. "We were bloated," Nord said bluntly, "and I came down heavy on that. Dick had begun laying off people, but we had to go through more pain, downsizing before there even was such a word."

In less than six months, GIA's staff shrank to just 275 people. No department was exempted, and many were consolidated. "It was a very depressing and very frightening period in those first months," recalled a veteran GIA manager who survived the cuts. "There were constant layoffs. There were a lot of nervous people until we hit bottom and started up again." In actuality, only about half of those who left GIA during that period were laid off by Nord or at his direction. The rest left on their own, both in California and New York. Still, the job security of the past decades was gone, and GIA's staff wouldn't again be as large as its peak of 500 until the end of the 1990s, almost 20 years later.

On July 31, 1983, Glenn Nord became only the third president of GIA in over 50 years.

AT GIA'S EAST COAST OFFICE, the early 1980s were "an extremely difficult time for all of us after the uncontrolled growth of the 1970s," said Tom Yonelunas, then New York Education manager. At the start of the decade, there had been some 120 people on staff, a third of them in education, the rest in the laboratory.

As in Santa Monica, the collapse of the diamond boom and GIA's financial restructuring forced the New York branch to do everything it could to reduce overhead and survive. "Enrollments dropped tremendously," recalled Seung-Hae Moon, then an instructor in New York. Between 1984 and early 1985, Bert Krashes and Tom Yonelunas began the process of consolidating all New York operations onto the second floor of the 580 Fifth Avenue building, a relocation that continued through the balance of the decade.

By early 1984, GIA New York was down to four classrooms—three for resident training and one for local one-week programs—and less than half the staff it had in 1980. But there were silver linings, too. By economizing and lowering overhead, Education improved efficiency and increased the number of students per classroom. Systems and procedures at the Gem Trade Laboratory, including security and the flow of gems, were reviewed and improved. In 1984, the laboratory began accepting international memberships.

Ironically, this difficult period also saw some improvement in the laboratory's rocky relations with the New York gem and diamond trades. In the late 1970s, the trades provided the base of GIA Gem Trade Laboratory clients, and the diamond dealers in particular wanted more input, especially given the long delays they experienced at the height of the investment boom. In January 1980, an industry advisory committee was formed. It was composed of Krashes and Crowningshield, as well as leaders of the New York diamond trade. The aim was to improve the functions of the Gem Trade Laboratory and to enhance its services to the industry and the public.

Formation of the committee helped alleviate the adversarial relations between GIA's laboratory and the local trade. Krashes' cooperative efforts encouraged dealers to keep supporting GIA with business during the lean early '80s, although many of them were going through difficult times of their own. "They went from being bitter about GIA to the point where everyone helped support us out of compassion, providing excellent advice and counsel," recalled Yonelunas. "The committee and its members became an incredible asset."

NOT SURPRISINGLY, Nord's no-nonsense approach, and the decisive actions he took, quickly earned him a reputation among many in the industry as a tough businessman. That reputation clung to him for years, even up to the writing of this book two decades later. Nord's management style and personality, so dramatically different from Liddicoat's, were major factors in how he was perceived.

NORD QUICKLY
EARNED A
REPUTATION AS A
NO-NONSENSE,
TAKE-CHARGE
ADMINISTRATOR.

Liddicoat was a genial, thoughtful, unassuming leader, who had spent his life in teaching, research, and service to the industry. He led by example, had a great vision for GIA, great gemological skills, and a great talent for motivating people.

Nord, on the other hand, was all business. He was a take-charge administrator who knew that to carry out its mission, the Institute had to be efficient, competitive, and operationally sound.

"[Nord has] the toughness and drive to set policy and see it carried out," one diamond dealer and former GIA student told *Modern Jeweler* in 1983. "GIA has gotten so big in the past 30 years, it practically needs a general to run it."

"Downsizing people was tough on Dick and it was tough on me, too," Nord said much later. "I couldn't sleep many nights, knowing I would have to let someone go the next day who was a good employee. I knew it hurt people, good people." Because of that, he was especially sensitive to morale, and did a number of things to boost it. He stayed true to his word at keeping people informed, telling them where the Institute stood financially. As much as possible, Nord kept the staff members appointed by Liddicoat. "I tried to work with the people we had. We were shaking things up enough without bringing in new people," he said.

He didn't ask more of GIA's staff than he asked of himself. Nord, like Liddicoat, was a workaholic. He arrived daily at 7 a.m. and worked long days and even weekends. "With our business going downhill, and me doing what I had to, it wasn't good for morale to do otherwise," he explained. He made a point of taking daily walks around the Institute, both to be visible and to stay in touch with the staff. Nord also provided a more tangible and unexpected morale-builder by giving everyone a bonus in December 1983.

"It was a 'thank you,'" said Nord. "In those first six months, we took ourselves from a tough situation to the point of breaking even again. These were all good people, and they were working very hard to produce and make the Institute go." By then, the Institute's long-term survival was no longer in question, so he continued the annual bonus the entire time he was president.

Richard Liddicoat signs a copy of his *Handbook of Gem Identification* at his 70th birthday party at the Santa Monica campus. Liddicoat was a "working chairman," traveling to gemological events and spending much of his time at GIA.

MEANWHILE, DICK LIDDICOAT GREW MORE COMFORTABLE with his new role as chairman of GIA. Now semi-retired, he wasn't directly involved in Nord's decisions and changes, though Nord talked with him frequently and kept him informed of what was happening. Liddicoat took his new post seriously. He was a working chairman, observed one Canadian reporter who visited him in early 1986. He came in every day at 9 a.m. and stayed until late afternoon. He played some golf and worked on his stamp collection. But his real hobby, indeed his life, was the Institute, and his commitment to it was as strong as ever.

When he was not traveling for the Institute, Liddicoat spent nearly all his time at GIA. He stopped by every evening—his house was only a couple of miles away—and came in on the weekends to work. Old habits and loyalties were too ingrained to break. With all the jobs and responsibilities he now had as chairman, he said, "There was too much happening for me to stay away."

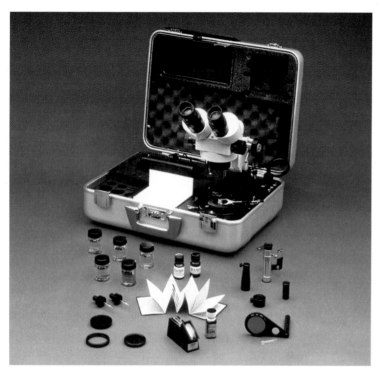

In 1984, GIA GEM Instruments bounced back with a new catalog featuring state-of-the-art instruments such as the MaxiLab.

"Dick once told me there was never a time when he didn't look forward to Monday morning," recalled George Kaplan in 2002.

■INSTRUMENTS

GEM Instruments and its products were like an overused engine— they needed a complete overhaul. The division's problems ran far deeper than the $1 million a year losses. Much of the inventory was outdated and unusable. Even in 1983, 1960s-vintage instruments were common. Overbuying had larded stockrooms with too many of the same parts or with parts for prototype equipment never completed, while other instruments had no replacement parts at all.

"We had to take GEM Instruments apart and put it back together again," said Nord. "But it would have been easier to shut it down and start over."

The makeover began soon after his arrival, when he met with GEM Instruments vice president Gale Johnson to discuss strategy. Outdated equipment was disposed of quickly. Prices were cut. Work began on redesigning all equipment and developing new instruments with cutting-edge technology. To keep production costs down, the division did more outsourcing. Nord himself went to Japan to buy some parts that were less expensive there than in the United States, and he implemented ways to improve the division's customer service and public image.

The results were evident within months. By early 1984, the manufacturing division had a new name, GIA GEM Instruments, "to better identify us with GIA and to let customers know our products have the backing of the Institute" said Johnson, and a bold new logo. GEM Instruments relocated across the street and set up a new showroom.

During 1984, a new 100-page catalog introduced an array of state-of-the-art gemological instruments designed to identify, grade, appraise, and merchandise diamonds, colored stones, and jewelry. Among them was the all-new GIA GEM MaxiLab, with 18 gemological instruments including the new Mark VI GemoLite binocular microscope.

Between 1983 and 1986, GIA GEM Instruments introduced more than half a dozen new instruments. Altogether, said Johnson, the changes marked "a renaissance for the company."

■NEW OPPORTUNITIES

By January 1984, after six months of relentless cost cutting and revamping of operations, things were on the upswing again. GEM Instruments (which, despite its troubles, still dominated its market) started to turn around. Test-market responses to early revisions of GIA's home study courses were positive and promised gains in enrollments. Though the Institute wasn't out of the woods yet, GIA's staff was lean, and its finances were finally stable. The total number of employees had dropped from a high of 500 in 1980 to 333 at the beginning of 1984.

"We had cut expenses everywhere," recalled Nord later. "We had put tight control on costs. We had cut space [consolidating operations in New York, and giving up thousands of square feet in Santa Monica]. We had taken care of our liabilities and had cash on hand. We were in good shape again."

That obviously pleased the board of governors. Indeed, his rescue effort had proved so successful that in January 1984—the deadline Nord had set for them to announce his replacement—the governors insisted that Nord continue as GIA's permanent president and chief executive officer. Kaplan told Nord they couldn't find anyone who knew GIA as well or could do as effective a job. This time, Nord didn't argue or resist. "All right," he agreed. "Let's see how it goes."

"Having worked as hard as we did to get a lot of things going," he explained later, "I wanted to hang around long enough to make sure they stayed in place."

NORD CONTINUED TO WORK ON GIA'S PUBLIC IMAGE. It wasn't enough to revive the Institute's good fortunes. He wanted to raise its profile and restore industry appreciation—and use—of its services to ensure that those fortunes remained stable and grew.

"We're not an ivory tower, distanced from the industry and public we serve," Nord said somewhat fervently on one occasion. "We are an integral part of the jewelry community—as a participant, not a figurehead." On

Whereas GIA advertising had always focused on home study, marketing efforts expanded during the Nord era to promote other areas of the Institute such as resident education (top) and the Gem Trade Laboratory (bottom).

At the early GemFests, GIA staff members introduced attendees to gemology and the Institute.

another occasion, he noted that "to do good work as educators, we must first reach out to the community we seek to educate. That means striving for high visibility in the public eye." It also meant some heavy-duty marketing.

A major full-color advertising campaign, including public relations materials, was launched through the trade press. It was hardly the first time GIA had advertised, but the focus previously was almost exclusively on promoting home study. Now GIA's advertising and marketing expanded to promote the entire Institute.

To do so, Nord, like a new homeowner inviting the neighbors over for a get-to-know-us barbecue, held an open house at the Santa Monica headquarters for anyone in the California jewelry community who wanted to visit. On a spring Sunday in March 1984, more than 800 people jammed the corridors and classrooms of the Institute to hear free lectures, see gemology demonstrations, and take advantage of special instrument and book sales. "Suddenly, it seems, staid and scientific GIA has doffed its scholarly robes, thrown open its doors and set out to spread the good news to whomever will listen about the joys of gemology," reported Joe Thompson, editor-in-chief of *Modern Jeweler*, in 1984.

Pleased by the response, Nord planned a bigger, better organized, and more elaborate event—called GemFest '84—to be held that summer immediately after the Pacific Jewelry Show in Los Angeles. He handed the idea over to the recently promoted manager of new project development, Bill Boyajian, with only one proviso: It had to appeal to a wide spectrum in the trade, including GIA alumni and students, as well as other gem and jewelry professionals.

Using what the Institute had learned in putting together the 1982 International Gemological Symposium, Boyajian and GIA staff designed a program for GemFest '84 that drew 320 people to Santa Monica for two days of technical seminars, demonstrations, and social events.

The response was strong enough to convince Nord to schedule GemFest as an annual undertaking. It would bring GIA's educational expertise into the open through seminars and social functions that let members of the industry get acquainted with one another, as well as with Institute staff. By 1986, GemFest was already what *Rock & Gem* magazine called "a major event" for jewelers, a fixture on the industry's annual schedule. In 1987, GIA launched GemFest East in New York in conjunction with the Jewelers of America summer trade show. A year later, it held a GemFest Europe in Vicenza, Italy.

The "open house" continued as an annual event into the early 1990s. And GIA GemFests became well-respected international events, held annually in conjunction with the spring Basel and fall Hong Kong trade shows, as well as elsewhere in Asia and Europe. "Now, GemFest is identified with GIA everywhere. It is gemologically oriented and very topical, a convenient way to create gem awareness and draw people wherever we go," said Boyajian as GIA entered the new millennium.

■ LANDMARK EDUCATIONAL MATERIAL
"Out-of-date" and "old-fashioned."

That's how management characterized GIA's courses—and especially its well-known diamonds course—in the early 1980s. Except for Dennis Foltz's revision of diamond grading assignments in 1979, none had been seriously revamped since Liddicoat had reorganized and rewritten founder Robert Shipley's courses in the late 1950s.

True, there were periodic reviews to add new material, and instructors updated lessons as needed. But the problems went deeper—to the structure of the courses, how they presented information, and their assumed audience.

Times had changed. Theories on education had changed. GIA students had changed. The industry had changed. The courses hadn't. They needed to be taken apart, reevaluated, and rewritten to meet new realities in the late 20th century. As Foltz said later, what GIA needed wasn't revised courses but different ones.

For decades, GIA's materials had been written for working jewelers, who had at least some basic knowledge of the subject. For example, in discussing carat weight, the diamonds course didn't explain what a diamond balance was or how to use it, because the course writers assumed students already knew that. But by the early '80s, students were asking more and more questions that indicated they *didn't* have such basic knowledge. The Institute was seeing a whole new generation of prospective jewelers.

What students expected from GIA courses was changing, too. They didn't necessarily want to learn the technical details of grading diamonds. "They just wanted a good background in their product," noted Foltz.

Also changing was the way educational materials in general were written and presented, thanks in part to the growing influence of television and changes in

TIMES HAD CHANGED. GIA STUDENTS HAD CHANGED. THE INDUSTRY HAD CHANGED. THE COURSES HADN'T.

The eclectic John Hummel was brought in to lead GIA's new course development department in 1983. With Dennis Foltz, he reshaped Institute courses during the 1980s and '90s.

publishing and educational theories. And since GIA was now widely accepted as the jewelry industry's "Harvard," it had a responsibility to ensure that its curriculum warranted this reputation, with cutting-edge training.

SO, IN EARLY 1983, Foltz set up the course development department. Its purpose was to review current courses, improve their presentations, create new courses, and develop state-of-the-art instructional methods. To run it, he hired John Hummel, a multi-talented writer and teacher. His task was to orchestrate the research, writing, and content of GIA home study and resident courses.

Hummel was one of the most unusual people ever to work at GIA. He boasted an extraordinarily varied career, none of it involving gems or jewelry. He was, said a friend, like "an onion. Just when you thought you had heard it all, he would do or say something that would reveal another layer."

Before joining GIA, Hummel had seen military service in Korea, earned a Ph.D. in French literature, and been a Fulbright scholar; he had worked as an accountant, a carpenter, a commercial fisherman, a credit collector, a high school English teacher, a university professor of comparative literature, and a freelance journalist. Yet it was just this unlikely smorgasbord of vocations that provided Hummel with the life experiences and knowledge needed to bring freshness to GIA's curriculum.

Together, Foltz and Hummel were an excellent team, their different skills and strengths complementing each other. Foltz contributed his knowledge and understanding of the industry as a veteran retail jeweler, as well as his familiarity with the challenges faced by home study students—most of Foltz's own education had come through correspondence courses. Recalled Betsy Schuster, then an instructor: "Dennis was the one with the vision and ideas, who said 'This is where we need to go,' and with his powerful personality, he had the drive to put it through."

While Foltz was like "a force of nature," as one colleague put it, Hummel was more casual and low key, customarily wearing a loose tie and open collar. He was a gentle mentor with a formidable intellect and infectious repartee. "John knew how to implement Dennis's ideas," Schuster said, because his experience in publishing gave him the know-how to present them in accessible, even entertaining, formats. His extensive education and years in teaching gave him an empathy with the students, and his editorial mastery enabled him to express complex ideas in terms and language that people could understand.

Foltz and Hummel redefined the philosophy behind GIA's training materials. Said Liddicoat later, "They shared a strong motivation to make our courses eminently readable for every level of educational background." And Nord supported their plans to revamp GIA's entire curriculum—a project that took the rest of the decade.

FOLTZ, HUMMEL, AND THEIR STAFFS were, in effect, starting from scratch. Education theory had changed enormously since the 1950s. Many of the decisions on changes in content and format came from a better understanding of the process of instruction and training. They studied changes in the use of graphic arts in the media and publishing. Television, for example, had become a pervasive influence in U.S. society and on students' reading and attention skills. They surveyed students and staff on ways to improve the courses, and consulted with industry experts. From all this, Foltz and Hummel set three important goals for the new courses: (1) attract more enrollees, (2) keep them studying, and (3) boost the average completion rates.

To meet the first goal, GIA more actively promoted employer-sponsored learning and expanded its efforts to include department stores, mass merchandisers and catalog showrooms, as well as major retail chains and small single outlets. The Institute marketed it as an efficient way to train employees without starting or expanding a training department.

Demand increased so dramatically that in January 1985, Bill Boyajian set up a special program just to handle company training. By July 1985, hundreds of people—and employees of four out of the 12 top jewelry retail chains in the U.S.—were enrolled in GIA home study courses via the Institute's company training programs. Eighteen months later, in late 1986, the Institute had some 20,000 course enrollments—many of them company paid or company reimbursed.

To achieve the second and third goals, Foltz and Hummel looked at why many GIA students didn't finish their courses. Most students were "terribly busy with full-time jobs, so we had to do a lot of things to accommodate them," said Foltz in 1986.

First, they decided to make all lessons of near-equal length, with very long ones divided into two or three parts. Each would be self-contained, but lead into the next. In effect, lessons were reconceived as "logically arranged steps

FOLTZ AND HUMMEL WERE AN EXCELLENT TEAM. TOGETHER, THEY REDEFINED THE PHILOSOPHY BEHIND GIA'S TRAINING MATERIALS.

RATHER THAN STRESSING PRODUCT KNOWLEDGE AND TECHNICAL INFORMATION, THE COURSES SHIFTED EMPHASIS TO USING PRODUCT KNOWLEDGE IN SALES AND MARKETING.

that ideally worked as stepping stones to eventually completing all our course material," Foltz explained.

Then, they adopted two new assumptions. One was that prospective students had no prior knowledge. The other was that the audience was anyone and everyone in jewelry retailing, including mass merchandisers and TV retailers. "We're still geared toward the independent jewelers," Foltz said a little later, but the courses would now be designed to be "useful to everyone in the jewelry industry."

Another change was the focus of the courses: Rather than stressing product knowledge and technical information, the courses shifted emphasis to *using* product knowledge in sales and marketing. GIA's board of governors, in a 1983 meeting with Nord and Foltz, had urged that more attention be paid to sales and marketing applications. Foltz's surveys also indicated many students took GIA training for a sound working knowledge of their products, not technical expertise. They wanted practical information they could use immediately in selling.

"Students tend to stick to our courses if they find something which can help them on the spot," noted Foltz. So, there was much more application of information to the sale of diamonds, gems, and jewelry. Diamond grades, for example, were introduced early in the new diamonds course, to help students use them as selling tools.

WITH THESE GOALS AND PARAMETERS IN PLACE, GIA started preparing new courses. The writing of the lessons was assigned to in-house staff, with input from outside editors and freelance professional writers. Copy was reviewed by Hummel and his staff, rewritten in terms of content, presentation, and instructional goals for each lesson, and evaluated for accuracy by specialists (such as GIA diamond graders, laboratory gemologists, and research scientists).

Hummel's influence in shaping the courses was enormous. He believed in a holistic approach to learning, recalled his friend and colleague Dean Stevens, editorial manager of the course development department in the late 1990s. A GIA course should engage the reader, not "talk at" him or her, Hummel said. It shouldn't be a dry presentation of facts or procedures, but have depth and texture. For example, in the new diamonds course, Stevens noted, "You learned about the 'Four Cs,' the GIA diamond grading system, and notable diamonds, but also followed the travels of [17th century diamond merchant] Jean-Baptiste Tavernier and gained an appreciation of art."

Language was also important to Hummel. He was "devoted to the fundamental principle that complexity can be made simple," said Stevens. "He understood what our students needed in the way of accessible, understandable, and appropriate course material [and] he went to great lengths to make sure that's what we, the writers in GIA's course development department, produced."

Visual presentation of the course material was critical, too, and here Hummel and Foltz also made significant changes. They closely studied the place of visuals—including the colorful and entertaining formats of popular magazines and television—in learning. In their research, they found that studies showed reading speed increased 25 to 30 percent when information was presented in double-column formats. They and their staff members put hundreds of hours into rethinking lesson formats and acquiring and producing photos, maps, illustrations, diagrams, and computer-generated graphics.

The fully revised colored stones program was part of a wave of courses printed in color and "in-house."

The results were GIA lessons that looked more like magazines, packed with color photos and illustrations, with sidebars containing entertaining but relevant anecdotes. They were a far cry not only from Shipley's mimeographed courses, but also from the sterile black-and-white lessons of the 1960s and '70s.

WERE FOLTZ AND HUMMEL GOING TOO FAR with their changes, or not far enough? In late 1983, they decided to test-market their ideas, starting with GIA's new colored stone grading course (the first not only to use the new format but also to be printed in full color and in-house) and a redesign of lesson one of the diamonds course. The response exceeded their expectations. Start-ups for the diamonds course alone rose 60 percent over the next few months. "We couldn't believe how effective it was," Foltz said later.

In late 1984 and early 1985, the first fully revised courses debuted. The pearls course, for example, contained almost 200 color photos and drawings and detailed information on culturing fresh- and saltwater pearls, managing a pearl inventory, and presenting cultured pearls to customers. It had buying, selling, and appraising sections, and offered hands-on grading exercises, using 30 strands of pearls loaned by GIA. Enrollments were so high in the first months that they put a strain on GIA's pearl inventory.

In April 1986, after almost three years of work, the new two-part diamonds program was finally ready for distribution. It was, said Foltz proudly, "a real step forward for the Institute and the industry."

Graphic artists at work in GIA's course development department during the mid-1980s. The revised lessons had a new format, more similar to that of magazines, with a heavy emphasis on color visuals.

The first part, diamonds, offered new lessons on diamond jewelry, store security, and the "romance" of diamonds. There were discussions of fancy-color and treated diamonds, the role of re-cutting in evaluating diamonds, new diamond sources (such as the former Soviet Union and Australia), important diamond cutting centers, and new diamond cutting technology.

Just as significant, and controversial, was what wasn't there. Gone after 50 years were discussions of "ideal cut" as the standard for round brilliants. Instead, the course taught that there could be variations from the so-called "ideal" proportions that many diamantaires would find acceptable.

The program's second part, diamond grading, focused on technical issues, with a format streamlined to speed progress. It was also designed to help retailers buy more effectively, with material, for example, on buying diamond parcels.

The new approach was further refined in GIA's revamped colored stones program, which appeared in 1987. It consisted of three courses—colored stones, gem identification, and colored stone grading (introduced earlier). Completing the entire program was made a requirement for the G.G. diploma.

MEANWHILE, NEW TECHNOLOGY WAS BEING ADDED to make learning quicker and simpler. One helpful tool was audiocassettes, introduced by Hummel, but even more effective was videotape, which made presentation of complicated procedures and concepts much easier. Use of videotape in the courses was instigated by Gary Hill, Foltz's new assistant manager of home study. Hill set up a video studio at home and began experimenting, using his video camera to shoot films of gem materials, gem testing, and refractometer readings—"all the things that were so very difficult for students to grasp when shown in live demonstrations," said Hill.

Thanks to the success of Hill's early efforts, videotapes were added to the home study program in the late 1980s, especially to those areas where students had to learn detailed procedures. The first course to use videotaped instruction was pearl and bead stringing, which debuted in 1988. Video was used even more prominently in counter sketching (which taught students how to draw attractive and convincing designs for potential customers), a new course released in 1990.

BY THE END OF THE 1980s, Foltz, Hummel, and the course development staff had compiled an impressive record. They had changed the direction of GIA training, revamped existing courses, developed several new courses for specific training needs in the industry, and made video- and audiotapes routine accessories.

Video comes to GIA courses in the 1980s: A segment being set up by Mike Ross (left, behind the camera), and video editing (right).

And the results were equally impressive. By the late 1980s, more than 17,000 students were enrolled in GIA's home study programs. And by 1991, GIA's diamonds course boasted a 50 percent completion rate, among the highest of *any* home study program in any industry or field.

■THE COMPUTER'S BLESSING

"I am convinced that the modern personal computer is a blessing [and if] we can master this technology, we can take a giant step forward in increasing the acceptance of home study education," wrote Dennis Foltz in a mid-1980s paper for the National Home Study Council.

GIA, which had already computerized its Gem Trade Laboratory diamond grading reports, was also quick to use computer technology—and later computer networks and the Internet—as an educational tool. That began in 1980, when jewelry store management instructor David Morrow created a simulated jewelry store program to teach students how to make decisions on merchandise, advertising, employees, and finances.

Computers had the most immediate, widespread impact in GIA's course development department and home study program. "[A] cursory review of customer trends tells us that our [home study] students want convenience,

During the 1980s, computers became standard in the creation of GIA course materials. Pictured on the right is instructor and course writer Bob Effler.

service and quality in everything they buy," wrote Hummel in that same NHSC paper. "With the help of the personal computer, we can do this. All we have to do is learn how to use it imaginatively."

Hummel and Foltz began doing that in the early 1980s. They mastered the PC basics within a couple of weeks, although, joked Foltz later, they "made just about every mistake one can think of, including the obligatory coffee-bath for the keyboard and jamming the computer diskette so far in the disk drive door that the machine almost had to be disassembled to get it out." But once they had mastered this new tool, they used it to radically revise GIA's entire portfolio of courses.

From 1984 on, all GIA courses were written, edited, and rewritten on computers. Not only did computerization provide an efficient means of updating and redesigning the courses, but it also increased productivity, boosting turnaround times and lowering costs. Home study instructors, too, found computerization invaluable in increasing the quality of their communications with students and the depth of information they could provide.

■ THE COLORS OF FRUSTRATION

GIA's long-awaited colored stone grading system, based on the ColorMaster device to measure and communicate color in gemstones, was formally unveiled with fanfare in a one-week class that started in May 1983 and a new home study course that debuted in January 1984. (The grading course was later incorporated into GIA's revamped colored stones program in 1987, when colored stone grading became a requirement for the Graduate Gemologist diploma.)

Two-thirds of the 30-lesson course dealt with colored stone grading based on color, clarity, and cut. The balance dealt with various factors that affect the value and marketing of colored stones (including "viewing environments," display, design, the effect of light, and color coordination), as well as appraising and how to buy competitively.

IRONICALLY, GIA'S NEW SYSTEM only seemed to increase confusion in the colored gem business, because three other systems were already being marketed to the trade. They were American Gemological Laboratories' Color/Scan, which used simulated master stones on grading cards; California Gemological Laboratories' Gem Color Guide, which used 80 color chips, but relied on GIA's ColorMaster to verify color and grading decisions; and Howard Rubin's GemDialogue™, which used a book of hue charts and color masks.

"If you thought it was confusing describing stone colors without any system, now pick the right color system from this mélange of possibilities," wrote *The Goldsmith*. The Accredited Gemologists Association tried to do just that in late 1983 by choosing one for its members' use, which AGA expected would influence the choice made by others in the gem and jewelry industry. But AGA issued a recommendation based on "practicality" and chose not one, but two—GIA and AGL. That left most people more confused than before, and led to a drop in sales of all four color systems for months afterward.

All of this strengthened resistance in some quarters of the industry to a colored stone grading system in general, and GIA's in particular. Many critics were concerned that a colored stone grading system could lead to a colored stone investment market and abuses similar to those seen during the 1970s diamond investment boom. For example, CIBJO, the international federation of jewelers and gem dealers, went on record in 1984 against any such system, fearing it would lead to certificates and possible investment fraud. A few other critics claimed, without evidence, that GIA invented its colored gem grading system to promote sales of the ColorMaster and recoup its heavy financial investment in the device.

At the Institute, Janice Mack believed support for colored stone grading declined after Liddicoat—who had urged her to create the system in the first place—retired as president in mid-1983. In January 1984, Mack returned to Washington state to get married and work in her husband's jewelry business. She was, she said later, "a little weary" from the half decade of tumult surrounding the creation and marketing of the system and the ColorMaster.

BY THE LATE 1980S, GIA still hadn't issued any colored stone grading reports based on its system, but it was trying new ways to improve the effectiveness of the ColorMaster and its colored stone grading system. In 1987, it studied whether it could apply its system, especially the nomenclature, to grading fancy-color diamonds. And in fact, it "was useful in helping us objectively establish the hue, tone, and saturation of many fancy colored diamonds," said James Lucey, then manager of education projects. Ultimately, though, the Gem Trade Laboratory felt that the colored stone grading system could not be directly applied to the grading of fancy-color diamonds.

MANY CRITICS WERE CONCERNED THAT A COLORED STONE GRADING SYSTEM COULD LEAD TO A COLORED STONE INVESTMENT MARKET.

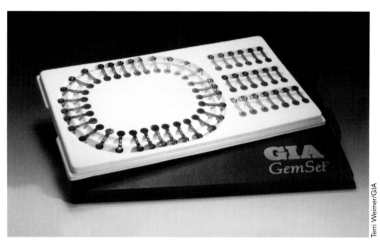

With the demise of the ColorMaster, the GIA GemSet became the Institute's primary reference tool for colored stone grading.

By 1993, it was evident that the ColorMaster's era was ending. It was rarely even mentioned anymore in GIA announcements about colored stone grading, and that same year GIA unveiled a more portable device called the GIA GemSet Color Communication System. Developed by independent color scientist Ken Roberts, GemSet used 324 polymer fingernail-sized "brilliant cut gem comparators" (each attached to a small tab for easy handling) with the colors identified by GIA terminology. Although the colors were cross-referenced to ColorMaster notations, GemSet was obviously intended to replace the ColorMaster. It would be, said GIA's announcement, "the primary tool in the Institute's colored stone training worldwide."

The ColorMaster story finally ended in 1995. Only about 500 had been sold between 1980 and 1995, and in September GIA quietly ended production, writing off almost half a million dollars in ColorMaster inventory and parts.

The colored stone grading system remained a valuable part of GIA education. In addition, its color nomenclature, especially for hue, was being used widely in the trade by the end of the 20th century. In 2002, GIA updated the system and more fully integrated it into its G.G. diploma program.

In 1998, Bill Boyajian told the World Emerald Congress in Bogotá, Colombia, that while he expected to see a trend toward colored stone description, grading, and evaluation in the early 21st century, GIA had no current plans to incorporate colored stone grading into its laboratory reports.

WHY DID COLORED STONE GRADING FAIL TO CATCH ON? One reason was the nature of colored gems themselves. "Diamonds are cut within a relatively restricted range for round brilliants," noted Liddicoat. "Colored stones, much of the time, are cut strictly for weight retention. So you can get fantastic variations, and each affects the appearance. That makes grading them difficult."

There was one other practical reason why color grading didn't catch fire in the late 20th century: The jewelry industry—and GIA itself—had lost interest. Treatments and disclosure became the major issues for colored stones, supplanting grading.

Despite the scientific value gained from it, the colored stone grading project never lived up to the high expectations with which it was launched. It was, Liddicoat said, "a major disappointment."

■ "A GIA MAN"

In July 1986, there was another unexpected change in GIA's top leadership: President Glenn Nord resigned, surprising many in the industry and at the Institute itself.

"I was burning too much midnight oil, working horrendous hours," he explained later. He had already considered stepping down in 1985 because of the toll that reviving GIA was taking on his health. But the matter was settled when he had a seizure during a De Beers Carat Club meeting in St. Andrews, Scotland, in May 1986. His condition was serious enough for him to cancel the rest of the trip and immediately return to California.

Following a battery of medical tests, his doctor told him, "Your health is too important. You must slow down *now*." Because of his brain aneurysm (which wouldn't be safely removed until the 1990s), Nord hadn't really expected to be president for very long, he said later. But in his short time there, Nord and the GIA staff scored some impressive accomplishments.

The Institute's finances were back in the black. GEM Instruments was on firm footing. Operations were efficient and businesslike, and the infrastructure was stable. He had put together a management team able to "take over the Institute if anything happened to me," as he put it.

He had encouraged an overhaul of the curriculum, and authorized the start of GIA's computerization—including purchase of a $500,000 five-color computerized press to print course materials in-house. He had also approved expensive but necessary research equipment, such as a state-of-the-art infrared spectrophotometer and the IBM System 9000 laboratory computer, to help Institute researchers analyze gem data.

Enrollments had risen, thanks to both revamped and new courses, promotional events such as GemFest, a dozen new one- and two-day seminars, and expansion of GIA's corporate training programs. Also important was the addition of financial aid for students. Though there had been a few scholarships since the early 1970s, it wasn't until 1983 that the Institute added a loan program and an office of financial aid, with veteran GIA employee T. J. Barrows as chief financial aid officer.

"PEOPLE WHO
HAVEN'T WORKED
FOR THE INSTITUTE
DON'T UNDERSTAND
WHAT I'M TALKING
ABOUT," SAID NORD,
"BUT THERE'S NO
PLACE LIKE GIA."

Under Nord's lead, the Institute continued expanding globally. In 1983, it sent its first delegation to China, and the Instituto Gemmologico Mediterraneo was retained to translate GIA courses into Italian and to support GIA home study students in Europe. The following year, it contracted with the Canadian Jewellers Institute to support GIA students in Canada. In 1986, GIA taught its first diamond grading classes in Geneva, Switzerland, and in Antwerp, Belgium.

Now, in mid-1986, just three years after he was appointed, it was time to leave. On July 29, 1986, citing the strains on his health, he submitted his resignation to GIA's board of governors, which accepted it with regret.

Nord resigned with mixed feelings, he noted afterward. "People who haven't worked for the Institute don't understand what I'm talking about, but there's no place like GIA. So, yes, I felt bad about leaving it again." Yet, as in 1974, he didn't really leave GIA. He remained on the board of governors, continued as a senior consultant, and in his activities and in his heart "stayed very close to the Institute."

For, as he himself often said, Glenn Nord was first and last "a GIA man."

THE NORD YEARS WERE A TURNING POINT in GIA's history. They ensured the financial survival of the Institute, revitalized and redirected its educational mission to the changing needs of the industry, and energetically raised its profile. But in doing so, something changed at GIA, in emphasis and attitude. The Nord years saw the Institute turn from what was largely a loosely structured academic organization into a more businesslike operation with a formal administrative structure that stressed productivity, initiative, expansion, and service.

"GIA's focus is education, first and foremost," Nord said midway through his tenure, but to maintain that focus, GIA had to operate like a smooth-running machine, with all its components contributing something to one another. Nord may have considered himself "a GIA man" but he was also a superb take-charge businessman who, said his protégé Bill Boyajian, "taught managers how to manage and to think of GIA not as a humble home study school but as an aggressive nonprofit institution to be respected," one that "could adapt and grow with modern times."

Not everyone at GIA, or in the industry, thought such a change was for the better. One longtime GIA instructor and manager, for example, believed the Nord years caused "a shift in GIA's philosophy, from service to the industry to the reliance on the financial bottom line." Even Bill Boyajian conceded, "We lost something during the hard years." In the struggle to survive, "the pendulum swung too far at times."

Others recognized the change, but understood the need for it. "Anybody who came in, like Glenn did, with the choice of saving this organization or seeing it go bust had to change the corporate culture," said David Morrow. "To make things efficient, he had to make a lot of tough decisions."

The Institute did become "more business oriented out of necessity" during the Nord years, noted Tom Yonelunas. "But we were trying to survive, so we had to focus not only on our mission but also on our financial structure and operations. Nord had no choice but to fix the problems, and it wasn't a popular position to be in."

Mauricio Minotta/GIA

Former GIA president Glenn Nord receives the Institute's highest honor, the Richard T. Liddicoat Award, in November 2001. Even after retiring in 1986, Nord continued to play an active role with GIA as a member of its board of governors.

But what Yonelunas calls "that dark period" also strengthened the remaining employees who would be GIA's senior management on both coasts well into the 21st century. "We all pulled together and survived, building a bond and commitment that still shows today," Yonelunas said many years later. And it was these people who would be the key movers and shakers in GIA, who, he said, would "make quantum leaps forward and be involved in explosive change and expansion" in the decades that followed.

Indeed, two of Nord's most important contributions—though it wouldn't become apparent until years later—were the eventual appointment of Bill Boyajian to succeed him as president and the earmarking of Tom Yonelunas to head the GIA Gem Trade Laboratory. These two men—near-perfect complements of each other—would help lead the dynamic growth of GIA for years to come.

In the final analysis, perhaps the best evaluation of the Nord years and their impact on GIA was given by George Kaplan, who had put Nord in charge to begin with: "He saved the Institute, and if it weren't for him, it wouldn't be the institution it has become."

PART THREE

expanding the legacy

CHAPTER 11

A new era:
In 1986,
Bill Boyajian
became
GIA's fourth
president.

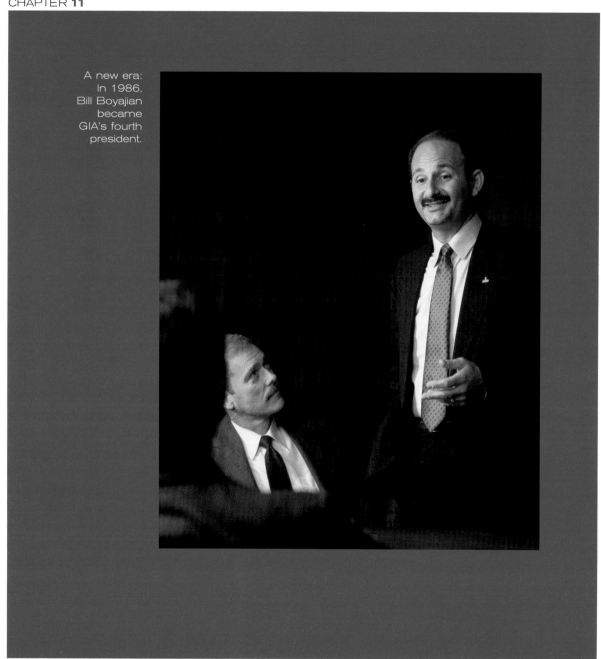

CHANGING OF THE GUARD

1986–2003

For GIA, the last years of the 20th century were among the most vigorous and challenging in its history. The Institute, well established again following the turmoil of the early 1980s, now turned its eyes to the future, both its own and the industry's. With new leadership at the helm and specific goals in front of it, GIA embarked on some of the most daring and ambitious projects it had yet attempted—fundraising, yet another new home, aggressive global expansion, and international gatherings designed to prepare the industry for the challenges of the 21st century.

At the same time, the Institute faced some of its biggest challenges. Internally, it went through several restructurings to improve efficiency while trying to cope with the loss of some of its best-known pioneers and managers. Externally, it had to deal with an unprecedented flood of new synthetics and treatments for diamonds, colored stones, and pearls; new mass technologies, like the Internet; and industry concerns about its controversial studies on diamond cut and plans to open an overseas grading laboratory.

Above all, it was during this period that GIA prepared for the new century and worked to establish itself as the world's foremost authority in gemology. Those two endeavors, in turn, set in motion a number of programs and projects designed, as the slogan of its decade-long development program put it, to "Secure the Future" for the Institute, the trade, and the public. It all began with the selection of a new president, his new team, and a new concept called, simply, the Master Plan.

ONE NIGHT IN JULY 1986, Bill Boyajian, GIA's marketing manager, was falling asleep in his New York City hotel room after a long day at the Jewelers of America trade show, when the phone rang.

"Hello, Bill," said the gentle voice on the other end of the line. "This is Dick Liddicoat. Can you come to the board of governors' meeting tomorrow morning at eight?"

"Yes, of course—but why?" Boyajian asked.

"Just come tomorrow, and you'll find out," Liddicoat replied and hung up.

Puzzled and somewhat unsettled, Boyajian tried to get some sleep.

It had been only 11 years since Boyajian had joined GIA, hired right after getting his G.G., but from the first day Liddicoat's eye had been on this enthusiastic, self-acknowledged "overachiever." Most new staffers started as

In 11 years at the Institute, Bill Boyajian had become a highly regarded instructor, speaker, and manager.

home study instructors grading lessons, or as staff gemologists in the Gem Trade Laboratory before being assigned to permanent jobs. But Liddicoat told Boyajian he wanted to give him a broad overview of the Institute and move him around to different areas. So, Boyajian spent his first year as a resident class teacher, a back-up instructor in the on-the-road classes, and a grader in the Gem Trade Laboratory.

In late 1976, following the move to Santa Monica, Liddicoat made him a full-time instructor in the resident colored stones and gem identification program, an assignment that brought out Boyajian's natural teaching and speaking abilities. Over the next three years, he became a popular instructor and speaker at GIA, at industry events, and at AGS Conclaves.

Boyajian's effectiveness was noted by extension class manager Mike Allbritton, who offered him a place on his team in 1979. Boyajian already had "an eye on moving up at GIA," he said later. To prepare himself, he was attending gem- and jewelry-related events locally, studying management and salesmanship, and trying to integrate gemology with his college background in economics and business to become what he called "a practical gemologist." So when Allbritton offered him the job, Boyajian went to Liddicoat for advice.

Allbritton's offer was a good opportunity and Boyajian wanted a new challenge, he told Liddicoat. But Liddicoat hated the idea of moving him to another area of GIA. "You can't leave the resident colored stones program," he said. "You *are* the resident program."

"Then give me the opportunity to make a difference here," replied Boyajian.

Within a month, Boyajian was named the new supervisor of the resident colored stones program. He hit the ground running. "I had so many ideas to implement," Boyajian recalled later. "That was a formative period for me." He worked closely with home study manager Dennis Foltz to align the home study and resident course materials and instruction—previously, each had operated more or less independently of each other—and with Tom Yonelunas, then education manager of GIA New York, to ensure that resident gemology instruction and materials on both coasts were consistent. Boyajian also began revising resident program support materials, including the well-known gemstone identification charts.

He also made some key hiring decisions, such as Debbie Hiss, an outstanding student who became a superb gemology instructor and popular speaker. Another successful choice was Gary Hill, who became assistant supervisor of the colored stones department, started GIA's video department, and would one day oversee GIA's move to a new campus.

Boyajian also hired Robert C. Kammerling, one of the most brilliant instructors and gemologists in the Institute's history. "Bob was a great asset to GIA, a 'gemologist's gemologist,'" said Boyajian later. Kammerling came from an accomplished medical family, but the excitement of travel lured him out of college to join the U.S. Civil Service. It was a stimulating job—occasionally a dangerous one—that took him to such regions as Ethiopia, Tibet, Afghanistan, and the Middle East. During those travels he developed a deep interest in gemstones, so much so that in 1981, at the age of 34, he resigned from his civil service post and enrolled in GIA's resident gemology program.

Boyajian first spotted Kammerling that same year while giving a classroom lecture. His thoughtful questions and obvious enthusiasm for gemology made him stand out from other students. "He was a brilliant guy, with one of the greatest minds I've ever known in gemology," recalled Boyajian years later. Kammerling's G.G. exam impressed him, too. "He had the highest score I had ever seen, and by then I had graded hundreds of them."

Six months after graduating, Kammerling joined Boyajian's staff, teaching courses in colored stones and gem identification. Intense and at times acerbic, while both intellectual and rugged, Kammerling quickly made his mark as an exceptional instructor, able to teach difficult gemological concepts. At the same time, he worked closely with Boyajian in writing and reworking materials for the resident gemology program and updating GIA's *Gem Identification Laboratory Manual*, still in use decades later.

A workaholic, like many at GIA, Kammerling was also a prodigious writer. Over the next 15 years, he wrote more than 400 articles, columns, and books that advanced gemology. He also worked on numerous research projects in the late 1980s, as head of GIA's technical development department. He later became assistant marketing manager and served as the Institute's public information officer for a number of years. In the 1990s, he was ultimately named vice president of research and development for the Gem Trade Laboratory.

It was Kammerling's intensity, along with his disregard for danger during his pre-GIA adventures abroad and subsequent visits to distant gem locales, that earned him the affectionate nickname among colleagues as "Kambo," a play on Sylvester Stallone's popular Rambo character.

KAMMERLING "WAS A BRILLIANT GUY, WITH ONE OF THE GREATEST MINDS I'VE EVER KNOWN IN GEMOLOGY," RECALLED BOYAJIAN.

Brilliant and driven, Robert Kammerling was a standout instructor and gemologist who rose to vice president of research and development at the Gem Trade Laboratory in the 1990s.

"I loved the way Bob's mind worked," said GIA colleague Dr. Mary Johnson, who was hired by Kammerling in the 1990s to do gemological research. "He could consider a problem from many different facets at the same time, identify the important issues involved, and see that we had the resources available to get the job done," she noted. Kammerling was also able, said Johnson, "to keep personalities separate from issues and work with anyone who had something to add to the understanding of a problem."

"What a producer!" Boyajian remarked later. "He taught during the day and then worked on these projects at night. Bob could pump out more work than anyone I ever met. He was a tremendous asset to the Institute."

BOYAJIAN'S TENURE AS RESIDENT INSTRUCTOR and program supervisor taught him how to be a leader. "I learned what good management is, how to move people in the directions you want them to go, and how to work with them as a team," he said later. Already a good speaker, writer, and gemologist, he was also nurturing his skills as a salesman.

That began in the early 1980s, with Boyajian's enrollment in a Dale Carnegie course on selling. "It was basic stuff," he recalled, "but it showed me how to bridge the gap and relate the science of gemology to those critical 18 inches" of counter space between jeweler and customer. After his sales talk at the 1982 Conclave, where he received a standing ovation, Boyajian developed a popular series of lectures on selling. He presented these talks at trade conventions across the United States, and in audiocassettes and videotapes sold by the GIA Bookstore.

All the while, Liddicoat was keeping his eye on Boyajian's development, and was impressed by his enthusiasm and dedication. At one point in the early 1980s, he even suggested Boyajian to GIA's board of governors as a possible successor to himself. At the same time, Boyajian began to suspect he was being groomed for the top spot. "There were little signs," he recalled later, like being appointed to the Institute's planning committee.

IN JUST EIGHT YEARS, Boyajian had become one of the most active managers at GIA, and one of Liddicoat's favorites. But his aspirations met an apparent setback in 1983, with Liddicoat's heart attack and replacement as president by Glenn Nord.

Yet Nord, from the moment he arrived as acting president, began surveying the landscape for someone to replace him permanently. It had to be someone with strong leadership and management skills who was well educated and dedicated to GIA, "someone young who could be president for years to come," Nord said. "A number of people were given the opportunity to show their management and leadership skills." One of the first to catch his attention was Bill Boyajian, the energetic and ambitious young guy—only 31 years old at the time—who headed the resident colored stones program.

Boyajian worked hard to earn Nord's respect and was tapped early on to lead a new department. In a meeting in Nord's office only a few months after taking over as president, Nord said to Boyajian, "I've been looking for a go-getter who is action oriented and development minded, someone who is an idea guy, for a new position: manager of new project development. I'd like you to take it."

Somewhat puzzled, Boyajian asked, "What's that?"

"Whatever you make it be," replied Nord. "You'll work the trade shows representing GIA, sell courses, develop new projects." In effect, Nord was offering Boyajian an open-ended assignment that would make him responsible for new ideas and programs, and for developing plans to execute them.

But both men saw this job offer as something larger, though they didn't say so at the time. For Nord, it was an opportunity to see what Boyajian could really do. And for Boyajian, "It was a chance to prove myself."

BEING MANAGER OF NEW PROJECT DEVELOPMENT wasn't a do-it-yourself job. Boyajian stayed in close contact with the Institute's other managers, helping them assess their departments' needs, developing projects for them, and encouraging each to contribute creative ideas for GIA's operations and programs.

Assisted by Kammerling and Gary Hill, Boyajian oversaw several initiatives for Nord, including a new video education program and an expanded training program for jewelry companies. He assisted GEM Instruments in assessing new equipment and organized GIA's participation in trade shows, while developing in-house events such as Nord's open houses and GemFests. Meanwhile, Boyajian continued to present his popular sales seminars at the Santa Monica campus and at trade conferences across the country.

FROM THE MOMENT NORD ARRIVED AT THE INSTITUTE, HE BEGAN SURVEYING THE LANDSCAPE FOR SOMEONE TO REPLACE HIM PERMANENTLY.

Impressed, Nord placed him in charge of the marketing department in May 1985. In his new position, Boyajian was responsible for sales, advertising, public relations, and marketing. It seemed a natural fit for his skills, but it was also, he said later, "a great challenge." Though he didn't have a formal background in marketing or advertising, Boyajian was a quick study.

He appointed Bob Kammerling (who had succeeded him as head of the resident colored stones department) as his assistant manager. Together they turned the department upside down, revamping marketing and direct mail, and working closely with home study manager Dennis Foltz to promote the Institute's correspondence courses and company training programs. Within a year, Boyajian and his staff had transformed GIA's marketing programs, boosting its profile in the industry. "It was one of the things I am proudest of," he declared later.

AND THEN CAME SPRING 1986, and Nord's seizure in Scotland. Nord had already picked his successor. "I had checked out a number of candidates," he said later, but Boyajian "stood out way above the rest. It became obvious after watching him that he was the one, and I knew Dick Liddicoat felt the same way.

"He's a man people can respect and trust. He had a total belief in what GIA can do for the industry and a dedication to gemology that I love," added Nord. "Bill had shown all the promise in the world. Now it was time for him to get his feet wet."

But Nord and Liddicoat had to move quickly, because there were others who believed they were stronger candidates.

"THE MOOD IN THAT ROOM WAS PRETTY TENSE," RECALLED BOYAJIAN YEARS LATER. "YOU COULD HEAR A PIN DROP."

THE MORNING AFTER LIDDICOAT'S PHONE CALL, Boyajian arrived at the Helmsley Palace (now the New York Palace) at 8 a.m. and waited outside the meeting room door—and waited, and waited. After an hour and a half, the door opened and he was invited in to sit at the table with GIA's governors.

Apparently during that 90-minute meeting, there had been substantial debate over who should be the Institute's next president. In fact, two of its vice presidents, Bert Krashes and chief financial officer William Bender, were also members of the board. But Nord and Liddicoat were adamant. They persuaded the board to offer Boyajian, then only 34 years of age, the venerable Institute's top job.

"The mood in that room was pretty tense," recalled Boyajian years later. "You could hear a pin drop." No one spoke except executive chairman George Kaplan.

"Bill," he said, "we've called you here today because Glenn has resigned as president for health reasons. We want to name you acting president of GIA. Will you accept?"

Without hesitation, Boyajian said, "Yes. Of course."

"Good," said Kaplan. "We want you to take over immediately."

So at about 10:00 that morning, he left the board meeting and walked down Fifth Avenue to Tom Yonelunas's office, where they drafted a brief press release announcing Nord's resignation and Boyajian's appointment as acting president.

Whereas Liddicoat (left) had the leadership style of a college dean and Nord (center) that of an astute businessman, Boyajian was a cross between his two predecessors.

BOYAJIAN'S "SWIFT ASCENT" TO THE PRESIDENCY, as *National Jeweler* magazine called it, surprised many in the industry every bit as much as Nord's unexpected resignation. "It was the shot heard around the world," Boyajian himself said. People were asking who this young guy was. At the manager level, he had leapfrogged over GIA directors and vice presidents to the Institute's premier post. Indeed, Boyajian, while well-known at GIA and in industry circles within the United States, was unfamiliar to many in the trade internationally.

However, Boyajian's selection wasn't as unusual as it seemed at the time. His youth ("34 going on 44," Boyajian joked) wasn't really an issue. GIA chairman Liddicoat pointed out that he was *exactly* the same age as Boyajian when he had taken over from Robert M. Shipley as executive director in 1952 (coincidentally, the same year that Boyajian was born). And, at that point, he had served less time at GIA (eight years, not including his four years in wartime military service) than Boyajian had. The board wanted a younger person, who once appointed could lead the

Institute for years. In addition, Boyajian had compiled an impressive resumé in just over a decade.

But most importantly, he had the backing of two former presidents. Liddicoat was "Mr. GIA," the most respected man in the international gemological community. How could they ignore his advice? And the board had trusted Nord enough to put him in the hot seat during a very turbulent time. How could the board now ignore his strong recommendation on who was best to take over the top job?

THE THOUGHT OF SUCCEEDING NORD AND LIDDICOAT overwhelmed Boyajian, he admitted later. He felt he was being prepared by Nord to eventually assume the presidency, but he didn't expect it to happen so soon. There were a lot of skeptics both inside and outside GIA, even Boyajian to some extent. "Frankly, I felt I wasn't fit to tie the shoes of Dick Liddicoat," he said. "I had so much respect for him, and for Glenn, whose experience and business acumen far outweighed my own." But within a short time, after settling into the job with the support of the Institute's staff and former presidents, the new leader's apprehension waned. "I knew everything was going to be okay."

▪REKINDLING THE FIRE

Boyajian's first task, as he saw it, was "rekindling the fire" at GIA. Nord had ensured the Institute's future, and Boyajian was determined to build its *esprit de corps*.

"Glenn did what had to be done to right the ship," said Boyajian later. "He did a marvelous job of restoring efficiency, good management, and a high degree of financial accountability. But we lost something during those hard times: The 'spirit of GIA' that Liddicoat had embodied for so many years needed to be revived.

"I WANTED TO REKINDLE THAT SPIRIT AND REIGNITE OUR FORCES, TO BRING EVERYONE AT THE INSTITUTE TOGETHER UNDER A COMMON THEME."

"I wanted to rekindle that spirit and reignite our forces, to bring everyone at the Institute together under a common theme."

That flame had to be stoked, of course, by the one who set the standards and attitude for an organization, the top executive. The self-assured Boyajian knew he could do it, though he wasn't always certain everyone else knew he could.

While neither the dean of gemology that Liddicoat was nor the astute businessman that Nord was, Boyajian did see himself—as he said more than once—as "a cross between Liddicoat and Nord." He believed he had the

Boyajian (center) formalized annual Staff of the Year awards. Left to right are 1996 award winners Eddie Decsi, Bev Zimmerman, Debbie Hiss, Sally Ehmke, and Gary Hill. Not pictured is Kim Cino.

personal warmth, like Liddicoat, to engender confidence and trust, while being assertive enough to run GIA as an efficient organization, like Nord. He combined these traits with his own skills as a teacher, manager, marketer, and communicator.

IN FACT, BOYAJIAN WAS A KIND OF EVANGELIST, encouraging GIA's people with the message of the Institute's importance to the industry and a vision of what it could become. It echoed GIA's early years, when its staff and supporters literally saw themselves as missionaries for the "gospel of gemology." And indeed, much of his leadership philosophy, said Boyajian, was "based on solid biblical principles on how to involve and lead people, to listen to their counsel and discern the right way to go."

"Bill's a great motivator," noted one Institute official. "If he wasn't president of GIA, he could be either a politician or a preacher, and be great at both."

Like Liddicoat, Boyajian was a "people person" who knew employees at every level by name. He believed in keeping his staff as informed as possible of GIA's plans and operations, and in involving as many people as possible—personally or through meetings and committees—in the administrative process. This "inclusive management" was essential, he believed, to an organization's success.

As part of Boyajian's restructuring, Dr. James Shigley (far right) was named the Institute's director of research. Two important members of Boyajian's inner circle were Gary Hill (top center) and Court Walker (top right).

Though determined in his views, Boyajian seldom raised his voice, according to one longtime co-worker. When he praised the work of individuals, he made a point of doing it in front of their peers. Boyajian was willing to take chances on the people he hired, if he was sure they had heart and were dedicated to the Institute. "Once certain of this, he left them alone to do their job," recalled one of his top staffers.

Boyajian was a true leader. He initiated annual management retreats, occasions to brainstorm and discuss ways to improve their departments and the Institute to better serve the industry. In addition to retreats, Boyajian spearheaded impromptu seminars. If he found a book he considered helpful and inspiring, he would order dozens of copies for the staff, plan a six-week class based on it, and present what he'd learned from it and how it related to the Institute. These sessions were open to any staff member who wanted to attend.

Occasionally, though, Boyajian tripped over his own zeal—GIA's unsuccessful attempt to open a lab in Antwerp in 1994 was a rare example. And at times, to some in the industry, he seemed either too conciliatory to the diamond trade or not accommodating enough to the retail trade. Overall, however, Boyajian's aim remained consistent: to lead the Institute in directions that served the best interests of the industry and the public.

BOYAJIAN'S RELIANCE ON "THE IMPORTANCE OF PEOPLE" was evident when he formed his inner circle of top managers. "My goal was to develop a strong management team," he said. "I like to surround myself with bright people and solicit their input."

Within days of his appointment, Boyajian began an extensive restructuring of the organization, a revamping that took more than a year. He appointed and promoted managers and executives who were dedicated, loyal GIA people committed, like him, to revitalizing the Institute. Specifically:

Dennis Foltz, formerly home study manager, was named director of operations, responsible for education development, administration, and services.

Gary Hill, who had created GIA's educational video department and assisted Boyajian in the resident colored stones program, was named assistant director of operations and later director of facilities.

Vince Manson, director of research since 1976 and acting director of education since 1984, now gave his full attention to education and planning.

Dr. James E. Shigley, who received his Ph.D. in geology from Stanford University, moved up to director of research, working with Boyajian and the GIA board's research advisory committee on setting the course of the Institute's scientific research and development.

Bob Kammerling was named manager of both marketing and new projects—Boyajian's old territories. The jobs of public information officer and director of technical development were later added to his duties.

Dick Agnew, who had been so important to the revamping of GIA GEM Instruments, was named managing director of that division.

Chuck Fryer, a 20-year veteran and head of the former Santa Monica lab for 15 years, was appointed director of gem identification at the Gem Trade Laboratory, overseeing that department on both the East and West Coasts.

Courtney A. Walker was hired as director of finance in January 1987, just months after Boyajian's appointment as president.

Tom Yonelunas, a superb administrator, was named head of the Gem Trade Laboratory in January 1988.

IN NEW YORK, TOM YONELUNAS was named manager of GIA's Eastern division, responsible for the daily business of the educational facility and—along with vice president Bert Krashes—management of the New York Gem Trade Laboratory. After Krashes retired at the end of 1987, Yonelunas became head of the New York branch as well as the Gem Trade Lab on both coasts in January 1988. Thomas M. Moses, one of GIA's most brilliant gemologists and a protégé of Robert Crowningshield, was tapped by Boyajian to become "the Crowningshield of the next generation," as he put it, in gem identification.

The sweeping staff reorganization demonstrated that Boyajian was serious about taking GIA to the next level. However, the abrupt changes caused some in the industry to wonder what was so wrong with the Institute. Those who thought this were missing the point, said Boyajian.

"What I did was recognize people who did good work," explained Boyajian. "This isn't a one-man operation; it is a multi-faceted, multi-talented organization. In leading and managing people, you must remember that *everyone* is important, and that no one person is as smart as our collective wisdom."

Indeed, many well-qualified managers got little press attention for their work, but were as essential as those in high-profile posts. One example was head of accounting Janet Ingall Fryer, the wife of Chuck Fryer. Originally

Tom Moses, one of GIA's most brilliant gemologists, was tapped by Boyajian to become "the Crowningshield of the next generation" in gem identification.

Jan Fryer held together the Institute's accounting infrastructure during the Nord and early Boyajian years.

from Scotland, she moved to California, got a job in GIA accounting in the 1970s and worked her way up to manager of the department. It was she who held the accounting infrastructure together during the Nord and early Boyajian years. "Jan was a Rock of Gibraltar, working 12 hours a day to make sure things continued to run during challenging times. She is an unsung hero," noted Alice Keller, then editor of *Gems & Gemology*.

What Boyajian was really doing was putting together a team to help him lead the Institute. Liddicoat had consulted an inner circle of officials, and Nord had formed GIA's first real management group. But it was Boyajian who expanded and formalized the concept. If the Institute was to be run like a corporation, he reasoned, then its president needed a team of executive-level directors, each responsible for specific operations, who would meet with him regularly to review, report, and advise on those operations and their contributions to GIA's overall objectives.

"These executives were people I could work with, people who believed in GIA, and people I could trust," Boyajian said.

A DEFINING MOMENT IN BOYAJIAN'S YOUNG ADMINISTRATION came in late 1986, just months after he became president. The setting was an all-management dinner he hosted at a restaurant in west Los Angeles, attended by about 60 people.

Boyajian had been reading John Naisbitt's book *Re-Inventing the Corporation*, much of which focused on corporate teamwork and empowering people in their jobs. It influenced much of his management style and formed the context of the motivational speech he delivered that evening.

Boyajian spoke about GIA's uniqueness, its tremendous diversity and strength. He cited the principles and values that guided the Institute, as well as the ethics he believed in. He told the managers that he wanted them to feel empowered to develop their own departments and their professional opportunities within the Institute.

It was a resounding speech, one that set the tone for Boyajian's leadership and the direction of the Institute for the coming years.

DURING HIS FIRST MONTHS, Boyajian established education and gemological research as priorities and turned his attention to meeting the rising trade demand for diamond grading reports. There was a renewed enthusiasm at GIA, and he had assembled a strong management team. Impressed with Boyajian's initiatives and leadership, the board of governors unanimously dropped the "acting" from his title and named him president at their September 26, 1986, meeting in Santa Monica. The speed of the confirmation, coming just two months after he was named acting president, surprised and pleased Boyajian, but he took it as a mandate by the board to initiate long-term planning and set a course for future development.

Not long thereafter, Boyajian took a significant step, one that set the direction of the Institute and its programs for the rest of the 20th century, and into the 21st.

It was called, simply, the Master Plan.

■ BLUEPRINTING THE FUTURE

As it entered 1987, GIA was in good financial shape and enjoying another surge in business, thanks to Nord's reforms and a revival in the global gem trade. That allowed Boyajian to push for more growth. "We put no limits on what the Institute could do to help the industry and the public," he said. "Our team wanted to go international, broaden our product and service offerings, and make GIA an even more effective institution."

But such growth had to be organized and controlled, with clear goals, rather than be reactive, as it had been for GIA in the 1970s. "We needed direction," Boyajian wrote later. "We needed to put our plans for the future on paper and in motion."

So Boyajian did something that had never been done at the Institute before: He initiated long-range strategic planning to chart GIA's future. "It was one of the most pivotal things I did as president," said Boyajian, looking back years later.

There had been annual budget planning meetings, of course, and the Institute had certainly capitalized on opportunities as they arose, such as the popularity of its diamond grading system. During his presidency, Nord and his top staff periodically brainstormed ideas for short-range projects and programs. But GIA's top officers had never sat down to compose a set of specific long-term goals and the means to achieve them. There was a vast difference between brainstorming and crafting a well-thought-out, detailed blueprint for future growth and development.

BOYAJIAN DID SOMETHING THAT HAD NEVER BEEN DONE AT THE INSTITUTE BEFORE: HE INITIATED LONG-RANGE STRATEGIC PLANNING TO CHART GIA'S FUTURE.

Ed Trenner, of MasterPlanning Group International, conducted GIA's strategic planning sessions from March 1987 to June 1988. Out of these sessions came the Master Plan, the blueprint that would guide the Institute into the 21st century.

THE IDEA FIRST OCCURRED TO BOYAJIAN at his church, where he and other volunteer officers participated in a strategic planning process conducted by MasterPlanning Group International (MGI), a business-consulting firm specializing in nonprofit organizations, to set long-range priorities for the church and the means to achieve them.

"The experience of using a facilitator to ask questions and lead you along a critical, objective, thoughtful process was so positive that I saw it could work in our nonprofit organization," said Boyajian.

The timing was right. In his first months in office, Boyajian had accomplished his initial goals. GIA was being reenergized. His leadership had been established, and his management team was in place. Now, in early 1987, was the moment for GIA's officials "to sit down, define the issues and needs facing the industry and the Institute, and decide where GIA should be by the year 2000," said Boyajian.

Boyajian wrote to the board of governors, "Developing a strategic Master Plan for the Institute is a vital element for our future success [so] that we can launch ourselves into the next decade, knowing where we want to go and how we are going to get there." With the governors' backing, he hired MGI and their associate Ed Trenner. Together, they and GIA's executive team set out to design a blueprint for the future of GIA.

The project took 14 months, from March 1987 to June 1988. It began with Boyajian and his wife meeting with Trenner in a 10-hour session of talks and tests to define and evaluate Boyajian's leadership attributes, his role at GIA, and the goals and challenges facing the Institute. Trenner insisted Joyce Boyajian take part. In that session, Trenner wrote Boyajian, Joyce demonstrated her importance to her husband's success as president, because she was "a strong 'first lady'. . . secure, devoted, and active, [with a] strong, supportive interest in your work with GIA."

Boyajian was "well-placed" as president because he didn't see himself as being there merely "to serve [himself] or GIA alone, but to serve the industry and the public," Trenner wrote in a subsequent report. His leadership style was that of a "developer . . . a people person, encourager, and a team leader."

One of Boyajian's goals for the Institute—taking it from a $20 million corporation to a $100 million one by 2000—"can't help but pull GIA forward in impacting the whole industry," said Trenner.

Then came a number of one-day retreats and meetings over the next several months with the Institute's top officials. "Team-dreaming," as Trenner called it, was critical to the success of the project, he said, in order for there to be "group ownership" of the GIA direction.

Those involved with this process included Dick Liddicoat and Glenn Nord. "If you understand the context of where you have been, then you know where you are going," explained Trenner. Others who helped draft GIA's blueprint for the future were Dennis Foltz, Tom Yonelunas, Chuck Fryer, Vince Manson, Jim Shigley, Dick Agnew, Court Walker, and of course Boyajian.

Trenner told them that the Master Planning process involved more than just crafting a plan. It was a way of *thinking about planning* that could help for years to come and was designed to stimulate their vision for the future. The end result, he said, would be "a crystal-clear direction with measurable goals that would provide a track to run on . . . and a place to put the new ideas that will come to you as you grow."

Trenner led them through a detailed assessment of the needs of the gem and jewelry industry and the public: "Keep asking yourselves the question, 'What needs exist in the industry, and how can GIA uniquely address them?'" he instructed the planning team. "Your answer will help you identify where and how you can best impact the industry and serve the public."

"That approach helped us focus not on ourselves, but on others," said Boyajian, "and *that* helped us formulate our mission statement, our values, and our objectives of how we would serve those needs."

THE SESSIONS WERE OFTEN INTENSE, as the participants discussed, discarded, and debated various issues. Boyajian, Manson, and Foltz were among the most vocal in expressing their views. The others were more reserved and reflective, contributing pertinent, thoughtful comments. A wide variety of topics were covered, from color grading to instructional videos, from creating an endowment for GIA to investing heavily in research and development. They shared their own dreams, goals, and frustrations with GIA's operations. Long-term fundraising—an essential ingredient of nonprofit status—was discussed, as were more immediate needs, such as replacing an outdated computer system or funding student loans.

"IF YOU UNDERSTAND THE CONTEXT OF WHERE YOU HAVE BEEN, THEN YOU KNOW WHERE YOU ARE GOING," EXPLAINED TRENNER.

263

THEY LEARNED TO
PLAN IN FIVE- TO
10-YEAR BLOCKS
AND TO THINK OF
GIA AS AN
INTEGRATED
INSTITUTION RATHER
THAN FOCUSING ON
INDIVIDUAL
DEPARTMENTS.

They learned to plan in five- to 10-year blocks, instead of just one or two years ahead, and to think of GIA as an integrated institution rather than focusing on individual departments. "That was the hardest part," said Boyajian. "There were multiple areas of endeavor. So when we talked about marketing, what did we mean? Were we talking about the Gem Trade Lab, GEM Instruments, or Education? It forced us to look at GIA as a whole."

Meanwhile, Trenner took copious notes and kept discussion within six definitive categories: personnel, marketing and communication, products and services, administration, finance, and research and development.

"Ed forced us to be very deliberate and disciplined, and to follow a structure (i.e., six one-hour sessions per day, one subject per hour)," Boyajian said. Trenner also provided an outsider's perspective, offering comments that might not otherwise have been considered. For example, he asked at one session, "How will the increase in TV home shopping affect jewelers and the sales of 'certified' diamonds?" At another, he told them they needed more factual data. "Market research is a must! I hear too much 'I think' and 'I guess,'" he said. "There is too little factual data in our meetings."

After each session, Trenner summarized the discussions, adding his own comments and recommendations. Over the months there were interim reports that GIA officials reviewed, followed by additional half-day brainstorming sessions.

IN EARLY 1988, the final draft of the document was presented to the board of governors for review. "These are the main themes that will guide us in the future," Boyajian told them. That spring, "The GIA Master Plan" was completed and approved by the Institute's top officials and the board of governors.

The 30-page plan—finely detailed but written so sparingly that it was virtually an outline—defined GIA's short-term (the next one to two years), mid-range (two to five years) and long-range (five to 10 years) goals, with specific objectives for each individual year. It clearly stated where the Institute should—and should not—put its resources and energies, along with what programs needed to be strengthened and how. It called for revisions in the core educational programs and research facilities, as well as serving the trade better through international expansion, diversification, and closer relations with other organizations in the industry.

OBJECTIVES OF GIA'S 1988 MASTER PLAN INCLUDED:

- Expanding the grading activities of the Gem Trade Laboratory

- Initiating institutional development, including a formal fundraising program

- Establishing a new world headquarters, a site that would allow unimpeded growth for the next half-century

- Increasing research and development activities

- Addressing the technological needs of the Institute and its students

- Broadening the Institute's curriculum and educational outreach

- Expanding the library and information center and its holdings

- Hosting a second International Gemological Symposium in 1991 (to mark the Institute's 60th anniversary)

- Accelerating global expansion

Over the next decade, all major proposals and projects would be measured against the 1988 Master Plan. Whether it was library expansion or a new gem collection, it was "all filtered through that grid," said Boyajian. "Is this right for GIA and the industry? Does it serve the public trust? It became our guidepost, a clear roadmap that kept us going in the right direction."

It represented, said Vince Manson, "the dream we're all moving toward." And moving successfully. By 1997, less than a decade later, Boyajian and his team had already achieved *95 percent* of the goals in the Master Plan. "It is incredible how close we have come to achieving something that seemed impossible, quixotic" only a few years earlier, said Manson, by then director of strategic planning.

And so, Boyajian and his team caught their breath, phoned Trenner, and sat down again in 1997 to set new goals and greater vision for the Institute and draft a new Master Plan for the 21st century.

OVER THE NEXT DECADE, ALL MAJOR PROPOSALS AND PROJECTS WOULD BE MEASURED AGAINST THE 1988 MASTER PLAN.

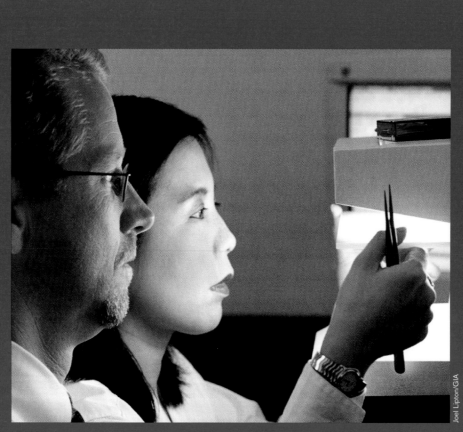

CHAPTER 12

Joel Lipton/GIA

Phil Yantzer, director of the West Coast grading laboratory, and lab manager Jennifer Hwang color grade a diamond.

THE HALLMARK OF INTEGRITY

1986–2003

In 1986, GIA and its new president faced a major crisis, one of supply and demand. The diamond industry was back, and so was the demand for GIA diamond grading reports, which had become indispensable tools to market fine-quality diamonds. But the Gem Trade Laboratory, the innovator and recognized authority in grading reports, was failing to meet the demand. Slow service times led to frustration and the feeling that the Institute was turning its back on the trade. Bill Boyajian, an unknown commodity in the eyes of the diamond industry, knew he needed to step in quickly.

Boyajian and newly appointed Gem Trade Laboratory managing director Tom Yonelunas acted immediately to expand the lab's diamond grading capacity and promote greater consistency in the grading process. Besides hiring additional staff and implementing new procedures, the laboratory started automating its processes, eventually developing a state-of-the-art operations and management computer system known as Horizon.

With these improvements came a host of new products introduced by the Gem Trade Laboratory in the late 20th century: laser inscription, new colored diamond reports, the GIA Diamond Dossier®, and a "new generation" of grading and identification reports.

Just as important was the Institute's closer communication with the diamond industry, while still maintaining complete objectivity and impartiality. Despite controversy over GIA's ill-fated attempt to open a grading laboratory in Antwerp and its ambitious study of diamond cut, this era saw the Gem Trade Laboratory become more responsive than ever to the needs of the trade and the public.

■LUNCHING IN THE LIONS' DEN

One of the first tasks Bill Boyajian faced as president was improving the Institute's relations with the diamond trade. There were a number of problems.

By the summer of 1986, the diamond business had awakened from its early-'80s slump, and pressure was again mounting on the Gem Trade Laboratory. Glenn Nord had been cautious about expanding the lab, but now the diamond dealers were clamoring for GIA to keep up with demand for its grading reports.

The trade had some very mixed feelings about GIA and the laboratory in the mid-1980s, recalled Tom Yonelunas. Despite the lab's industry advisory

William Goldberg (right) was one of the diamond industry leaders who, in 1986, urged Boyajian to improve GIA's laboratory service and relations with the trade.

committee, which was designed to coordinate and improve trade relations, some tradespeople complained that the laboratory still wasn't supportive enough of the diamond industry.

"They felt there was no vision for developing our services," noted Yonelunas years later. And indeed, *New York Diamonds* magazine reported in 1988 that the diamond trade often regarded the GIA laboratory "with a mixture of awe and annoyance"—awe for creating the grading system and reports that had changed the industry, and annoyance for failing to keep up with the demand for those reports. (Laboratory facilities on both coasts were so overwhelmed by trade demand in 1986 that GIA was temporarily forced to limit grading services to diamonds over one carat to reduce the backlog.)

So when Boyajian took over, "tension with the trade was high," said Yonelunas. None of the diamond dealers or manufacturers really knew him personally; they had heard that he was, as one put it, "a colored stone guy," who had spent years teaching and administering the Institute's resident gemology program in California. "There was uneasiness about how that would affect GIA's relationship with the diamond trade," said Yonelunas.

Almost immediately after Boyajian was named acting president of GIA, the Diamond Dealers Club in New York invited him to what Yonelunas called "a getting-to-know-you" luncheon.

In hindsight, the dealers needn't have been so worried. Boyajian himself wanted to "cultivate a friendly and yet arms-length relationship with the 47th Street diamond community," he said later. "I felt it was critical to meet with them personally and to listen.

"While I love colored stones, I learned quickly that the wheels of the industry and GIA rolled on diamonds. Diamond grading reports and diamond training are the two most important components of this institution. So I had to make the diamond industry my priority."

SEATED AT THE LUNCHEON TABLE in the Diamond Dealers Club that August afternoon were many of the leading figures in the U.S. diamond trade, people such as Louis Glick, William Goldberg, Eli Haas, Eli Izhakoff, Ray Pearlman, and Marvin Samuels. Boyajian—"young and a little naive," as he described feeling at that moment—was the only GIA official there, because the dealers not only wanted to size him up, but they also wanted to talk candidly to him about the laboratory and what they thought GIA should do to improve service and relations with the trade.

The dealers were cordial but insistent, articulate but fervent. "Frankly, they beat up on GIA and me," remarked Boyajian afterward.

They contended that the New York diamond trade had helped build the Institute's laboratory operation, and they stressed the importance of the laboratory to dealers and clients. They said that the terrible times of the early '80s were over, and it was imperative that GIA invest in its laboratory to meet the growing demand. The Gem Trade Lab had to become more service minded, more responsive to the needs and concerns of the industry.

With writing pad and pen in hand, Boyajian sat there, listening carefully to them for almost two hours and taking copious notes. At the end, he told them, "Gentlemen, I know I have a lot to learn, but I'll take what you say to heart and work with you. I will make this right. You'll see a difference."

It was quiet for a couple moments, and then Bill Goldberg, president and chairman of William Goldberg Diamond Corp., spoke up from the other end of the table: "Well, now I have something to say.

"I don't know about you gentlemen, but I like this guy. I think he's honest." And the others murmured their assent.

That lunch meeting broke the ice, said Yonelunas later. "Bill is a great communicator. They hit it off very well."

GIA Gem Trade Laboratory CEO Tom Yonelunas chats with diamantaire Stephen Cohen (right).

BOYAJIAN AND YONELUNAS MOVED QUICKLY to make good on those promises. Yonelunas packed his suitcase and became more visible in major diamond centers. He began attending every congress of the World Federation of Diamond Bourses, the first time that anyone from GIA had officially attended. Yonelunas and other officials traveled to meet face-to-face with trade leaders around the globe, obtaining input that strengthened the laboratory's commitment to the industry.

While reaching out, Boyajian and Yonelunas also helped the diamond trade gain a better understanding of GIA. In 1988, Boyajian urged the Institute's governors to elect Eli Haas, a leading member (and later chairman) of the Diamond Dealers Club, to the GIA board. Although the board of governors had long included members of the "ideal cut" diamond sector, such as then-chairman George Kaplan, Haas was the first dealer from the mainstream diamond industry.

Haas's presence on the board sent a signal to the diamond world that the Institute was open to addressing their concerns and interests. That same year—not coincidentally—Yonelunas was appointed to the board of directors of the Diamond & Jewelry Association of New York. "Such close contact

Bob Crowningshield assists a diamond grader in the New York lab, which expanded three times during the 1990s.

with the trade doesn't threaten GIA's impartiality," said Yonelunas. "Instead, it enhances our ability to respond to the industry's needs and, ultimately, to better serve the public."

Meanwhile, there was more aggressive recruitment of diamond graders and gemologists to improve GIA's turnaround time while coping with rising industry demand for grading services. Between 1986 and mid-1988, the grading staff in New York and California doubled in size. As a result of this and other measures, laboratory facilities on both coasts were able to decrease their average service time—to accept, grade, and return unmounted diamonds—and the number of diamond grading reports issued rose 27 percent in 1988. An additional 20 percent were issued the following year. In 1990, the Gem Trade Lab graded or reported on some $2 billion worth of diamonds at wholesale, including thousands of fancy-color diamonds, which were now being submitted regularly to GIA for colored diamond reports. By 1991, the laboratory employed 60 diamond graders and gemologists in New York (50 percent more than in 1988) and 40 in Santa Monica (more than double the number in 1988).

To keep pace with the ever-rising demand for its services, GIA expanded its New York location three times over the next several years. At the turn of the century, it occupied two floors in the 580 Fifth Avenue building—at 30,000 square feet, the largest tenant—allowing room for hundreds of diamond graders, gemologists, and support staff. In California, the laboratory relocated from its already-expanded 10,000-square-foot space in Santa Monica to GIA's world headquarters in Carlsbad, where it occupied more than 40,000 square feet by 2003.

All this occurred as trade demand for grading and identification of diamonds, colored gems, and pearls kept rising sharply. It was, as Yonelunas put it, "like fine-tuning an engine while speeding down the highway."

By 2003, the GIA laboratory had more than 500 staff members between New York and California, two-thirds of whom were diamond graders and technical personnel. They were grading many hundreds of thousands of diamonds a year, with a wholesale value of some $6 billion, and making an impact throughout the world. Yet signs indicated that demand would continue to grow, and so should the laboratory. Aggressive expansion of physical space and staff size was planned in both domestic locations to meet the demand of its clients well into the 21st century.

In 2003, the GIA Gem Trade Laboratory employed more than 500 staff members, two-thirds of whom were diamond graders and technical personnel.

Joel Lipton/GIA

IN ADDITION TO GROWING CAPACITY, ensuring consistency in grading and operating procedures on both coasts was also a top priority of GIA's new leaders in the late 1980s. Boyajian, shortly after being named acting president in the summer of 1986, told *Jewelers' Circular-Keystone* that one of the important issues facing GIA was ensuring the consistency of Gem Trade Laboratory reports. Yonelunas, too, vowed that consistency was one of the three essential standards (with quality and productivity) toward which the laboratory would strive.

A major thrust in this direction had come in 1987, when Boyajian named Yonelunas chief executive officer (CEO) of the Gem Trade Laboratory, and Chuck Fryer director of gem identification services. That August, a week-long summit of top GIA and Gem Trade Lab officials was held to review gem identification and diamond grading procedures as well as communications between the East and West Coast laboratory offices. The aim was to develop or improve means for ensuring consistency in all procedures, while reducing cycle times and increasing capacity.

A number of changes and improvements emerged from that summit. One was an exchange program between the two laboratory locations, with personnel from one office working a week or more at the other at regularly

Sheryl Cashmore, a manager at the West Coast laboratory, guides Asako Whennen in the diamond grading process.

Joel Lipton/GIA

scheduled intervals. This ongoing exchange between both coasts—still in effect many years later—not only reinforced accuracy and consistency in grading, identification, and research, but it also, according to West Coast director Sally Ehmke, "promoted camaraderie, which ultimately led to a more open environment where ideas are freely exchanged and challenges are discussed and met."

The summit also led to a new procedure called "doubling up," whereby representatives from both coasts participated in major initiatives. When the laboratory created its revolutionary Horizon computer system in the mid-'90s, for example, each of the groups involved in planning and supervising the project contained representatives from both locations. "Two are more than twice as smart as one," said Yonelunas, "and this approach ensures that whatever we implement is consistent between the two coasts."

Consistency also was improved in other ways in the late 1980s. More diamonds were routinely sent to both offices to verify and monitor grading results, and advances in telecommunications brought even greater communication between the two coasts.

In 1988, two years after the DDC luncheon, Goldberg phoned Boyajian and asked, "Remember what you said you would do when you came out to see us? Well, what you said you'd do, you did!"

And in early 1989, David Steinmetz, then chairman of the Diamond Dealers Club's Gemological Committee, noted, "Grading results are consistent regardless of which laboratory location issued the report."

THE LABORATORY CONTINUED TO GROW and mature. In 1989, graders' initials were removed from the final reports. Though a standard feature since GIA began issuing reports in the 1950s, by the late 1980s laboratory operations had become so sophisticated that individual initials on reports were superfluous. The initials were replaced with "GIA Gem Trade

Laboratory," written in longhand beneath the printed name. That anonymity more accurately indicated that a report was the work not of one or two graders but of several, including senior staff members who acted as arbiters when there was a difference of opinion. Indeed, by the beginning of the new century, items were being routinely examined by a minimum of four laboratory employees, and as many as 12 or more diamond graders and gemologists, depending on the situation.

At the same time, new procedures ensured that graders were unaware of whose stones they were analyzing, an important enhancement of what Yonelunas called GIA's "consensus grading process based on independent analysis." Several graders independently viewed a diamond. After a preliminary grade was established, senior graders again independently assessed the diamond until a consensus grade was determined. If a client disputed a grade, the diamond could be rechecked, but not by the original graders. Rather, senior gemologists or lab supervisors who were not involved in the original grading—and, again, did not know the client's identity—would perform the recheck.

These procedures were followed at both the West Coast and East Coast locations. But while both operations had the same client base,[1] shared data and staffers, and adhered to the same grading and identification methods, they *weren't* slavish copies of each other. Each addressed specific needs and had different service methods. For example, the West Coast facility graded most of the smaller (less than 0.70 carat) diamonds. Most items submitted to the West Coast office came via registered mail or armored courier to the California office on South Hill Street in the jewelry district of Los Angeles. By the mid-'90s, this facility also had established a service with Brinks Inc. at the Los Angeles International Jewelry Center, which allowed local clients to submit items directly to Brinks for delivery to the West Coast location and have them returned in the same manner.

The East Coast laboratory, at 580 Fifth Avenue in the heart of New York's diamond district, was in the very building where many of its wholesaler and manufacturer clients had their offices. As a result, many of the New York clients simply took their items personally to the laboratory without leaving the building, and were able to receive expedited service for their most important diamonds. For clients with larger diamonds, for whom time was of the essence, GIA unveiled a "Priority Service" in New York in

Twenty-five-year laboratory staffer Bruce Lanzl (top) was director of West Coast grading operations in 2003. On the East Coast, veteran Dan Gillen was director of grading services for the laboratory.

---

[1] The laboratory's clients included diamond manufacturers, wholesalers, retailers, and the public. The services they offered included diamond grading reports, colored diamond grading reports, and colored diamond identification and origin reports. There were also identification reports for mounted and loose colored stones, pearls, and gem carvings. Either lab also would update or verify any previous report issued.

1992. Large or important diamonds, usually those weighing four carats or more, would receive special attention, with service typically taking only a few days.

ONE OF THE LABORATORY'S MOST POPULAR OPTIONS as it entered the 21st century was laser inscription of diamonds. Although the Gem Trade Lab originally introduced its micro-laser inscription service in September 1982, after it leased a device using a new patented technology developed by Lazare Kaplan & Sons, that service was not cost effective for most diamonds under one carat. In the late 1990s, however, improved technology coincided with growing trade demand for a cost-effective way to identify and market "branded" diamonds.

Using state-of-the-art technology, laboratory technicians could place an inscription on the girdle of a diamond as small as 0.18 carat, without affecting color, clarity, or other quality characteristics. With the system's highly precise laser beam, the technicians could engrave alphanumeric characters (about 60 microns high) that could be read with a 10× loupe or a microscope but weren't visible to the unaided eye. A diamond submitted for grading could be inscribed at the same time with a corresponding GIA report number for a nominal fee.

"A diamond inscribed with a GIA report number provides an additional sense of security when buying and selling, and instills greater consumer confidence," said Yonelunas. Inscription also enabled retailers to "add value" to a sale, because consumers had the option of commemorating a special occasion with an inscribed personal message or date. Not surprisingly, many client firms wanted to reproduce their corporate name, logo or slogan, or other company-specific information.

A particularly special inscription involved GIA vice president Bert Krashes, one of the Institute's most honored and respected leaders. At a party held November 8, 1998, after the GIA Board of Governors meeting during which Krashes retired from the board, Yonelunas surprised him with a lapel pin. The pin's diamond was inscribed with the number 19491998, representing Krashes' 49 years of service to GIA.

"We wanted to do something special to pay tribute to a man whose infallible energy, expertise, enthusiasm, and commitment have played such a large part in the Gem Trade Laboratory's continued success," said Yonelunas. "This unique man deserves a unique diamond."

ALTHOUGH THE GEM TRADE LABORATORY had graded many notable diamonds since the early 1950s, including the Hope, one of the best industry endorsements of the laboratory's grading procedures and reports came in 1999, when GIA was named the official grading laboratory for De Beers's limited-edition Millennium Diamonds. Through that prestigious appointment, GIA provided grading and laser-inscription services to the 14 sightholders selected by De Beers to market an anticipated 20,000 mostly one-carat round brilliant diamonds that carried a unique De Beers mark on their tables.

It was, said Yonelunas, "a discerning vote of confidence in GIA's ability to provide expert gemological services consistently throughout the world."

Among the prestigious diamonds graded by the GIA Gem Trade Laboratory is the world-famous Hope diamond.

■A NEW "HORIZON"

At the start of the 1990s, the Gem Trade Laboratory turned its attention to improving its technological and administrative systems. Although the largely paper-based system had been effective and useful in its day, it did not meet the security, tracking, or data-archival needs of the modern Gem Trade Lab. A new computer system installed at the start of the decade improved operational efficiency, consistency, and internal security, but Tom Yonelunas soon realized that the laboratory required more than just a standard computer system if it was to keep up with increasing demand.

"We had reached a point where adding staff was not producing a corresponding increase in capacity. We had outgrown our business systems—computer technology, administrative infrastructure, inventory management—the tools that drive and support every operation," said Kim Cino, then manager of administration for the laboratory.

"Although some of our business was supported by computers," added Yonelunas, "the gemological side—grading, plotting, and other gemological procedures—was not. It was glaringly apparent that we needed to take a bold step in re-engineering our operations to increase our capacity to yet another level."

In 1993, Yonelunas put together a core team of more than a dozen staff members from both coasts, representing a cross section of laboratory grading and support activities. Over 18 months, they reviewed every aspect of operations. "We looked at exactly how items move through the laboratory, and how redesigning the process could accommodate the information and

Don Mengason/GIA

Kim Cino, director of administration at the Gem Trade Laboratory in 2003, led the Horizon development project for GIA in the mid-1990s.

servicing needs of the industry," said Yonelunas. Along the way, they also solicited input from key industry players, technology and business management consultants, and other GIA professionals.

The conclusion: The laboratory needed to create its own customized business system "designed from the ground up," using state-of-the-art computer technology to completely revamp its work processes and streamline its grading operations. Doing so would improve efficiency, significantly increase productivity, accelerate the recording of information, and provide improved customer service to laboratory clients.

But the laboratory staff members were experts in gemology, not information technology. So Yonelunas turned to Oracle, a top business software and technology firm. Combining their expertise with the gemological and operational experience of the laboratory team would create a system uniquely suited to meet the current and future needs of the Gem Trade Laboratory and the industry.

In September 1994, Oracle and the Gem Trade Lab team began the design phase of the project, which Yonelunas and his staff dubbed "Horizon"— "because of its ability to take us as far as we can envision and beyond," he said. They defined in detail what was needed technically and then focused on designing an operations system that would facilitate grading and identification activities with the maximum degree of efficiency.

The entire project took several years, with the laboratory team "every day living, eating, and breathing the restructuring of our very unique business processes," said Yonelunas. The final nine months were spent creating the actual software. At one point, a dozen contracted software programmers congregated in a small room within the laboratory to write new computer code and develop software for Horizon based on Oracle's advice and GIA's gemological needs.

Completion of the first phase of the Horizon network and operations system was announced in August 1996. "We are not changing the way we grade, or gemology," Yonelunas assured clients. "We are streamlining and improving the overall approach to the operation which will, over time, increase our work flow."

Put that way, the results of the Horizon project sounded mundane. In fact, it was a revolutionary operations management system, the first of its kind in the gem and jewelry industry.

"Some of the most exciting features of the new system are the digital creation, plotting, and storage of shape and facet diagrams," said Cino. "These allow for more efficient communication with clients and staff, while the electronic scanning and archiving of support documentation enables immediate access to historical information."

Graders now had personal computers at their desks, all linked to Horizon. Rather than using colored pencils, pens, and graph sheets to plot inclusions and record their findings by hand, graders used specially programmed "workscreens." They had a variety of online tools to record their opinions on polish and symmetry, or to plot clarity. In addition, the system provided instant access to take-in data (though not client names), customized graphics, and a digital library of hundreds of diamond faceting styles, from which graders could select the most representative diagram for the item they were examining.

Horizon streamlined the inventory management and tracking systems while capturing vast amounts of useful gemological data. For example, when a diamond was received by the laboratory, it was first weighed on an electronic balance and measured with a precise, noncontact optical measuring device in the weights and measures department. Using Horizon's proprietary software, this device captured hundreds of linear, angular, and proportional measurements, which were uploaded into Horizon's system for later reference.

Horizon also turned the laboratory into a virtually paperless operation. Before, computers had only been used to record take-in data and print receipts or the final report. Everything in between was done on paper, such as worksheets and plotting diagrams, which accumulated with each step in the process.

But with Horizon, when an item came in, the only paper generated throughout the entire process was a receipt, a small label, and the final report. Everything else was recorded electronically. With the Horizon system, difficulties in searching and retrieving information on grading reports were gone—as was the need for a new five-drawer file cabinet every week.

DESPITE GLITCHES DURING ITS INSTALLATION and break-in period—which caused serious servicing delays, yet are not uncommon in a technological undertaking this large—the benefits of Horizon soon became apparent to clients. Capacity increased significantly, as the time needed for plotting during the grading process was cut by 30 percent in most cases. More information could be captured and analyzed more intensively. Any item could be located immediately at any stage of the process.

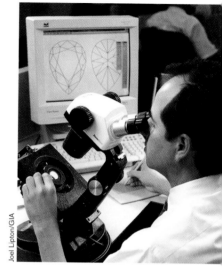

Joel Lipton/GIA

Sergio Espinoza of the West Coast grading laboratory plots a diamond using the state-of-the-art Horizon computer system. Brought online in 1996, Horizon became a powerful tool in meeting the enormous demand for GIA laboratory services.

HOW DIAMONDS ARE GRADED AT GIA

As an independent organization that stresses security and confidentiality, the GIA Gem Trade Laboratory rarely supplies specifics on its diamond grading procedures. But the following provides a look at the meticulous steps involved in grading colorless and near-colorless diamonds at its East and West Coast locations in the early 2000s. Each step is carefully designed to assure that the diamond submitted receives tight security, proper care and handling, and accurate and consistent grading.

Items are submitted by mail, armored courier, or in person. Every package received by mail or courier is thoroughly inspected and opened with precise witnessing requirements to maximize security and documentation. Transactions in person are conducted between the client and the GIA customer service representative in a private, secure booth.

For each item submitted, the client indicates the type of service requested and provides a description of the shape, the declared weight and value, and all client account information. All this is immediately entered into GIA's Horizon operations management system, and a unique bar-coded identification number is assigned to the diamond and placed on the stone paper. With this bar code, GIA can track every step an item takes during its journey through the laboratory.

Joel Lipton/GIA

The GIA laboratory pays special attention to the security of the facility, including its personnel and its clients' gemstones.

The item is then taken to inventory control, where it goes through various procedures. First, it is measured and weighed to the nearest hundred-thousandth of a carat (0.00001 carat) on a digital electronic scale. Its condition is documented, and it travels through several screening and testing steps to determine if it is a diamond, a synthetic or simulant, or if it has been subjected to any treatment process, including high pressure/high temperature (HPHT) annealing. If it is a synthetic or treated diamond, it is pulled from the grading process for advanced testing by the gem identification services group. For natural diamonds, a small label, devoid of any client information, is printed out and placed with the item in a custom-designed, foam-padded transparent case, so both are visible at all times. From this point on, all grading procedures are completely anonymous.

Next, all diamonds submitted for a GIA Diamond Dossier go to the inscription department, along with any others for which this service has been requested. Here, a micro-laser beam inscribes the item's unique GIA report number–which is archived in the laboratory's extensive global database (the laser inscription registry)– or a personal message, brand name or logo, or client identification number.

Now the diamond is ready to enter the grading process. Diamonds flow through many grading steps, each expedited randomly by GIA's inventory control department. Every diamond is independently examined by a minimum of four–and often many more– graders until a consensus is reached. Each step is conducted with the highest levels of security and anonymity, and each also provides an independent examination by a more senior diamond grader or gemologist. Throughout the grading process, diamonds are continually tested and carefully inspected to distinguish synthetics and detect enhancements such as laser drilling, coating, fracture filling, or HPHT annealing that might not have been clearly evident during the initial screening.

Clarity and finish are determined with a binocular microscope at 10× magnification, and confirmed with a standard 10× fully corrected loupe. Five criteria are considered in clarity grading: size, number, location, nature, and relief or color of inclusions. During examination with the microscope, the identifying characteristics are noted and plotted on a diagram that represents the shape and faceting style of the diamond being graded. For the Diamond Dossier, which does not include a plotting diagram, the general shape is selected and identifying clarity characteristics are documented on GIA records. At this time, the proportions of the diamond–its measurements, depth percentage, table percentage, girdle thickness, culet size, and crown angles–are verified.

In color grading, several graders independently examine the diamond against GIA's master color comparison diamonds (D-to-Z) and record separately their color grade opinions. Graders rotate hourly with other tasks to minimize eye strain and thus ensure the quality and consistency of the process. After a preliminary color grade is established, senior color graders independently examine the diamond's color to form a consensus. As with clarity and finish, many graders may be required to finalize the laboratory's opinion on the color grade.

Once every step in the diamond grading process has been completed, all diamonds go through additional weights and measures verification procedures, report processing, and preparation for return to the client.

"These procedures were specifically designed in conjunction with our Horizon system to conduct our activities in the most efficient and secure manner, with the highest level of integrity," said Tom Yonelunas, the laboratory CEO.

Joel Lipton/GIA

Each item is labeled and then placed in a transparent case for its transit through the GIA laboratory.

HORIZON ASSISTED IN
THE RECOVERY OF
DOZENS OF ITEMS
REPORTED LOST OR
STOLEN IN ITS FIRST
FIVE YEARS ALONE.

Horizon also enabled the Gem Trade Laboratory to track any item for any reason in perpetuity. For instance, if an owner of a diamond report notified GIA that the gem was lost, misplaced, or stolen, the laboratory could flag the record in Horizon's archives so that a notification appeared if the diamond was ever re-submitted. If (often when) that happened, GIA informed the appropriate law enforcement and insurance officials. Horizon assisted in the recovery of dozens of items reported lost or stolen in its first five years alone.

Horizon's planners designed it to grow, to add and support laboratory services "without affecting existing operations or our ability to satisfy client needs," noted Yonelunas. Constant improvements helped the laboratory see near-continuous double-digit growth for years.

Yonelunas envisioned more advances, especially ones linking Horizon and laboratory information with the Internet to bring GIA and its clients closer together. "We're seeing more and more ways of accommodating a world that is getting smaller and smaller," he said. "As GIA increases its global business, it will be important to transcend regional and international time differences to give everyone the information they require. Horizon was developed as a platform on which the Gem Trade Laboratory could grow and expand to meet and exceed the needs of the trade in service to the public. We see the system as a continual work-in-progress that evolves to a new level to meet new challenges and help streamline our operations nearly every day."

■REPORTS, CUTS, AND LABS

Despite their successes, GIA and the Gem Trade Laboratory didn't always have an easy time at the end of the 20th century with either diamond dealers or jewelers. Two issues in particular caused serious discord.

One involved GIA's plan to open its own laboratory in Antwerp, Belgium, one of the world's leading diamond trading centers. The controversy was brief—a few weeks at most—but intense. The other was an issue that had simmered for years concerning diamond cut and GIA grading reports.

GIA's reaction to both had far-reaching implications for the laboratory and how it served the industry and the public.

IN 1994, GIA HAD ONE OF ITS MOST BRUISING BATTLES with the diamond industry when it attempted to open a laboratory overseas. The plan caused so much furor on both sides of the Atlantic that GIA president Bill Boyajian later called it "the eight days from hell." It was one of only a few examples where a GIA plan to grow did not come to fruition. Yet it eventually led to changes in the Institute's handling of its international laboratory services that opened the way for more expansion, though in a different way.

Setting up a "laboratory branch" abroad was one of the long-term goals in GIA's 1988 Master Plan and part of Boyajian's own plan to "internationalize" GIA. It was spurred by growing global demand in the late 1980s for diamond grading reports and the need to serve key world centers. "We were also concerned that, while everyone was using the same [GIA-created] terminology and system, they weren't all grading to the same standards," Boyajian explained to *National Jeweler* later. "They're our standards, but there's no accountability" for others using—or misusing—them.

The Gem Trade Laboratory already had an overseas presence at that time. Years before, GIA had authorized its AGT affiliate in Japan to issue GIA diamond grading reports in its laboratory. In 1989, GIA established a similar affiliation with the London laboratory of the Gemmological Association of Great Britain to issue GIA grading reports for diamonds under two carats (as in Japan). While neither affiliation lasted into the 21st century, both provided an incentive to grow elsewhere.

By 1994, Boyajian had decided to move forward with an independent laboratory outside the U.S. "It seemed plausible [for GIA] to establish [its own] overseas lab location to uphold GIA standards," he said. The Institute wasn't alone in thinking this was a good idea. Trade leaders and groups in Tel Aviv, Johannesburg, Bangkok, and Bombay (now Mumbai) had already requested that GIA open a lab in their cities. But the site chosen was Antwerp, a major trading center through which 70 percent of the world's diamonds passed, and one where dealers had expressed support for such a laboratory.

After moving quietly in its preparations in early 1994, GIA confirmed in May that it planned to open a small, six-person diamond grading lab in Antwerp by year's end. Boyajian expected to hear some grumbling, but he was unprepared for—and even startled by—what *Jewelers' Circular-Keystone* called "intense opposition" from within both the New York and Antwerp diamond trades. Belgium's Diamond High Council (HRD) accused GIA of hiring away two of its senior lab managers. In a letter to GIA, HRD demanded that the Institute suspend its plans to open a lab in Antwerp or face legal action.

Meanwhile, many New York diamond dealers worried that they would lose the unique marketing advantage that having the GIA laboratory there (alone) gave them. Most fine diamonds came through the Gem Trade Lab in New York, providing the city's dealers with ready access to many high-quality stones.

THE ANTWERP PLAN CAUSED SO MUCH FUROR ON BOTH SIDES OF THE ATLANTIC THAT BOYAJIAN LATER CALLED IT "THE EIGHT DAYS FROM HELL."

Others wanted GIA to remain an exclusively American entity. "They used GIA's New York–issued certificates to enhance their own image internationally," noted *Modern Jeweler* magazine in a look back at the tempest a few years later.

But a number of New York dealers also thought GIA was overextending itself, since there were still lengthy turnaround times, especially in New York. The Institute should concentrate on strengthening service in the U.S., they told GIA officials, rather than start a new venture overseas. (Actually, said GIA officials in reply, the laboratory had tripled its capacity over the preceding half-decade, and overseas expan-

Diego Lezama Orezzoli/Corbis

The Institute's 1994 plans to open a laboratory in Antwerp, Belgium, met with strong resistance. After canceling the Antwerp project, GIA focused on strengthening its domestic lab activities and expanding internationally through forwarding services.

sion would actually take some of the pressure off domestic operations.) Dealers were so incensed that members of the Diamond Dealers Club began talks with the American Gem Society about opening their own U.S. diamond grading lab, to compete with GIA.

"There was *tremendous* resistance to the idea of an Antwerp lab," said Yonelunas later, so much so that less than two weeks after the project was formally announced—and even though it was in its final stages, with people hired and ready to start—Boyajian, Yonelunas, and the GIA governors reevaluated the situation and decided not to open the lab. Boyajian announced the decision at a meeting of the Diamond Dealers Club in June. In doing so, he conceded that the idea had created "enormous concern" within the diamond trade, but even years later he was still troubled that "starting a little laboratory" produced such an emotional outcry from both New York and the HRD.

"I never imagined the kind of reaction that came," Boyajian said. Shutting down the project was one of the hardest decisions he ever made as GIA president.

Still, something good can grow out of an apparent debacle. The Antwerp event was a turning point for GIA's international expansion, or at least in *how* it expanded. Instead of opening labs overseas, Institute officials decided to concentrate on strengthening laboratory services in the U.S. and meeting global demand through a worldwide network of distribution centers to take in gemstones and forward them to GIA.

"We focused on the United States, where we knew there would be growth in the future, and where we had expanded several times and would again. We did everything we could to build our international laboratory reach without being overseas," said Yonelunas. By 2003, laboratory forwarding services were acommodating demand in Los Angeles, Miami, Chicago, Tokyo, London, Antwerp, Tel Aviv, Hong Kong, India, and Johannesburg.

IF THE BATTLE OF ANTWERP WAS BRIEF BUT INTENSE, the dispute between jewelers and GIA over diamond cut and grading reports heated to various levels for years. However, it was sparked not by the grading reports themselves, but by the significant rewrite of the Institute's diamonds course, released in 1986. The rewritten course eliminated the "American Ideal" cut as the model from which "corrected weight" would be determined in the Institute's diamond training—where it had been for 50 years. Doing so shocked and angered many jewelers, especially those in GIA's one-time sibling organization, the American Gem Society, and "ideal cut" suppliers such as former GIA executive chairman George Kaplan of Lazare Kaplan Inc.

Some jewelers claimed that the Institute should uphold industry standards in its training, not challenge them. But GIA officials, including Boyajian, said that the most important reason for the change was that GIA could not scientifically substantiate the Tolkowsky model as the standard from which to judge other round brilliant cut diamonds.

Criticism of the course changes ignited some jewelers' long-simmering frustration with GIA's diamond grading reports themselves. As the diamond business experienced a resurgence in the late 1980s, consumers increasingly relied on GIA's third-party objectivity to verify the quality and descriptions of diamonds they bought. Likewise, there were more diamond sellers— known in the trade as "upstairs dealers"—who had little product knowledge but relied heavily on GIA reports to sell their goods. That gave GIA's diamond reports an importance equal to, if not greater than, what they had during the investment boom of the late 1970s.

Some jewelers felt that the reports (or "certs," as many in the trade still called them) enabled anyone to sell diamonds, increasing competition while lessening the consumer's need for the expertise of a trained jeweler and the "romance" in buying diamonds and diamond jewelry. The paper, not the stone, had become the most important element in diamond sales, critics claimed.

GIA COULD NOT SCIENTIFICALLY SUBSTANTIATE THE TOLKOWSKY MODEL AS THE STANDARD FROM WHICH TO JUDGE OTHER ROUND BRILLIANT CUT DIAMONDS.

ELIMINATING GRADING
REPORTS WOULD HAVE
BEEN "LIKE TRYING TO
STOP THE SPREAD OF
COMPUTERS," NOTED
BOYAJIAN.

IN OCTOBER 1986, JUST MONTHS AFTER the new diamonds course was unveiled, a prominent AGS jeweler sent a letter to 27 other leading jewelers around the country, many of them AGS members, which he asked them to sign and forward to the GIA Board of Governors. The petition urged GIA to stop issuing its diamond grading reports because, he wrote, they had "become a monster."

The jeweler contended that the detailed reports enabled many diamond investment promoters and sellers, often with no knowledge of diamonds other than what was on a GIA grading report, to set up shop "in small upstairs rooms" and sell diamonds "solely on the basis of what was on a [report]." The reports not only made it difficult for veteran jewelers to make reasonable profits on "important size diamonds," he said, but it was also becoming "impossible for the jewelers—many trained by GIA— to compete against the renowned credibility of the GIA" as exemplified in the reports.

The jeweler also claimed the reports were "incomplete" and misleading because they didn't provide a grade for diamond cut, an important factor in evaluating a diamond's quality. Stop issuing the reports, he said, and the problems they cause would soon disappear.

But while most of the 27 jewelers may have agreed with his arguments, only nine actually signed the letter to the GIA governors. Eliminating the GIA reports, said the others, would only encourage other gem labs to fill the gap with their own reports.

Boyajian denied that the grading reports promoted diamond investment at the expense of jewelers or encouraged unscrupulous diamond sales. In an open letter in *Jewelers' Circular-Keystone* in early 1987, he contended that it was "the GIA diamond grading system and unquestioned integrity and prestige of the GIA laboratory which, more than anything else, prevented widespread misrepresentation of diamond quality in the industry. . . ."

And by that point in the late 1980s, he noted, eliminating the reports would have been "like trying to stop the spread of computers." The GIA grading reports were widely used by domestic and international dealers because they facilitated trading and assured quality, confidence, and consistency in grading. They were also used by many jewelers *especially* when selling large, expensive stones. Clearly, he said, "the GIA quality analysis reports aid in selling diamond jewelry." Most importantly, they enhanced public trust and confidence in diamonds.

The issue, though, erupted again in 1993 with articles in the trade press following a joint report by the Jewelers of America (JA), the Jewelers

Vigilance Committee (JVC), the Diamond Dealers Club (DDC), and the American Gem Society calling for GIA to make a number of revisions in its diamond grading reports.

WHAT TO SAY ABOUT CUT—OR SHOULD THEY SAY ANYTHING AT ALL? THERE WAS NO CONSENSUS IN THE INDUSTRY.

BOYAJIAN CONTENDED THAT SOME CRITICS of the diamond grading reports were more concerned about competition than they were about misuse of reports. Nevertheless, Boyajian, Yonelunas, and other GIA officials agreed that some changes in the reports could be accommodated. But what to say about cut—or should they say anything at all? There was no consensus in the industry.

Some, like the Japan Jewelry Association and AGS, wanted cut grades (which most Japanese labs had been issuing for years). AGS defended use of the "ideal cut" and eventually included a cut grade on its grading reports when it opened its own laboratory in 1995. Others such as the JVC, DDC, and JA opposed saying anything about cut at all. Yet many jewelers, according to a *Jewelers' Circular-Keystone* poll in the early 1990s, did want GIA to address the cut issue on its grading reports.

And if it did, should cut criteria be inclusive or exclusive, apply to all shapes or just round brilliants (the most popular cut)? Limiting grades to only the round brilliants would make certificates for that cut more desirable than those for fancy-shaped diamonds, claimed some dealers. All the criticism and debate led GIA to reevaluate its diamond grading reports and consider what objective criteria in defining diamond cut might be added.

"The effect was that Bill and I decided the reports *did* need some moderniz-ing, including some additional information concerning cut," said Yonelunas. Indeed, Boyajian considered diamond cut "perhaps the single most strategic gemological issue in the industry" at that time, and one that GIA had to address.

But since cut was the most complex of the 4 Cs to understand and assess, and since there was no industry consensus on the issue, GIA decided to build its case through solid research before making any changes to its reports.

That in turn led the Institute to undertake what would become a multi-year research project into diamond cut, one of the most important—and contro-versial—research projects in GIA history.

MOST DIAMOND-CUT GRADING SYSTEMS in the 20th century evolved from work Henry Morse and Charles Field did in the late 1800s. Before the turn of the century, the types of diamonds manufactured by Morse and Field

These three round brilliant cut diamonds demonstrate how cut affects the face-up appearance. The one on the lower right (F color) is less bright than the other two (above, H color, and lower left, E color).

were already referred to as "American cuts," and by 1917 they were also referred to by some as "ideal cuts." Although several individuals used "ray tracing" in the early 20th century to explore diamond cut, perhaps the most famous was Antwerp diamond cutter Marcel Tolkowsky, who described his two-dimensional model of the behavior of light in fashioned diamonds in a 1919 publication, *Diamond Design*. While some subsequent research modified his work, there were few serious attempts to study the subject of cut itself for decades after Tolkowsky published his treatise. Without a sound theoretical basis or method to measure brilliance, fire, or scintillation effects, what constituted better appearance in a diamond was actually based on, and varied with, individual and market preferences. By the late 20th century, the effect on diamond appearance of changes in proportions was still little understood.

A major stumbling block to researching this problem was the absence of an accurate method for modeling the complex interaction between light and a faceted transparent material. Indeed, a complete analysis of the appearance of a diamond that incorporated the effects of all facets and the behavior of light had long been considered unobtainable.

By the late 1980s, however, technology had developed to the point where computers could be used effectively to investigate diamond appearance. So, in 1987, GIA launched an ambitious research project into the interaction of light with a faceted diamond to develop a comprehensive understanding of the impact of different proportions on the appearance of a diamond.

The project began with the development (by computer scientist T. Scott Hemphill) of a sophisticated three-dimensional ray-tracing program to measure how light travels through a colorless, flawless round brilliant cut diamond. Using this program, he and his colleagues constructed a theoretical computer model of light interacting with a faceted diamond, which they then used to evaluate the influence of cut on various aspects of diamond appearance. They concentrated first on brilliance, the aspect that was considered the most important.

To incorporate overall diamond brilliance (the amount of white light returned from a diamond) into their calculations, GIA researchers developed a numerical value (or metric) called "weighted light return" (WLR).[2] They examined how WLR values changed with variations in cut proportions—in particular, crown angle, pavilion angle, and table size—and found the relationships were often complex. In all, the researchers calculated WLR values for more than

---

[2] Simply put, WLR is the "weighted sum of the amount of light returned through the crown of the virtual diamond to all positions of observation above the girdle, using a specific lighting condition."

20,000 combinations of diamond proportions and identified many combinations with equal or higher WLRs than so-called "ideal cuts." "We have found new evidence that many long-held assumptions regarding diamond make may have to be updated in light of our research," said Boyajian in early 1994.

The first results of this ongoing study were published in the Fall 1998 issue of *Gems & Gemology*. The article concluded that many combinations of proportions—rather than a single "ideal" set of narrow ranges—can yield equally bright round brilliant cut diamonds. That conclusion flew in the face of numerous cutting systems that put forth their own single set of "ideal" proportions for round brilliants. "Use of the term 'ideal' is thus confusing . . . like 'blue-white' and 'perfect' decades ago," wrote Boyajian in an editorial that accompanied the article. "Although it is not GIA's role to discredit the concept of an 'ideal cut,' on the basis of our research to date we cannot recommend the use of this term in modern times."

This round brilliant is actually a computer-generated "virtual" diamond with proportions that were calculated using GIA's mathematical model.

But GIA was not ready to change its grading reports or institute a cut grade—at least not yet. As that 1998 article stated, it was also important to address the effect of different proportions on fire and scintillation, as well as the impact of other factors such as lighting conditions. GIA began to develop new metrics for appearance aspects other than brilliance, and proceeded to model various real environments.

Three years later, in the Fall 2001 issue of *Gems & Gemology*, GIA researchers published their results for fire, as represented by the metric "dispersed colored light return" (DCLR). The project continued to be complex and painstaking, as researchers proceeded with observation testing to refine the existing metrics, and looked at the impact of different lighting conditions and scintillation effects. GIA has since indicated that it would eventually expand the proportion-related information included in its reports.

"The approach we're taking is the right approach, one step at time, working through the issues," said GIA research director Jim Shigley. "We're building new fundamental ideas on how cut affects diamond appearance."

MEANWHILE, LABORATORY OFFICIALS CONTINUED to reevaluate what information appeared on the grading reports and how the reports were represented.

The first major redesign of GIA reports appeared in spring 1995, when GIA introduced its revised and improved grading report for colored diamonds. The new "Colored Diamond Identification and Origin Report"—or "color only" report, as it was known in the trade—was the result of GIA's years-long review of its colored diamond grading criteria and its ongoing studies into colored diamond nomenclature as it related to color concepts (the

The Diamond Dossier, introduced in 1998, satisfied a new demand for GIA grading reports on diamonds under one carat.

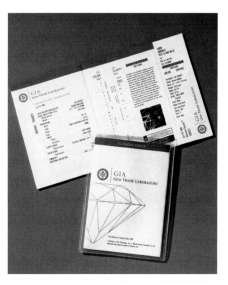

results of which were detailed in a Winter 1994 *Gems & Gemology* article by John King and colleagues).

The revised report included new color grades and expanded color terminology, based on those years of research. Its format was revamped to provide its information more concisely and clearly. There was a paragraph explaining the relationship between color and its components—hue, tone, and saturation—plus a more prominent advisory that the recipient "consult an accredited jeweler or gemologist about the importance and interrelationships of cut, color, clarity and carat weight" (which was added to the traditional diamond grading report as well). And for security and authenticity, the new report had a GIA hologram and a lightly printed background screen under the report entries, in addition to numerous other overt and covert security features.

GIA continued tweaking its various reports with new features—new mastheads, more use of color, and new covers—over the next few years. But the most innovative changes in GIA's reports occurred at the turn of the century.

First came the compact GIA Diamond Dossier, introduced in fall 1998. Quickly nicknamed the "Dossier" in the trade, this report was created to satisfy a new phenomenon of the late 20th century: a steadily growing number of consumers who wanted independent laboratory grading reports with their diamond purchases, regardless of the size. Recognizing GIA's reputation for integrity, many asked specifically for a GIA report.

Market research and work on designing the new service began in the mid-1990s. The resulting Diamond Dossier combined both grading and GIA's recently improved micro-laser inscription registry service for loose (unmounted) diamonds in the D-to-Z color grading scale that weighed 0.18 to 0.99 carat.

The new grading report folded to 5 × 3.5 inches—about the size of a U.S. passport—making it easier to handle for filing, store displays, and selling situations. Contemporary in design, it offered the same type of information on shape and cutting style, measurements and weight, proportions, finish, and grades for clarity and color as appeared on GIA's traditional grading reports.

With the Dossier, the GIA report number was laser inscribed on the diamond's girdle for fast and easy identification of both the diamond and its Dossier document. The inscription could be seen with 10× magnification and was registered in GIA's confidential archival database. But there was no diamond plotting in the report because, said Yonelunas, the report number inscribed on the diamond was "an excellent alternative" for identifying diamonds under a carat.

A perforated tab on the side of the Dossier provided a summary of the grading information; this could be detached easily and kept for future reference or packed with the diamond in its parcel paper. Security features such as the hologram protected the document from tampering and unauthorized reproduction. And there was one other selling point: The new service cost 25 to 40 percent less than the full diamond grading report (though GIA still continued to offer standard grading reports for diamonds over 0.18 carat).

Altogether, said laboratory officials, the new service would enable the Institute to satisfy trade demand while increasing consumer confidence.

In hindsight, the Dossier was the single most successful product or service launch in GIA history. By late 1999, within a year of its introduction, the Dossier already accounted for one of every five diamonds submitted to the laboratory for diamond grading. By 2003, Dossier services represented more than half of the diamond grading business, by volume, in the Carlsbad laboratory.

THE DIAMOND DOSSIER WAS JUST THE BEGINNING. Over the next two years, GIA redesigned its entire family of laboratory reports.

In January 2000, with the advent of a new millennium, the Institute unveiled its "new generation" of grading and identification reports. The reports had a contemporary design that was easy to read and understand, yet they contained more data. Each came with a smaller laminated report summary, which could be filed for reference and had its own detachable tab, with another summary that could be detached and put into a parcel paper. Each report also incorporated a number of state-of-the-art security features, exceeding document-industry security guidelines.

While the "new gen" reports had a fresh look, GIA didn't tamper with much else. "Wanting to be sensitive to over 50 years of service and millions of GIA reports in circulation, we preserved the size, format, and exact gemological information and nomenclature," said Yonelunas. Even so, the result was "a consumer-friendly and secure product designed to benefit the trade and public, and anticipate technological advances in the new millennium."

GIA's "new generation" grading and identification reports were issued beginning January 1, 2000. Modeled after the Diamond Dossier, these reports provided even greater security and convenience than their predecessors.

Geologist Dona Dirlam, here thumbing through volumes from GIA's rare book archives, built the Liddicoat Library and Information Center into the largest, most comprehensive resource of its type in the world.

CREATING A UNIQUE INFORMATION RESOURCE

1986–2003

August 21, 1989. It was a glittering summer night of champagne, laughter, and honors, a black-tie evening of men in tuxedos and women in elegant gowns. It was a night important enough to attract hundreds of leading gem and jewelry industry figures to the Gemological Institute of America.

It was the night of the formal dedication of the Richard T. Liddicoat Gemological Library and Information Center, including the newly acquired, world-renowned Sinkankas collection.

It was the night of the official unveiling of what one writer called "the greatest collection of gemological literature ever assembled."

THAT AUGUST NIGHT WAS A LONG WAY from where it all began, in the office of GIA founder Robert M. Shipley. The very first library of the Gemological Institute of America was a single bookcase, half as high as a man, that consisted of Shipley's books and magazines, which he loaned to staff and students.

Through donations and purchases, the collection gradually began to grow. The Shipleys, Anna McConnell Beckley (the Institute's first librarian), and early instructors made sure that important gem and jewelry books and trade journals were added. The library expanded to several bookcases during the decade of the 1930s and was moved to a separate room in the Institute's headquarters. By the 1950s, it included a number of works by GIA's own officials and leading advisors, such as Shipley's *Diamonds of the World*, Liddicoat's *Handbook of Gem Identification*, Virginia Hinton's *Introductory Gemology*, and Dr. Edward J. Gübelin's *Inclusions as a Means of Gemstone Identification*.

Yet by the start of the 1980s, half a century after the Institute was founded, the library contained just over 2,500 volumes, plus a periodicals collection, all kept locked away in a small room on the second floor of the Santa Monica headquarters. Students and staff had to make an appointment if they wanted to use the facility. It was hardly an adequate information resource for the gem and jewelry industry's leading educational institution.

Then Dona Dirlam arrived, and everything changed.

IT BEGAN BY CHANCE, on a wintry Monday night in Madison, Wisconsin, in 1979. High school teacher and graduate student Dona Dirlam was walking through the snow when she noticed the lights of a jewelry store across the street. It was a new store, one she hadn't seen before, and she crossed over to it. Inside, her eyes were immediately drawn to a little display box with a large pink stone in it.

"That's kunzite," she told the owner.

"That's right," the surprised jeweler replied. "How did you know?"

Dirlam told him about her childhood fascination with a box of Oregon agates, which had led to an interest in gems and geology, a bachelor's degree in science education, and a teaching credential in earth sciences from the University of Minnesota. A teaching job had brought her to Madison, where she taught high school geology and seventh-grade earth science. Dirlam had begun working on a master's degree in geology and geophysics at the University of Wisconsin.

The jeweler was delighted. He brought out a box filled with half-carat sapphires in a rainbow of colors. Dirlam had never seen such wonderful things. "And if you think that's neat, wait 'til you see this," replied the jeweler, who showed Dirlam a one-carat D-Flawless, radiant-cut diamond. "I had never seen a diamond that was so well cut and clean," she recalled. "It was stunning."

With Dirlam's obvious interest in gems, the jeweler—himself a GIA graduate—suggested she enroll at the Institute. She had never heard of it, but what the jeweler told Dirlam excited her. The very next day, she phoned GIA and registered for an upcoming resident gemology course. In June 1979, after finishing her master's degree and quitting her teaching job, Dirlam packed up her car and drove to Santa Monica to begin her studies.

Dirlam loved the course and graduated at the top of her class. Inspired by a lecture on gem formation by Dr. Vince Manson, she interviewed with him for a job with the research department. There were no openings, but until there was one, he urged her to stay and work as a diamond grader at the Gem Trade Laboratory in Santa Monica.

Dirlam accepted the position and enjoyed it, but she was still hungry for gemological information. She made frequent appointments to use the GIA library, checking out trade magazines and gemological journals and sharing noteworthy articles with her colleagues.

This went on for a few months until June 1980, when Dirlam got a call to report to Richard Liddicoat's office. She was bewildered. "I didn't think he even knew who I was," she said later. "I couldn't imagine why he wanted to see me. I thought I had done something wrong!"

Actually, Liddicoat had learned about her frequent visits to the library and her interest in gemological literature. He needed someone to take over the job of GIA librarian, someone with a background in gemology, geology, and teaching. All three converged in Dona Dirlam.

"This was Mr. Liddicoat," she recalled with a laugh. "How could anyone say no to *Mr. Liddicoat*?"

DIRLAM TOOK HER NEW MISSION SERIOUSLY and immediately began making changes. First, she opened the library to students and staff, eliminating the appointment system. Meanwhile, she reorganized the library itself. For decades, its books had been arranged by topic, and within those categories by author, rather than by the standard system used in most libraries. There wasn't even a card catalog. Finding a book had always depended on the librarian's familiarity with it. This casual system had worked okay when the Institute was much smaller, but Dirlam recognized that a more formal organization was needed. By early 1982, GIA's library was catalogued according to the Library of Congress system, enabling users to find books quickly and easily.

In addition to revamping the library, handling phone requests, assisting students and staff, and writing articles for Institute publications, Dirlam also began giving special attention to the rare-book collection. She started by ordering the construction of special cabinets to protect the books. At the same time, she was actively expanding it through purchases and donations, encouraging friends of the Institute to make tax-deductible gifts of gemological materials.

BY 1984, THE GIA COLLECTION had grown to more than 3,000 books and 110 different periodicals. According to Liddicoat, it was "a unique and valuable collection," virtually the only public library of its kind in the world. It was also becoming an important information center. In just the few years since Dona Dirlam had taken over, there had been a dramatic increase in requests for reference information. Dirlam's goal, she said in mid-1983, was nothing less than making the library "the foremost center for gemological information, both current and historical."

"I COULDN'T IMAGINE WHY HE [MR. LIDDICOAT] WANTED TO SEE ME," SAID DIRLAM. "I THOUGHT I HAD DONE SOMETHING WRONG!"

Elise Misiorowski was the first person hired by Dirlam, in 1984, to support the fledgling library. Over the years, Misiorowski made significant contributions as a jewelry historian and eventually was named director of the GIA Museum in 2001.

As the library's contents grew, so did the need for space. In 1984, the library was moved to a two-room suite on the second floor, doubling its square footage. That year also saw the start of what would become the Institute's information and research library staff.

"We needed more staff by the mid-1980s just to handle the growing number of phone calls requesting information," said Dirlam. "The more you help people, the more they call back for help, and then tell other people. So the calls kept increasing, and that meant more staff."

After four years as a one-woman department, her first hire, in 1984, was Elise Misiorowski, a gemologist who had worked as a diamond grader at the Los Angeles lab and served on the research team that developed GIA's colored stone grading system. Caught in the layoffs of 1982 and 1983, Misiorowski became a gem trader. When offered the opportunity to return as a member of the library staff, she jumped at the chance. She became Dirlam's right-hand person, playing a vital part in the library's development into the 1990s.

IN 1988, DIRLAM ADDED TWO MORE gemologists to her staff: Robert Weldon, a talented multilingual photographer hired right out of class, and gemologist-appraiser Juli Cook. That same year, they began preparing a 3,800-square-foot area on the first floor of the Santa Monica headquarters—the fourth home of the library in less than a decade—in anticipation of adding one of the most famous gemological libraries in the world, the Sinkankas collection. It was an acquisition that would catapult GIA's holdings into world-class status as a specialized library.

■THE SINKANKAS COLLECTION

Retired U.S. Navy Captain John Sinkankas, though neither a jeweler nor a gem dealer, was a monumental figure in the gem world. He was gemology's Renaissance man—author, artist, world traveler, gemological authority, gem cutter, rare-book seller, and book collector par excellence. He was not just enamored of books; he was, as one colleague described him, "the world's premier bibliophile for gemological topics." During a half-century of writing and researching, Sinkankas and his wife Marjorie created what became the most important private collection of literature on gems and minerals the world had yet seen.

Sinkankas's fascination with rocks and gems began during his childhood. Early in the 20th century, at the age of seven, he wandered into one of the famous zeolite quarries near his hometown of Paterson, New Jersey, just as some taprock was being dynamited. When the smoke cleared, he saw cavities with green prehnite and dog-toothed calcite crystals, "the most wonderful sights" he had ever seen, he recalled decades later. His mineral collecting hobby continued into adulthood and through World War II, when he served as a naval aviator.

After the war, while stationed at Norfolk, Virginia, Sinkankas taught himself gem cutting. He became such an accomplished lapidary that some of his creations—including a 7,000-carat rock crystal quartz egg and the world's largest golden beryl (2,065 carats)—were put on display at the gem hall of the Smithsonian Institution.

In 1948, Sinkankas began contributing to *Rocks and Minerals* magazine, becoming editor of its amateur lapidary section in 1951. His articles caught the attention of D. Van Nostrand Company, which signed him to write a book on the subject. The result was *Gem Cutting: A Lapidary's Manual* (1955), the first of more than a dozen books he authored or edited over the next half century. Most became authoritative standards in the field. "If your library doesn't contain at least one of the . . . major texts written by John, you are not a true student of mineralogy or gemology," declared *Rock & Gem* magazine in 1990.

Renowned lapidary and author John Sinkankas, who passed away in 2002, built the world's finest private collection of gemological and mineralogical literature.

SINKANKAS BEGAN COMPILING his personal library of gem-related titles in the late 1940s in postwar Europe, where his work as a naval officer often took him. "Marvelous books were showing up from all kinds of private collections," he recalled years later. "Rare books were easily available and relatively inexpensive." But it was while writing *Gem Cutting* during the 1950s that Sinkankas began to seriously and systematically expand his library.

"I dug up every lapidary reference I could find," Sinkankas recalled, but there weren't that many available. No single library offered the concentration of books he needed. "In order to write with authority," he said, "I began collecting books to advance my own writing, finding it easier to build my own library than depend on collections assembled by others."

Sinkankas corresponded regularly with book dealers, especially a small network of antiquarian booksellers who kept their eyes open for the types of

HOWES OFFERED TO
SELL SINKANKAS AS
MANY BOOKS AS HE
WANTED—FOUR
DOLLARS FOR LARGE
ONES AND A DOLLAR
FOR SMALL ONES.

gemological books he needed. He traveled the world buying books from private collections, and after retiring from the Navy in 1961, he and Marge started their own mail-order antiquarian book business.

But Sinkankas's most remarkable book purchase occurred in Los Angeles, not far from his San Diego home, in the late 1960s. By then his fame as a lapidary, author, and bibliophile was well established. Prominent Los Angeles jeweler B. D. Howes wrote Sinkankas to tell him about an extensive book collection he might like to see. Expecting "a modest collection of prosaic volumes about jewelry," Sinkankas and his wife visited Howes's store and were led back into a huge room lined with books "written in as many languages as Europe has countries," he recalled later.

Howes had collected most of the volumes, including many classic 16th-century books on engraved gems written in Latin, German, and French, after the Second World War. But he no longer wanted to own so many books in languages he couldn't read. He offered to sell Sinkankas as many as he wanted—four dollars for large ones and a dollar for small ones. Sinkankas, who could make his way through German, French, Lithuanian, Italian, and Swedish, immediately accepted. "It was the most remarkable find in my life," he said later. Sinkankas, Marge, and Howes "loaded up the back of our half-ton truck with so many books I was afraid the police would ticket me on the way home!" he chuckled later.

BY THE 1970s, JOHN AND MARGE SINKANKAS owned some 10,000 volumes, as well as more than 4,000 articles, reprints, and pamphlets. Sinkankas didn't keep this treasury to himself; he shared it with librarians and writers seeking answers to gemological questions. Dona Dirlam learned of the Sinkankas collection in her first week as GIA librarian. Betsy Barker, her predecessor, had often contacted Sinkankas for information, and she suggested that Dirlam do the same. "He has a simply amazing gemological library, the largest in the world," Barker told her, adding as an afterthought that Sinkankas had said he was thinking of selling it.

"Right from the beginning, buying it sounded like something we should do," said Dirlam. If GIA could acquire the Sinkankas collection, she reasoned, it would provide an invaluable resource for the Institute and its students, the industry, and the public. At the time, however, with GIA's declining revenues, she felt it was no more than a wild dream.

In the meantime, Dirlam took Barker's advice and contacted Sinkankas with a question about Egyptian emeralds. It was the start of her long professional relationship with John and Marge Sinkankas. As Dirlam expanded the library, she purchased books from the couple's rare book business. Then, sometime during the early '80s—neither could recall exactly when—she asked Sinkankas if he would be willing to sell his collection.

Sinkankas knew the Institute well. He had taken its home study course and earned his G.G. diploma in 1952, while still on active duty in the Navy. He was impressed by the "unfailingly courteous" GIA staff. In 1981, when the Institute launched its revamped *Gems & Gemology* journal, Sinkankas was invited to join the editorial review board. He also contributed articles and book reviews and was eventually appointed associate editor. In 1982, during the closing session of the Institute's first international symposium, Richard Liddicoat cemented that relationship by presenting Sinkankas with the "Distinguished Associate of the Gemological Institute of America" award for his contributions to gemology.

SINKANKAS FELT GIA WAS THE ONLY SUITABLE PLACE to house his life's work. There it wouldn't be dismantled and scattered, as had happened with the rare book collections he had seen in postwar Europe. In early 1983, with Sinkankas's verbal promise, Dirlam approached Liddicoat with her plan.

Dirlam had strong allies in her effort to acquire the collection. Liddicoat was for it, as was GIA governor Dr. Kurt Nassau. But the strongest and most convincing advocate was Glenn Nord, Liddicoat's successor. As early as 1984, Nord told Dirlam and some associates that one of his top priorities was acquiring the Sinkankas library. It would be, he said, a focal point of the Institute's future development.

So he and Dirlam began informal negotiations with Sinkankas. In a letter dated August 14, 1985, Nord secured a formal written offer from the Sinkankases. The letter also set the specific purchase price for the library— $755,898—and a 10-year period (ending in August 1995) in which GIA could exercise its option to buy the collection *in toto* or in "large lots as funds are accumulated" for the purchase. The offer was contingent on the understanding that GIA would purchase the entire library, even if it took several years to do so. Under no circumstances, Sinkankas wrote, would he allow the sale of individual items and the breakup of the collection.

Nord actively worked behind the scenes, buttonholing governors at board meetings and industry events to argue the case for acquiring the collection. At the same time, he built up enough operational surplus so that GIA could afford it. "Glenn Nord really had an eye on this library and wanted to get it for GIA," said Sinkankas later. "If anyone was instrumental in securing it for the Institute, it was him."

UNDER NO CIRCUMSTANCES, SINKANKAS WROTE, WOULD HE ALLOW THE SALE OF INDIVIDUAL ITEMS AND THE BREAKUP OF THE COLLECTION.

FOR DIRLAM, THE
ACQUISITION WAS THE
CAPSTONE OF A
TENACIOUS SEVEN-
YEAR EFFORT TO TURN
HER ONCE "WILD
DREAM" INTO A
MAGNIFICENT REALITY.

Ultimately, it was Bill Boyajian, Nord's successor, who handled the final negotiations with Sinkankas. At a February 1987 luncheon meeting at the Sinkankas home, attended by Boyajian, Dirlam, and GIA operations director Dennis Foltz, the final details were ironed out. On April 30, 1987, the Institute's board of governors formally approved the purchase of the entire John and Marjorie Sinkankas Gemological and Mineralogical Library.

For Dirlam, it was the capstone of a tenacious seven-year effort to turn her once "wild dream" into a magnificent reality.

AND WHAT AN ACQUISITION IT WAS! The contents of the Sinkankas collection dated from 1511 to 1988. Many of the volumes were from the 1700s and 1800s, but there were also major works from the 1500s and 1600s. It contained books, journals, articles, and pamphlets on almost every aspect of gemology, jewelry, geology, and lapidary arts, and in several languages.

There was, for example, the first gemology text in English, *A Lapidary: or, The History of Pretious Stones: With Cautions for the Undeceiving of All Those That Deal with Pretious Stones*, by Thomas Nicols (1652). The collection also included one of the earliest books on the commercial aspects of cut diamonds, *A Treatise on Diamonds and Pearls*, by David Jeffries (1750). There were rare editions with beautifully hand-wrought drawings of gems and gem crystals, many in watercolor. Others offered eyewitness accounts of gem finds and of deposits no longer active.

Aside from its sheer size, another feature that set the Sinkankas collection apart from any other was its completeness. For each important volume, Sinkankas had sought every edition in every language. There were, for example, 26 editions of *Pliny's Natural History* alone. At least half the collection contained material in languages other than English, including volumes in Latin, Renaissance French, and Russian.

It wasn't easy for the Sinkankases to give up such a collection. Before Dirlam arrived to transfer the books, John and Marge—like parents saying goodbye to children going on a long trip—went through the collection, handling each volume and carefully placing their nameplate on the inside cover.

"It was a very profound time for them," said Dirlam. "It was important that they have the opportunity to touch each one before the collection was passed on."

In January 1988, Dirlam formally took possession of the collection on behalf of GIA. Initially, she thought it would take a week for her and one of her librarians to prepare and box up all the books at the Sinkankas home in San

The Sinkankas collection contained a number of rare and important volumes, such as *Les Six Voyages de Jean Baptiste Tavernier* (1679). The engraving on the right shows the famed traveler buying gems from native miners during one of his journeys.

Diego. But the first day she realized that the process would take much longer and require more help. Eventually a party of 10 people worked for two weeks wrapping, packing, and boxing books. More than 400 boxes were loaded into trucks and sent to Santa Monica.

Altogether, the Sinkankas collection added some 10,000 books and over 6,000 article reprints and pamphlets to the GIA library's existing collection of 4,000 books for general circulation, 125 different trade journals, and some 14,000 slides. Together, they created a resource unlike any in the world.

BACK TO THAT GLITTERING EVENING ON AUGUST 21, 1989, when some 300 guests got the first glimpse of the Richard T. Liddicoat Gemological Library and Information Center. During the official opening ceremony, they heard firsthand accounts from Dirlam, Liddicoat, and Boyajian on the acquisition of the Sinkankas collection and what it meant to GIA and the gemological community. Another highlight was Sinkankas's off-the-cuff comments on how he and Marge had created their personal library,

John and Marjorie Sinkankas (center) attend the dedication of the Richard T. Liddicoat Gemological Library and Information Center on August 21, 1989. The evening also marked the official unveiling of the library's newly acquired Sinkankas collection of gem and mineral literature.

including book-buying adventures in Europe, the Howes acquisition, and his longtime relationship with GIA. Mayor James Conn presented Bill Boyajian with a letter of commendation from the city of Santa Monica acknowledging GIA's contribution to education in the community. At the end of the night, departing guests were handed reprints of *Gems & Gemology*'s Spring 1989 article on the Sinkankas collection.

It was an impressive debut for what one writer called "the greatest collection of gemological literature ever assembled."

ACQUISITION OF THE SINKANKAS COLLECTION had several effects on GIA's library, besides making it the world's largest gemological information center.

It provided the impetus for converting GIA's library into a state-of-the-art facility at its Santa Monica headquarters. The expanded 3,800-square-foot area included a secure, climate-controlled room where the Sinkankas volumes and other rare and fragile books could be preserved. The volumes were put on earthquake-proof metal shelving set on rollers, and the room was equipped with an extensive fire-suppression system.

Acquisition of the collection also brought about computerization of the library. In preparation for cataloging the huge Sinkankas library, Dirlam and her staff devoted the entire year of 1987 to compiling a computerized database of the library's extensive 35 mm slide collection. Completed in November 1987, this database enabled users to quickly retrieve images as varied as a Fabergé gold box or an emerald from Zambia. It soon became one of the library's most popular features.

When it came time to catalog the Sinkankas collection in 1989, the library staff, under the direction of technical librarian Rose Tozer, now had a computer vocabulary for indexing gemology and jewelry information. Once the vocabulary was completed in 1990, and applied to the slides, maps, auction catalogs, and journals, it was the first computerized catalog of gemological works available anywhere. Ultimately, all of the library's holdings—including the 7,000-volume circulating collection and other rare books—became part of a network of computer-searchable gemological databases.

Visual Resources manager Judy Colbert searches the slide collection for an image. In 2003, the library held over 28,000 slides, photographs, and digital images related to gems and jewelry.

When GIA moved to its new Carlsbad headquarters in 1997, the nucleus of the campus was the Richard T. Liddicoat Gemological Library and Information Center. At almost 9,000 square feet, it occupied more than twice its previous space and featured expansive areas devoted to reading and research. Every workstation was equipped with computers, and a separate location was set aside where students and the public could access the Internet. Also available was a viewing area for the library's extensive collection of industry videotapes, supported by George Carter Jessop, of the same jewelry family that encouraged Shipley to give his first gemology course in 1930.

ALTHOUGH THE SINKANKAS COLLECTION was the library's largest and most important rare book acquisition, it was also just one step in Dirlam's goal of making the Institute's gemological library and information center the most important in the world. Through lectures, articles, and press releases, she regularly encouraged GIA students, alumni, and others in the industry to donate books, gem source maps, journals, early gemological equipment, renderings, and early auction catalogs to the library. She cultivated a

Joel Lipton/GIA

Left: Research librarian Cathy Jonathan shelves one of the Liddicoat Library's 30,000 books in 2003. Right: Students watch an instructional videotape in the library's specially designed viewing area.

network of rare-book collectors and book dealers and became a regular customer at book auctions.

One special find was the collection of Swiss jeweler Theodore Horovitz, whose thousand-volume private library—with some books dating to the 16th century—was auctioned in Geneva in 1998. Thanks to a $32,000 donation from diamantaire Ishaia Gol, president of the Ishaia Trading Corp., Dirlam was able to acquire several priceless volumes from the Horovitz collection.

"My education at GIA was invaluable," said Gol in explaining his generosity later, "so I knew how significant it would be for GIA students from all over the world to have access to these remarkable antique reference tools to better understand their chosen profession."

The Liddicoat Gemological Library and Information Center continued to receive donations and support. Andrew Cohen Inc. set up a collection to purchase additional books on jade and jade carving in 1996. Then in 1998, through a generous gift from Cartier, Inc., the rare-book room housing the Sinkankas library was named the Cartier Rare Book Repository and Archives. After the passing of John Sinkankas in 2002, a memorial fund was established in his name to add additional rare volumes.

Joel Lipton/GIA

As another feature of the Liddicoat Library, Dirlam also started a collection of historical videos. She began obtaining videos of pertinent TV programs, and worked with GIA's award-winning cameraman Pedro Padua to video-tape oral history interviews with some of the important figures from the Institute and the industry.

Together, all the collections—rare books, images, maps, and videos—had a single purpose: "We want to make this library the archive of the international jewelry industry, and an important part of our mission to ensure the public trust in gems and jewelry," said Dirlam. Using the technology of the 21st century, these resources formed the foundation for a digital asset management system that would provide access to resources throughout GIA as well as to the industry and public, the first step in a comprehensive knowledge management plan.

DONA DIRLAM'S CHILDHOOD FASCINATION WITH EARTH SCIENCES blossomed into a remarkable career in gemology. With the help of a dedicated staff that eventually totaled 12 librarians, she created a world-class, state-of-the-art gemological information resource, accessible and useful for GIA students and staff, the industry, and the public.

Since 1997, the Richard T. Liddicoat Gemological Library and Information Center has occupied nearly 9,000 square feet of space at the Institute's Carlsbad headquarters.

Dr. James Shigley, GIA's longtime director of research, uses Raman spectroscopy to analyze a yellow diamond.

Michael Justice

THE INDUSTRY'S
AUTOMATIC ALARM SYSTEM

1986–2003

The 1980s ushered in an era of new treated and synthetic gem materials, which began to appear in the marketplace in unprecedented quantities and varieties. Many were the product of sophisticated technology, as manufacturers invested far more money in producing these gem materials than testing laboratories could spend in identifying them. And as GIA Research director Dr. James Shigley once noted, "People who treat gemstones usually do not come and tell us their secrets." Meeting these increasingly complex gem identification challenges was crucial for the gem and jewelry industry.

As the need for practical research became ever more critical, the Institute pursued a range of scientific investigations that addressed the concerns of the industry. Working closely with the Gem Trade Laboratory, GIA Research routinely encountered a wider variety of specimens than any other research lab. When treatments and synthetics defied classical gem-testing tools such as the microscope and the refractometer, more sophisticated methods were applied. The department's use of high-tech analytical equipment became increasingly important to maintaining public confidence in the industry.

BASIC GEMOLOGICAL RESEARCH HAS ALWAYS BEEN a GIA hallmark. The Institute was a pioneer in the study of gem treatments, such as G. Robert Crowningshield's groundbreaking discovery in 1956 of a key criterion to identify irradiated diamonds. But for decades research was performed "on the job" in the laboratory, rather than being a more sophisticated, formal process.

That began to change in 1976, when Richard Liddicoat hired geologist Dr. D. Vincent Manson to create a research department for the Institute. Its purpose was to expand the knowledge of gems by using modern technology to gather and study the complex physical, chemical, and optical properties of all gem materials—natural, treated, synthetic, and imitation. That knowledge would become the bridge between scientific inquiry and concerns of the trade.

"We are dealing with a changing marketplace, so we have to understand what new material is being introduced, and quickly grasp its properties and limitations," said Manson. "We have to develop new methodologies, new equipment, and new approaches to determine any differences easily. In this sense, research provides an automatic alarm system."

The discovery of unusually vivid tourmaline from Paraíba, Brazil, was just one of the exciting developments toward the end of the 20th century.

Harold & Erica Van Pelt

AS GIA'S GEM TRADE LABORATORY grew in the late 20th century, so did its research department under Dr. James Shigley, who became director in 1986. The Institute's deeper commitment to gemological research came just in time, as profound changes were taking place in the gem market.

Nontraditional jewelry outlets—mass merchants such as catalog showrooms, discount retailers, TV home shopping programs, and later the Internet—stimulated consumer demand, especially for colored gems. Feeding this growing market for colored stones was a significant increase in mining at new sources, such as East Africa and Madagascar. While commercial quantities of rubies continued to flow from traditional sites in Burma (Myanmar) and Thailand, for example, they also were produced at new sources in Tanzania and Vietnam. One of the most exciting discoveries of the era was made in Brazil, where unusually vivid blue and green tourmalines first emerged from the state of Paraíba in the late 1980s.

The 1990s marked perhaps the most significant "pearl era" in modern history. During the decade, the production and variety of cultured pearls increased dramatically. These included black Tahitian, white South Sea, and "golden" pearls from Indonesia and the Philippines. Meanwhile, vast improvements were being made in the quality, quantity, and size of freshwater cultured pearls from China.

The diamond industry, which began the 1980s in a global funk due to recession and the collapse of the investment boom, started to recover mid-decade. It ended the '80s much stronger, spurred by record-breaking demand for diamonds in the Far East and prosperity in the U.S. Significantly, annual diamond production during this 10-year period soared from 40 million carats to more than 100 million. This was due not only to expanded production at existing mines, but also to new sources such as Australia and Botswana, both of which shot up from zero production in 1980 to 34 million carats and 15 million carats per year, respectively, in 1989. This greater production, especially of lower-quality goods as from Australia, spurred the emergence of major new cutting centers such as India, which boasted some 700,000 cutters in the 1990s. And near the end of the century, Canada promised to become a significant new producer of diamonds.

Courtesy of Argyle Diamonds Pty. Ltd.

Courtesy of BHP Billiton Diamonds Inc.

This surge in demand, availability, and sales of gem materials coincided with a parallel rise in gem enhancements, synthetics, and simulants. At the same time, Russia and other countries of the former Soviet Union were seeking commercial applications for high-tech weapons technology that had been developed during the Cold War. These included, for example, synthetic crystal growth for electronics, communications, and lasers. Indeed, increasingly sophisticated equipment and technical knowledge in the 1980s and '90s brought a proliferation of gemstone treatments and synthetic gem materials that was unprecedented in the history of gemology.

Worldwide diamond production exploded from the 1980s into the 21st century, thanks to new sources such as Australia's Argyle mine (left) and Canada's Ekati mine (right).

■ OUT OF THE LAB:
TREATMENTS, SYNTHETICS, AND SIMULANTS

The treating of colored stones to improve their appearance became routine by the end of the 20th century, to the point where almost every known gem material was subjected to some form of enhancement. Some treatments of the 1980s and '90s were really new variations of old techniques. Heating gemstones to change their color, for example, dates back to ancient Egypt. By the end of the 1990s, however, an estimated 95 percent of all rubies and sapphires entering the market had undergone some form of heat treatment. The widespread heat treatment of corundum was a serious issue for GIA researchers because of the difficulty in telling if a specific gem had been heated, and in interpreting the nature of the substances that were left

Photos by Maha Tannous/GIA

Harold & Erica Van Pelt

The photos on the left show an emerald before (top) and after clarity enhancement. The fracture filling of emeralds became a critical issue for the industry in the 1990s. The ruby and sapphire colors seen on the right, some mimicking the rare "padparadscha," were produced by the diffusion of beryllium into the stones.

behind by the heating process. In 1984, Robert E. Kane of the Gem Trade Laboratory published a classic study on heated rubies with large, glass-filled cavities—in one case, such a glass filling added more than a carat to the weight of the stone.

Another modernized treatment that confronted the Institute's researchers was the centuries-old practice of filling "surface-reaching" fractures in emeralds. Historically, this was done using various oils (especially cedarwood oil) and a natural balsam resin. During the 1980s and 1990s, many new types of emerald fillers were introduced, some of which were notoriously unstable. Bad press and lawsuits weakened the demand for emeralds, and this treatment became a critical trade issue. In 1991, Bob Kammerling and John Koivula led the first major study of the effect and durability of Opticon as an emerald filler. The two next-door neighbors literally took their work home with them, cleaning and treating emeralds in their own kitchens late into the night.

Six years later, GIA Research launched an extensive study of emerald fillers, led by Dr. Mary Johnson. Researchers tested 39 different emerald filler substances to find their identifying "signatures." And in late 1999, Shane McClure announced a new system that he and other staff members had developed and tested on more than 500 filled emeralds to determine the extent of clarity enhancement. Based on the results of that research, the Gem Trade Laboratory in 2000 began issuing a new emerald report that described the degree of clarity enhancement (*minor*, *moderate*, or *significant*) in natural emeralds.

One newcomer to the industry was diffusion treatment, which came to the fore in the late 1980s. Using a combination of chemicals and high temperature, color-causing agents were diffused into near-colorless corundum, primarily to create a layer of dark blue sapphire just below the stone's surface. A complex twist to the issue of diffusion came in late 2001, when the industry learned of a new treatment that could change the abundant light pink sapphire from Madagascar to the beautiful pinkish orange color of the rare "padparadscha" sapphire. Studies by GIA and other researchers found that the new color was produced by diffusing beryllium into the gemstone. The Institute joined several major gem-testing laboratories in investigating the process and publishing key ways to identify the treatment.

All the while, the Institute tackled several other treatment techniques, including irradiation, coating, dyeing, bleaching, and impregnation. For example, the first comprehensive study of bleached and polymer-impregnated jadeite, also known as "B jade," was led by GIA researcher Dr. Emmanuel Fritsch in 1992.

The orange to blue "flash effect" is characteristic of diamonds that have been clarity enhanced by the filling of fractures with a lead-based glass.

IN THE AREA OF DIAMONDS, two new treatment techniques generated great concern in the late 20th century. One was the filling of surface-reaching fractures, the first major enhancement of near-colorless diamonds. In 1983, Zvi Yehuda in Israel developed a process to fill surface-reaching fractures in polished diamonds with a lead-based glass. As with clarity-enhanced emeralds, the presence of this material made fractures less visible; it improved apparent clarity by one or two quality grades, with no apparent weight gain. In 1987, evidence of fracture-filled diamonds in the marketplace first emerged in reports from Japan. That same year, the Gem Trade Laboratory on both coasts received and examined diamonds with "treated surface-reaching breaks." Institute officials immediately realized that the successful fracture filling of commercial diamonds had introduced an entirely new variable to the grading of color and clarity in diamonds.

The situation posed a threat to the selling of near-colorless diamonds, the mainstay of the jewelry industry, and GIA moved quickly to help. It launched a comprehensive investigation of this new enhancement, led by Kammerling and Koivula, to document the process and alert jewelers to its characteristic signs. By 1989, they had discovered that the glass filler was not stable to all routine jewelry cleaning and repair techniques, and had charted a number of features that identified fracture-filled diamonds. Most important was the signature "flash effect" seen when a filled break was viewed down its length (typically yellowish orange with darkfield illumination, then "electric blue" when the stone was rotated).

GIA reported this groundbreaking research in comprehensive 1989 and (when new fillers appeared) 1994 *Gems & Gemology* articles and through a 1995 lecture-blitz of U.S. diamond clubs by researchers Kammerling, Tom Moses, and Shane McClure. The Institute also provided an identification chart and a how-to video for jewelers. By making practical detection techniques readily accessible throughout the trade, GIA helped deflate the threat.

THE OTHER MAJOR DIAMOND ENHANCEMENT came seemingly out of nowhere in 1999. For much of the 1990s, GIA had investigated rumors about the possibility of decolorizing gem-quality diamonds. Then, as the decade was drawing to a close, rock-hard proof emerged from a most unlikely source: Lazare Kaplan International (LKI), a longtime supporter of GIA and the laboratory.

On March 1, 1999, Pegasus Overseas Limited (POL), a new subsidiary of LKI based in Antwerp, announced it had an exclusive agreement with General Electric Co. (GE) to market "select" natural diamonds whose "color, brilliance, and brightness" had been enhanced by a new technological process developed by GE scientists. (POL sold only GE-processed diamonds, so its customers knew they were buying treated gems.) The process, said GE and POL, was "permanent and irreversible," and didn't rely on conventional treatments such as irradiation, laser drilling, surface coating, or fracture filling.

None of the major gemological research organizations (including GIA, HRD, the Gübelin Gem Lab, the SSEF Swiss Gemmological Institute, and De Beers) was informed about the treatment before the launch or consulted during its development, either of which would have helped GIA and other gem labs develop identification criteria, educate the industry, and protect the consumer.

Indeed, LKI had *already* sent hundreds of the processed stones through GIA (and some through other labs as well) for grading reports before the announcement.[1] The new treatment was not detected in any of them. The intent, said POL and LKI later, was to prove that the new enhancement was undetectable. They assumed that if these labs didn't spot it, then neither would other gemologists or consumers.

However, the effect of that revelation was to alarm the trade and anger the major laboratories. Bill Boyajian insisted that the industry be informed when new treatments were developed. "The specific process is GE's business,"

---

[1] The original POL announcement said that each stone would be accompanied by standard certification from a leading gem lab authenticating color, clarity, proportions, and shape.

Boyajian said in March 1999, "but the ability to identify the treatment and ultimately identify the diamonds treated by the process is the diamond industry's business. If diamonds are treated in any way, the trade has a right to know, and ultimately so does the consumer. The integrity of the industry is at stake!"

Boyajian and others in the industry called for immediate cooperation with the Institute's research department and demanded that GE and LKI provide information to help detect the process and minimize the potentially negative impact on the diamond marketplace.

On April 16, 1999, after several informal talks by phone, Boyajian hosted a summit in New York to resolve issues with GE and LKI officials. Discussions were "candid and open," he said afterward, and there was "a willingness by all parties to do the right thing." In the end, GE and LKI agreed that LKI would laser-inscribe "GE POL" on all GE-processed diamonds to identify them. GE and POL would resubmit all 858 processed diamonds they had previously sent to the GIA laboratory for new grading reports that would include a comment explaining the laser inscription. All three parties agreed to help the trade describe these diamonds "in an appropriate manner with respect to identification and complete disclosure." And GIA began a project, with the support of GE and POL, to identify characteristics of GE-processed diamonds and better understand diamond decolorization.

By September 1999, thanks to the Institute's researchers and graders, Boyajian could tell a diamond industry conference in Israel that GIA had identified some "very subtle and unusual characteristics" in these rare type IIa GE diamonds. Soon thereafter, GE confirmed that it was using a high pressure/high temperature (HPHT) process.

By the early 21st century, HPHT treatment was being used not only to decolorize diamonds in facilities other than GE's and in countries other than the U.S., but also to create various attractive hues in off-color diamonds. By that point, however, GIA and the other leading research laboratories had developed solid criteria to identify HPHT treatment. In 2002, just three years after the treatment was introduced, the Gem Trade Laboratory stated that it could identify the vast majority of HPHT-enhanced diamonds in the marketplace.

ALTHOUGH SYNTHETIC GEM MATERIALS were overshadowed by the issue of treatments, they still had a profound impact on the industry. Many of the new synthetics introduced during the 1980s and '90s originated outside the jewelry industry, developed by scientists involved in crystal growth for

Photos by Phillip Hitz/Gübelin Gem Lab

These two illustrations show brown type IIa diamonds before (top) and after high pressure/high temperature (HPHT) treatment by General Electric Co.

Maha Tannous/GIA

Numerous synthetics and simulants were introduced or gained a strong commercial presence during the 1980s and '90s. These include, from the top (left to right), synthetic versions of: Row 1—red spinel, blue sapphire, citrine, red beryl, emerald; row 2—blue spinel, black opal, white opal, amethyst; row 3—moissanite, ruby, alexandrite, diamond.

electronics, communications, and laser applications. As a result of rapid advances in computer technology and improved equipment design—accelerated by the end of the Cold War—commercial crystal growth processes were constantly being refined, to the point where they became nearly identical to nature's growth processes. New and highly evolved synthetic rubies, sapphires, and emeralds—and literally tons of synthetic amethyst—all demanded the attention of GIA and other gemological researchers.

Still, the most significant developments in gem synthesis involved diamonds. The Institute had been tracking synthetic diamonds since 1970, when General Electric announced its development of synthetic diamond crystals with gem potential. However, it wasn't until 1984 that Sumitomo Electric Industries of Japan sold the first gem-quality synthetic diamonds, grown by a high-pressure technique for industrial use. GIA Research soon devised methods of detecting these new synthetics.

Over the next few years, there were steady improvements in gem-quality synthetic diamonds. By the early 1990s, yellow synthetic diamonds suitable for jewelry use also were being grown in Russia, the Ukraine, and China. Although the overall quantities remained small, GIA analyzed the characteristics of all these products, and developed techniques to identify and distinguish them from natural diamonds.

In the fall of 1993, Institute researchers Shigley, Moses, and Kammerling summed up the results of almost a decade of investigation into synthetic diamonds. "Rough and faceted gem-quality synthetic diamonds can be identified, using standard gemological equipment and methods readily available to jewelers and diamantaires," their *Loupe* article concluded. "[The] advanced technologies available in many gem-testing laboratories (such as infrared spectroscopy) can provide further confirmation of synthetic origin."

In 1995, GIA researchers published a chart on the separation of natural from synthetic yellow, blue, and near-colorless diamonds. The following year, De Beers researchers introduced two new instruments, the DiamondSure and DiamondView, designed specifically for laboratory identification of synthetic diamonds. This was a welcome addition, since the Gem Trade Laboratory was testing every diamond submitted for grading to verify that it was natural, as well as untreated.

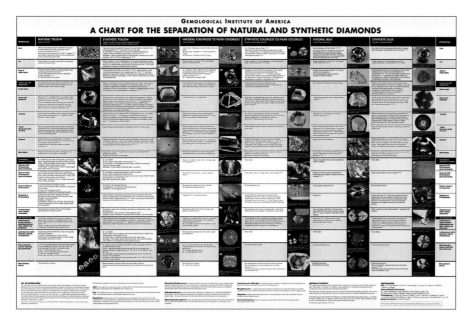

GIA Research's chart for the separation of natural and synthetic diamonds, published in 1995, was created by Jim Shigley, Emmanuel Fritsch, Ilene Reinitz, and Tom Moses.

In late 2002, Shigley and colleagues reported on the first commercial production of gem-quality synthetic diamonds specifically for jewelry, by Gemesis Corp. in Florida. They concluded that these diamonds, too, could be identified by the techniques developed since GIA researchers examined those first GE gem-quality synthetic diamonds.

The most commercially significant laboratory-created diamond look-alike to emerge in the late 1990s, however, was not a synthetic diamond but a simulant: synthetic moissanite. Unlike synthetic diamonds, which share the same chemical, physical, and optical properties as natural diamonds, synthetic moissanite is actually laboratory-created silicon carbide. This material first appeared in a near-colorless, gem-quality form in 1995, and by 1997 synthetic moissanite was being manufactured and marketed as a diamond substitute.

Consumers soon learned about synthetic moissanite from exposés aired on the Discovery Channel and "ABC World News Tonight." These reports caused alarm by portraying the new material, which fooled the thermal diamond probes many jewelers relied on, as a product that could be misidentified as diamond. GIA Research, collaborating with Dr. Kurt Nassau, completed its study on synthetic moissanite in late 1997. The results, published in the Winter 1997 issue of *Gems & Gemology*, revealed several practical methods for distinguishing synthetic moissanite from diamond.

Shane McClure/GIA

Synthetic moissanite was the most commercially important diamond simulant to emerge in the late 1990s. Its double refraction (and the resulting doubling of back facets seen above) made for a fairly straightforward separation from diamond.

Infrared spectroscopy, here being used by former GIA researcher Dr. Emmanuel Fritsch, was routinely applied to the identification of treated gems and the separation of synthetic from natural stones.

■DISCLOSE . . . OR BE DISCLOSED

There is nothing inherently wrong, of course, with creating new treatments or synthetics. They make more gems available to the public, at affordable prices. Some processes, such as the Zachery treatment of turquoise, even make the gem material more durable. Treated and synthetic gems have a legitimate place, as long as all the facts are clearly presented. Historically, problems have arisen for the industry when the details of treatments and synthetic materials weren't fully disclosed to customers, causing the public's confidence to slip.

Because of the high volume of gemstones submitted for reports, the Gem Trade Laboratory has often been on the front line of discovering new synthetics or treatments. "We're always playing catch-up, because we often learn about a new treatment when a treated stone shows up at GIA for testing," noted Shigley in 1993.

Over the years, the Institute has worked to develop closer ties with gem manufacturers, scientists, and other industries involved in synthetic gems and treatments—in the U.S. and abroad—to see new processes as soon as they were developed and to help establish identification criteria. Nevertheless, GIA Research—like a gemological detective service—has typically had to work backwards, starting with a finished product, then deducing its distinctive characteristics, mode of creation, and origin.

Meanwhile, the gem researcher's investigative tools were also changing significantly. Until the late 1970s, lab and research gemologists relied primarily on classical methods and equipment, such as the binocular microscope, the spectroscope, the refractometer, and ultraviolet lamps, to identify gems and detect treatments. But rapid technological advances in gem synthesis and enhancements required GIA (and other advanced gem labs) to use ever more sophisticated equipment in their detective work. In the 1970s, GIA researchers first used the electron microprobe to determine the chemical composition of gem materials, and they acquired a scanning electron microscope (SEM) to observe structural features at extremely high magnification.

Often, the "new" technology was adapted from other fields. "During the 1980s, we learned to borrow and borrow well," noted a 1990 *Gems & Gemology* editorial. X-ray diffraction analysis, a common tool in mineralogy, had long been used to accurately identify gem materials based on their crystal structure. And advanced spectroscopic methods—ultraviolet-visible, infrared, X-ray fluorescence, and Raman—had already achieved widespread use in chemistry.

Although the UV-visible spectrophotometer became a real workhorse for identifying origin of color in diamonds and other colored stones, infrared spectroscopy brought many breakthroughs in gem identification during the 1980s. This tool could separate a number of natural from synthetic materials when there were no inclusions—as in the case of amethyst—and it could detect polymers injected into materials such as opals or jadeite. Using X-ray fluorescence, researchers investigated the separation of natural from synthetic rubies as well as freshwater from saltwater pearls. Laser Raman microspectroscopy became one of the most important instruments in gemological research during the 1990s. It saw widespread use in identifying inclusions and fillers, even those beneath a gemstone's surface.

GIA Research used all of these sophisticated techniques to identify gemstones and document new materials for its ever-expanding database.

■GLITTERING MYSTERIES: FANCY-COLOR DIAMONDS

Another area that held researchers' attention during this time was fancy-color diamonds—natural, treated, and synthetic.

For most of recorded history, colored diamonds were mentioned only rarely, but this began to change in the latter part of the 20th century. Thanks to new sources and improved cutting technology, natural-color diamonds entered the marketplace in greater numbers. In particular, Australia's Argyle mine began producing intense pinks and "champagne" diamonds in the mid-1980s. At the same time, manufacturers developed cutting styles that maximized the color in many diamonds. As colored diamonds became more available, so did stories about them in the consumer media and trade press, pushing demand and value higher.

One famous demonstration of the new premium being placed on natural-color diamonds was the Hancock Red. This 0.95-carat round brilliant diamond, graded "Fancy purplish red" by GIA, had been bought by a Montana collector in 1956 for $13,500. History was made on April 28, 1987, when Christie's sold the same gem at auction for an astounding $880,000. At over $926,000 per carat, it was more than seven times the previous record per-carat price paid at auction for a gemstone.

With demand for fancy-color diamonds growing, and the technology to produce color in diamonds (primarily through irradiation and annealing) readily available, more color-enhanced diamonds entered the market. That made distinguishing between natural- and treated-color diamonds a critical issue to the trade in general and to the GIA laboratory in particular. After all, the value of a fancy-color diamond depends on the rarity of its naturally occurring color, even more than its cut or clarity. Indeed, the famous Hancock Red diamond had eye-visible inclusions.

Tino Hammid/GIA

Demand for natural-color diamonds grew sharply in the latter part of the 20th century. The Hancock Red, a 0.95-carat Fancy purplish red diamond, was auctioned for a record per-carat price of $926,000 in 1987.

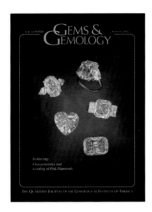

Fancy Vivid Pink

Fancy Deep Pink

Fancy Red

The Institute's research into colored diamonds yielded a definitive study on pink diamonds and their color grading in 2002. *Gems & Gemology* was GIA Research's primary vehicle for communicating its findings to the industry.

By the 1990s, thousands of colored diamonds came to the laboratory for origin-of-color reports each year. The importance of those color reports to a diamond's value was so great that almost every significant natural-color diamond sold from the late '80s into the 21st century was accompanied by a GIA Gem Trade Laboratory report.

WHEN THE GEM TRADE LABORATORY BEGAN ISSUING origin-of-color reports in 1956, it launched what GIA officials later called "a process of systematic standardization" in describing faceted colored diamonds. Unlike GIA's D-to-Z grading system for colorless to light yellow diamonds, which is based on the *absence* of color, the grading system for colored diamonds is based on the *presence* of color. Using a controlled viewing and lighting environment and an elaborate set of color comparators, a trained grader could consistently locate the characteristic color of a diamond and assign it a grade. The hue chosen was modified by a "Fancy-grade" term (such as *Fancy Light, Fancy,* or *Fancy Intense*), which described ranges of the combined effect of tone and saturation.

As more colored diamonds entered the market in the late 1980s and early '90s—expanding the ranges of hue, tone, and saturation—GIA began exploring refinements to its grading system. To better articulate depths of color in diamonds, in 1995 the laboratory added two additional terms—*Fancy Deep* and *Fancy Vivid*—and began to apply the full range of Fancy-grade terms to all hues. The expanded terminology was provided concisely and clearly in a revised grading report introduced that year.

GIA's rigorous research into colored diamonds continued, under the leadership of laboratory projects officer John King. In 1998, it concluded a several-year study of blue diamonds, and in 2002 it produced a comprehensive *G&G* article on grading pink diamonds. They were the most definitive studies ever published on the grading of these enigmatic diamonds.

■ RESEARCH APPLIED

By the 1990s, the GIA research department—the analytical facility was renamed the G. Robert Crowningshield Gemological Research Laboratory in 1991—was recognized as one of the finest gemological research facilities in the world. The rapid advances in computer technology enabled gemologists to quickly and methodically analyze data that otherwise might have taken years to evaluate. By the late 1990s, Gem Trade Laboratory instruments were storing vast amounts of electronic information, expanding a database that already exceeded 100,000 individual gems. This database included test results, descriptive information, numerical measurements, weights, proportions, chemical analyses, visible spectra, and images (such as photomicrographs).

And when GIA Research didn't have, or couldn't afford, the needed equipment for a special project, it turned to cooperative or pay-per-use projects with universities, major high-tech companies, and gemological organizations in other countries to gain access to their state-of-the art technology. Early in the 21st century, at least a third of the major research projects had some outside connection. One of its most significant affiliations was with Dr. George Rossman (a member of the GIA Board of Governors since 1995) of the California Institute of Technology. So profound were his academic contributions that, in 1998, the International Mineralogical Association approved the naming of a species of tourmaline *rossmanite* in his honor.

One of GIA's most significant affiliations was with Dr. George Rossman of the California Institute of Technology.

WHAT WAS THE DIFFERENCE between GIA's research, grading, and gem identification activities? Where did one end and the other begin?

When Vince Manson set up GIA Research in the mid-1970s, the separation between grading and identifying gems in the labs and the pure scientific study of gem materials and color by his department was obvious. Manson's group focused on basic or fundamental research on gems, while the Gem Trade Laboratory worked almost exclusively on applied research solutions. But those lines blurred in the 1980s, as the laboratory relied increasingly on the research department's analytical instruments to deal with the growing number of treated and synthetic gems. As research spent more and more time dealing with the industry's practical problems, particularly gem identification, it overlapped so much with the Gem Trade Laboratory that outsiders could barely distinguish the two.

And that was how Institute officials liked it. Research at GIA, said Boyajian, was "driven by the needs of the industry and the public as we see them in the Gem Trade Lab." By the end of the decade, there was "no hard barrier between research and the rest of the Gem Trade Laboratory," stated Tom Yonelunas. "Everything that comes in here needs a decision. Important subjects need to be thoroughly researched for the trade and for consumer protection."

Staff researchers worked closely with lab gemologists on data collection and technical projects, such as the ongoing emerald filler studies and identification of pearl treatments and HPHT-annealed diamonds. Meanwhile, the Gem Trade Laboratory on both coasts was a rich resource of gem materials. "A steady river of gemstones flows by us each day," said Shigley. Using another metaphor, he added, "What comes through the lab is a window to the world for GIA Research."

Among the Institute's top researchers in Carlsbad at the turn of the century were (from left) John Koivula, Dr. Mary Johnson, and Shane McClure.

INTO THE 21ST CENTURY, GIA RESEARCH HAD A STAFF OF NEARLY 40, most of them on the West and East Coasts, with a handful in Antwerp. That was twice the size it had been a decade earlier, and included people "shared" with the laboratory.

Yet demands on time and resources also continued to grow. Gemological research was still a relatively new discipline, lacking the accumulated body of knowledge so many other scientific fields had. And, as noted earlier, many manufacturers provided little or no help in identifying the treated or synthetic gem materials they introduced. So GIA researchers often had to start from scratch, gathering and organizing data before they could begin to understand or explain it.

"First, we acquire samples, which could involve thousands of colored diamonds or a few synthetic gem materials. Then we decide what gem testing equipment to use," said Shigley. "We also contact experts in academia for their insights. Last, we gather the data in a nondestructive way and try to interpret what it means as a basis for developing new identification criteria."

Depending on a subject's importance and the availability of resources, a project may take weeks, months, or even years. "At the end of all this," Shigley added, "we try to come up with a practical solution, which we present to the trade. Sometimes a practical solution is not possible, in which case we attempt to develop methods for gem testing that can be used within the laboratory."

Research without application and communication is, of course, fruitless. So a key mission of GIA Research was to relay its findings to the industry.

The primary means was through detailed, peer-reviewed articles in *Gems & Gemology*, the Institute's scholarly quarterly journal. It was in *G&G* that the first comprehensive articles appeared, for example, on gem-quality synthetic diamonds, fracture-filled diamonds, clarity-enhanced emeralds, color grading colored diamonds, the influence of blue fluorescence on the appearance of "colorless" diamonds, and the effect of cut on polished-diamond appearance. Research staff also produced articles for other journals and presented regular updates in *The Loupe*, the Institute's quarterly news publication, and *GIA Insider*, a bi-weekly electronic newsletter.

One of the most prolific authors was John Koivula, a geologist and chemist who joined the Institute in 1976. Koivula revolutionized the use of the gemological microscope for identification and photomicrography, working with famed Swiss inclusion expert Dr. Edward Gübelin. By 2003, Koivula had published more than 700 articles and two books.

Besides their contributions to the gemological literature, GIA researchers exerted far-reaching influence in other ways. They worked with the Institute's

Education department to incorporate their findings into the courses, and they made presentations at industry and professional conferences. Research staff also contributed to the development of precise gem-testing equipment that could be marketed through GIA's instrument division, helping to enhance the work of jewelers and gemologists.

The toughest obstacle researchers faced in giving their findings and advice to the trade was often the trade itself. Vince Manson observed in 1984 that many in the industry had "opposing objectives." They wanted GIA's research to help them stay competitive, but they also wanted "simple black-and-white, true-or-false answers to our problems. They didn't want to know that everything isn't always clearly positive or negative. With synthetics and treated stones, we don't always have clear-cut cases. Sometimes we can't positively identify the [natural or synthetic] origin of a gem or whether or not it has been enhanced."

Almost two decades later, Jim Shigley echoed similar comments. Indeed, Shigley would occasionally joke with Bob Crowningshield or Dick Liddicoat that they had "made research in their day look easy, coming out with practical, simple solutions—and now people expect simple, quick, yes-or-no answers to much more complex gemological problems!"

Along with Tom Moses (far right), John King and Dr. Ilene Reinitz were standout researchers from the New York staff.

THE CHALLENGES GIA RESEARCH FACED AS IT ENTERED THE 21ST CENTURY were far more difficult than those of any previous era. "We are confronting well-funded research in the manufacture of synthetics and treated gem materials, and there are more people treating or synthesizing gems than there are researchers and laboratory gemologists who identify them," said Shigley.

"Today, our visibility is high and people often look to us for answers," continued Shigley. And because of the dedication of GIA's researchers and the excellence of their work, "they tend to believe and rely on the answers we provide. We try to be all things to all people, because people expect us to be."

Ultimately, GIA Research became the cornerstone that would support the Institute's education, laboratory, and instruments divisions. GIA had emerged from the days when Robert M. Shipley and his son performed testing with rudimentary (and often borrowed) equipment to become one of the most important gemological research centers in the world—and a mainstay of public confidence in gems and jewelry.

Instructor Martin Harmon trains a resident gemology student at the Carlsbad campus in 2002. While the G.G. program remained GIA's educational cornerstone into the 21st century, the Institute expanded beyond gemology to achieve excellence in teaching other sought-after skills such as jewelry manufacturing, design, retail management, and more.

LEARNING FROM THE FOREMOST AUTHORITY

1986–2003

The end of the 20th century was a time of ups and downs for GIA as an educational institution. On the one hand, it was a time of great progress and growth. On the other hand, it was yet another period of loss. But while GIA would mourn the passing of key staff members, it would build on the foundation they had helped lay.

Already the premier training ground of the U.S. gem and jewelry industry, the Institute went truly international, successfully exporting its educational offerings throughout Asia and Europe. By 2003, GIA boasted 13 branches in nine countries on three continents.

Moreover, the Institute responded to the industry's training needs with innovative course materials and new diploma programs. It also created some revolutionary new methods of course delivery that made GIA's education accessible to anyone, anywhere, anytime.

■ A SEASON OF CHANGE AND LOSS

The decade of the 1990s was a turbulent period for GIA's education division. That flux wasn't reflected in the quality of its educational material, nor was it evident to GIA's thousands of students in the U.S. and around the world. But internally, GIA Education went through a series of restructurings to improve its operations, while also experiencing the loss of some of its most important leaders and pioneers. The changes began in 1990, with a series of staff promotions. Most importantly, Dennis Foltz, who only a few years earlier had been manager of home study education, was named vice president of education and operations.

In 1993, Foltz persuaded Janice Mack-Talcott, one of GIA's most popular instructors in the 1970s, to return to the Institute as director of education. Foltz especially liked her strong retail jewelry background. But there was another reason for hiring Mack-Talcott. Foltz had learned he was ill with cancer. He moved quickly to transfer many of his responsibilities to her, and together they implemented a new management structure.

In April 1995, Bill Boyajian, mindful of Foltz's deteriorating health, recruited Brook Ellis to join GIA's executive management team as vice president of operations. In this role, he would be responsible for coordinating many of the Institute's divisions, especially its multinational educational operations. Ellis,

Brook Ellis joined the Institute's executive management team in 1995 and was named vice president of education a year later.

formerly a vice president of fine jewelry for Henry Birks and Sons, one of Canada's leading jewelers[1], had been a member of GIA's board of governors for 12 years. Like his father, Ellis was a graduate of GIA's home study program. He brought with him a wealth of expertise in the gem and jewelry industry and—in keeping with an international organization—a global perspective.

Ellis's duties expanded further at the end of the year when Mack-Talcott, who was finding the weekly commute between her home in Washington State and GIA's headquarters more difficult than anticipated, resigned as director of education. While not officially named to replace her, Ellis eased into many of her duties, assisting an increasingly weakened Foltz.

Changes were also occurring in course development. Under the leadership of John Hummel, now its director, course development had grown from two people in 1983 into an award-winning operation with state-of-the-art equipment, a $1 million annual budget, and a staff of more than 20 in 1997.[2] Although Hummel retired that same year, he continued as a consultant to GIA.

Together, Dennis Foltz and John Hummel had changed the content and direction of GIA's training in the 1980s and '90s. Foltz had been the architect, the guiding hand, the visionary. Hummel was the learned and innovative craftsman who applied their ideas to GIA's training with what Liddicoat called "motivation, inspiration, and sometimes pure entertainment."

These men's ideas and words had touched the lives of tens of thousands of students around the world. Then, suddenly and too soon, both were gone. Foltz died of cancer in 1996 at the age of 60, in Los Angeles. Hummel died in early 1998 at the age of 62, after suffering two heart attacks while touring South African diamond mines on special assignment for GIA. He passed away in a Johannesburg hospital, with his son at his side.

TWO IMPORTANT PEOPLE LINKED with GIA's early history also passed away during this time of transition. One was Dorothy Smith, the Shipleys' first full-time employee, whose encouraging notes in the 1930s meant so much to GIA's early correspondence students. During the Institute's formative years, she had been one of the Shipleys' most loyal friends and supporters. Smith died in July 1999 at the age of 90, in Bishop, California.

---

[1] Henry Birks was also one of the first jewelers in North America to support GIA founder Robert Shipley in the early 1930s.

[2] Hummel also found time to edit the 1994 edition of the *GIA Diamond Dictionary*, which became the first GIA publication to be released as a CD-ROM.

Another loss was pioneering gemologist Eunice Miles, who died in March 1997 at the age of 80, following a stroke. Miles was the first female gemologist to join GIA's Gem Trade Laboratory in New York City. In her four-and-a-half decades with GIA, Miles made important discoveries in diamond identification. In semi-retirement, she was director of GIA's job referral service in New York, and upon retirement was named the Institute's historian.

"Eunice's vast network of friends and colleagues who she helped to find work and contacts [in the trade] was staggering," wrote Peter Theriault of the Northeast Lab in Camden, Maine, in 1997. She never asked anything in return, continued Theriault, except that those she helped "carry the mantle to help others, just as she had done in her long career."

ANOTHER LOSS CAME MUCH TOO SOON. Robert Kammerling, 48, one of the most talented and versatile staff members in GIA's history, died suddenly in January 1996. Kammerling was recruited by Boyajian shortly after he graduated in 1981 to teach colored stones and gem identification. He became one of the Institute's most popular instructors and wrote course materials for the gemology program. During his tenure, he rose through management to become, in 1995, vice president of research and development in the GIA Gem Trade Laboratory.

Kammerling co-authored (with Harvard's Dr. Cornelius Hurlbut) the second edition of *Gemology*, contributed to the *GIA Diamond Dictionary*, and wrote some 400 articles and columns on gemology for trade journals worldwide. One of his many passions was *Gems & Gemology*, which he served as associate editor and co-editor of the Gem News and Gem Trade Lab Notes sections. Robert Kammerling, wrote Boyajian, would "long be remembered as one of the heroes of modern gemology."

BUT OUT OF THE LATE 1990s CAME A REBIRTH for GIA Education. In 1996, Brook Ellis was named vice president of education. One of Ellis's first efforts was rebuilding the division's management structure. Susan Johnson, who had turned the GIA Alumni Association over to Patrick Ball when she became dean of students in 1997, was appointed director of education administration. In her new job, Johnson oversaw admissions, student services, financial aid, accreditation, career services, and education records. Bill Herberts was named manager of resident education, eventually becoming director of education operations in 2002, where he oversaw GIA Education's delivery of resident, extension, and home study courses. In course development, Duncan Pay took over for Wendy

ROBERT KAMMERLING, WROTE BOYAJIAN, WOULD "LONG BE REMEMBERED AS ONE OF THE HEROES OF MODERN GEMOLOGY."

Into the 21st century, directors Duncan Pay, Susan Johnson, and Bill Herberts (from left) were key leaders in GIA Education.

Melissa Jacobs/GIA

Graham, who had succeeded John Hummel in 1997. Pay made enormous strides early in the new century by completely revamping, once again, the all-important G.G. program. Carrying the torch from Foltz and Hummel, Ellis and Pay became the principal architects of the new generation of GIA's education programs.

One of the most telling appointments, however, was the promotion of 20-year veteran Seung-Hae Moon to director of global education. Moon assumed responsibility for GIA's branch education offices in the U.S. and its network of campuses and affiliated schools around the world. With this promotion, the Institute recognized that it had evolved into a truly global organization.

■THE INTERNATIONALIZATION OF GIA

Tokyo. Osaka. Vicenza. Seoul. Taipei. Bangkok. Hong Kong. Moscow. London. Beijing.

It reads like an exotic travel itinerary, but it's actually a list of the hubs of the growing international network of schools and affiliates of the Gemological Institute of America. But it wasn't always so.

As recently as the late 1980s—despite an affiliate school in Japan, extension classes from Toronto to Australia, and many thousands of home study students around the world—the Institute itself was largely a domestic operation, run by Americans with just one campus, in California, and one branch, in New York. Changing that was one of Boyajian's goals when he became president, and it was put in writing as one of the priorities of the 1988 Master Plan.

In a way, GIA's international outreach had really begun in the early 1930s, with Robert Shipley's first forays into Canada. Leading Canadian jewelers had played important roles in the Institute's development from the beginning as GIA officials, students, and supporters. But the Master Plan envisioned something more. Boyajian recognized that although GIA had reached out internationally for decades, it was still "very insular and American," even as the gem and jewelry industry had become less regional. So, like the industry and public it served, GIA's outlook had to become global.

This global commitment became visible in several ways. One was the second International Gemological Symposium in 1991, when the Institute invited the international gem and jewelry community to Los Angeles to celebrate the Institute's 60th anniversary. There was the worldwide growth of the GIA Alumni Association, with dozens of alumni chapters around the globe and thousands of members. GIA also increased its participation in international trade shows, including those in Basel (Switzerland), Hong Kong, Vicenza, and Taipei, and held GemFests internationally on a regular basis, starting in 1988.

But the Institute's most important outreach was the network of schools it planted throughout the world. GIA had established its first licensed school overseas in Japan during the early 1970s, and in the late 1980s GIA officials began looking at new opportunities for growth. They considered Singapore, Thailand, Hong Kong, and China, but the site they chose was South Korea. Its architects were a visionary businessman named Dong Keuk Kim and a dynamo named Seung-Hae Moon, then manager of GIA Education in New York.

Gregory Zabilski

Gem cutting and manufacturing businessman Dong Keuk Kim (left) teamed up with the Institute's Seung-Hae Moon (right) to bring GIA training to South Korea in 1989.

AS A SERIOUS ACADEMIC DISCIPLINE, gemology in South Korea was still in its infancy in the early 1980s. Many Korean jewelry businesses were small, family-run operations that relied solely on the experience of their proprietors. There were a variety of idiosyncratic systems for grading diamonds, and lab reports were unfamiliar to consumers. At the time, there were fewer than 40 G.G.'s in the entire country. There was, to put it mildly, widespread uncertainty when it came to sound gemological knowledge.

Several factors changed that, however. One was the government's loosening of travel restrictions early in the decade. Affluent South Koreans were soon exposed to a variety of luxury items abroad, spurring a sharp rise in demand for diamond jewelry back home. Diamond ownership became an important status symbol, and by the mid-1990s the average diamond in an engagement ring in South Korea was 0.57 carat, the largest of any country. The most important event, however, was the 1988 Seoul Olympics, which brought a huge influx of tourists into South Korea. With the world's attention focused on Seoul, the government had little choice but to open the country's markets and relax restrictions on imported luxury goods, notably a 60 percent tax on jewelry and prohibitions on importing diamonds. The South Korean market blossomed as consumers flocked to jewelry stores and more companies imported diamonds and finished goods.

An extension class in South Korea during the 1990s. GIA Korea helped transform the country's gem and jewelry industry.

All this spurred rising interest in gemological education. Many South Korean jewelry trade leaders wanted uniform gemological standards and professional education for the rapidly evolving industry. One of them was Dong Keuk Kim, the owner of the Far East Gem & Jewelry Company. His gem-cutting firm was in Iri City, the cutting and manufacturing center of South Korea's export market. In the 1980s, Kim had hired some South Korean Graduate Gemologists to provide customer support. Impressed with their professionalism and knowledge, he considered bringing GIA training to his own country. Some of his American customers suggested he contact a Korean-American GIA employee in New York named Seung-Hae Moon.

In February 1989, the two met at the Tucson gem shows. Kim told Moon that he wanted to sponsor a GIA school in Seoul. She was interested, but she also knew that the Institute had experienced a very unsatisfactory sponsorship relationship in South Korea in the mid-1980s. This had left students without any instruction, GIA embarrassed, and South Koreans in general suspicious of the American school's reliability.

Still, Kim thought history could be overcome, and together they drafted a proposal. The Institute responded by sending Moon and Vince Manson, then director of strategic planning, on a week-long trip to South Korea to assess the market and GIA's potential there. The two visited South Korean jewelry businesses and met with government, trade, and commerce officials. By the time they returned, Manson was convinced the Institute had a future in Korea. Kim's qualifications, integrity, and broad knowledge of the many different segments in Korea's rapidly changing jewelry industry made it clear that GIA could move ahead quickly. But before Boyajian would agree to the creation of a school in South Korea, he insisted on one thing: that Seung-Hae Moon move there to get it started.

In August 1989, GIA and Kim signed a contract establishing the Gemological Institute of Korea, renamed GIA Korea one year later. As an affiliate, it would conduct official GIA-approved courses. Kim would share tuition proceeds with the Institute and, under a separate licensing agreement, sell GEM Instruments through his company. GIA would provide educational materials and instructors. Moon became the school's general manager, while continuing to oversee the New York office until 1991, when the Seoul branch had grown so large as to require most of her attention.

During the last quarter of 1989, Moon set off on a media tour of South Korea, promoting GIA and its gemological training. The effort was remarkable, not only for promoting universal standards and education in a country of independent family jewelers, but also because its messenger was a woman. "I was both a cultural oddity and a role model," noted Moon much later. She was respected for her education and career accomplishments, and for the fact that she could raise a child and still hold an important job. "In the Korean mind, all those things reflected well on GIA," she said.

At the same time, Kim was busy putting together the capital investment for GIA Korea. He underwrote the lease of the campus in Seoul and the cost of equipment and staff salaries, all the while recruiting students and promoting the Institute.

In 1990, GIA Korea offered its first extension classes and a seven-week resident diamonds program, with all the materials printed in Korean. The following year, a four-month resident colored stones program was introduced, and a Korean translation of the home study G.G. program debuted. By 2003, GIA Korea had graduated over 1,200 G.G.'s and 500 design students.

In just over a decade, GIA Korea significantly changed the South Korean jewelry market and industry. Firms that years before knew neither the Institute nor its lab reports now regularly advertised that they had Graduate Gemologists on staff and used GIA's diamond grading system. South Korean consumers regularly looked for G.G. credentials when they shopped for jewelry. Many GIA Korea graduates opened their own companies and developed successful businesses.

AS GIA KOREA WAS JUST GETTING STARTED in the early 1990s, GIA's Japanese affiliate had been in existence for two decades. AGT had offices, classrooms, and labs in Tokyo and Osaka, with a full-time staff of 35 Graduate Gemologists. It had graduated 1,500 G.G.'s, GIA's largest alumni base outside the U.S. The influence of the Institute's training and its grading system was spreading throughout the Japanese industry.

In July 1993, Yoshiko Doi's efforts to introduce GIA training and standards into Japan came full circle. At Boyajian's urging, AGT was renamed GIA Japan. Doi was delighted with the decision, as AGT had always regarded itself as part of the GIA family. The change also ignited a project Doi had been planning for a while: Japan's own resident gemology program.

As in the U.S. years earlier, the success of the home study program in Japan had spurred demand for a full-time resident program for young

AGT, the Institute's Japanese affiliate founded in 1971, became GIA Japan in 1993. The Tokyo campus is located in the Ueno jewelry district.

Anna Chang, a 1978
GIA Santa Monica
graduate, later returned
to her native land and
established GIA Taiwan.

adults seeking a career in the jewelry business. In November 1993, GIA Japan ran a successful test program, and in May 1994 it formally launched a six-month resident program.

By 2003, GIA Japan was the leader among the Institute's growing network of overseas branch institutes. Having produced more than 3,000 Graduate Gemologists, its pioneering educational work had created tremendous confidence both within the Japanese trade and among consumers.

WITH THE SUCCESS OF ITS EFFORTS in Japan and Korea, GIA quickly moved in the early 1990s to establish schools in the burgeoning markets of Taiwan and Hong Kong. The Taiwan initiative was led by one of the island's very first G.G.'s, Anna Chang.

A 1978 graduate of the resident program in Santa Monica, Chang worked as a grader in GIA's Los Angeles laboratory for three years before returning to her native land to set up the China Gemmological Laboratory with three fellow G.G.'s. She eventually became a well-known gemology authority in Taiwan, helping establish the GIA Alumni Association chapter there, conducting Diamond Promotion Service (DPS) seminars, and presenting annual one-week GIA classes in Taipei between 1988 and 1991. By the early 1990s, Chang believed the time was right for GIA to go into Taiwan. Dennis Foltz listened to her plan and agreed, naming her director of Chinese gemology and assigning her two assistants to translate GIA's home study courses into Chinese. In 1992, GIA Taiwan was established in Taipei.

In addition to promoting the popular new Chinese home study courses, GIA Taiwan—under the administrative management of Linda Ku—added several classes over the next few years. All were taught in the Mandarin dialect. In 1994, GIA Taiwan graduated its first 20 G.G.'s. It also reached out to the public in the late 1990s, offering free monthly seminars for consumers on basic jewelry knowledge, including how to read a GIA laboratory report.

Meanwhile, the Institute was also exploring its options in Hong Kong, led by then–Asian operations director Randy Park. GIA already was familiar with the territory, having sent one-week extension classes there on a regular basis since the 1970s. It had held classes in connection with the major Hong Kong fair every September, and its alumni chapter there had been active since 1984. By the early 1990s, Hong Kong was the center of Asia's jewelry and diamond industry both geographically and economically. Looking ahead to the end of British rule in 1997, GIA officials saw the strategic importance of Hong Kong in reaching the huge economy of mainland China, home to one-fifth of the world's population.

By 1994, GIA was satisfied that it could make a successful, financially sustainable entry into Hong Kong. It had an enthusiastic sponsor in Lorenzo Yih, founder and chairman of Lorenzo Jewelry and associate chairman of the Hong Kong Jewelry Manufacturers Association. A new, well-equipped school occupied a floor of its own in Yih's plant in Hunghum, Hong Kong's jewelry manufacturing district. Within two years, GIA Hong Kong had 200 students, including several from mainland China. It had grown enough by 1998 to move into larger quarters at the tip of Kowloon Peninsula, not far from Hong Kong's famous retail section on Nathan Road. That same year, GIA Hong Kong also launched two accelerated graduate diamond programs, one in English and one in Cantonese. Students came to class three times a week and completed all assignments and exams within 10 weeks, which allowed more time in class for grading diamonds than was possible with the standard distance education programs. In 2002, the Institute assumed the sponsorship of the Hong Kong education branch, seeing it as a strategic entry point for China.

Indeed, the Institute had already begun exploring ways to enter the market in mainland China. The Chinese diamond market had grown over the last few years, and with it emerged the need for solid gemological education, especially

The creation of GIA campuses in Taiwan (left) in 1992 and Hong Kong (right) two years later set the stage for the Institute's entrance into mainland China.

GIA Thailand director Christopher Keenan (center) joins the first Graduate Gemologists from the school.

in diamond grading. In May 1999, GIA launched its graduate diamond diploma program in association with the National Gemstone Testing Center (NGTC) in Beijing. It included two distance education courses, diamonds and diamond grading, and a diamond grading extension class (taught by Phil York, with Chinese translations provided by Vivian Wang of GIA Taiwan). In April 2001, GIA reached an exclusive agreement with the NGTC to bring the Institute's educational offerings to Beijing and other Chinese cities.

ANOTHER VISIONARY OF THE EARLY 1990S was Chirakitti Tang, the genial president of Oriental Lapidary Group in Bangkok and a founder of the Thai Diamond Manufacturers Association. Tang was a pivotal player in the establishment of GIA Thailand. He acquired the necessary equipment, provided the space, and contracted with GIA to fill the classes. According to Bill Boyajian, "We would not have initiated a program in Bangkok as quickly without a supporter like Tang to maintain the infrastructure that it takes to put on even one class of GIA quality." But a successful operation also meant forging bonds with all the leaders in a given area, and the Institute made a point of establishing good relationships with key members of Bangkok's gem and jewelry trade.

GIA Thailand opened its doors in mid-1993 with two seasoned instructors: Christopher Keenan, a long-time veteran of New York's education program; and Carl Chilstrom, one of the Institute's most versatile and experienced staffers. Keenan oversaw daily operations from its opening and ultimately would lead GIA Thailand into the new century. In January 1994, GIA Thailand graduated its first class of G.G.'s.

The school grew quickly as it served a variety of students nearly as diverse as that in the Santa Monica headquarters. They included Thais in the local gem and jewelry trade, expatriates living in Thailand, international students from neighboring Asian countries, and even students from as far away as Europe, North America, and Africa. In March 1997, GIA Thailand moved to larger quarters in Bangrak, the gem center of Bangkok, and came under the sponsorship of the Institute itself. The facility continued to expand, accommodating nine classrooms and hundreds of students by 2003.

As with all of the Institute's schools, GIA Thailand became an important conduit to the region's tradespeople for current gemological knowledge and information. According to Keenan, with so many new treatments, synthetics, and other gem products entering the global market, those in the trade "have to keep on top of these vital new developments."

As the 21st century began, GIA continued expanding its presence in Asia, offering classes in the Philippines, Singapore, and Shanghai, among other locations worldwide. Establishing a presence in India was also a strong possibility. Boyajian felt that India could become one of the Institute's fastest-growing markets due to its large population, emerging middle-class, and enormous diamond industry.

WHILE ASIAN SCHOOLS AND MARKETS demanded much of GIA's attention in the 1990s, the Institute's officials hadn't forgotten Europe. In fact, the Institute had a toehold there as early as 1983, when it licensed Raffaele Zancanella and the Institute Gemmologico Mediterraneo (IGM) in Cavalese, Italy, to translate GIA courses, assist local students, and teach extension classes.

In 1991, the Institute took the next step in its commitment to Italy and began looking for a campus site in Vicenza. The city, well known for its gold jewelry manufacturing operations and well situated in the heart of Italy's "Golden Triangle," was selected both because of its location and because of the strong support GIA had received from the Vicenza Trade Fair Board and from local manufacturer Pierluigi Dalla Rovere.

In early 1992, GIA Italy opened under the leadership of director Federico "Fred" Stocco. Stocco, born in Venice, was raised from the age of four in Brooklyn, New York. Assisting him as head of administration was his wife Kathy, a Michigan native. (In Fred Stocco's words, "Dennis Foltz hired me, but Bill Boyajian was the smart one—he hired Kathy.") The Stoccos opened the school with the G.G. program, adding extension classes and seminars later, including bilingual offerings. GIA Italy rapidly became the hub of the Institute's activities in Europe. De Beers sponsored special seminars called "A Day with Diamonds," which Stocco taught in Italy, Switzerland, Russia, and as far away as Dubai and Saudi Arabia. The Stoccos oversaw and hosted GIA-sponsored GemFests, receptions, and alumni reunions at the important VicenzaOro trade fairs. They also exhibited for GIA at other major jewelry fairs in Europe.

In 1998, the school moved to an 8,000-square-foot state-of-the-art facility in Vicenza. By 2003, GIA Italy boasted some 60 Graduate Gemologists a year.

GIA Italy director Fred Stocco and his wife Kathy opened the facility in 1992 and made it the hub of the Institute's European activities.

A group of Russian students, led by Dr. Julia Solodova (front, second from right) joins instructors Phil York and Mary Fitzgerald (far left), Richard Liddicoat and Bill Boyajian at GIA's Santa Monica campus in 1995. Two years later, GIA Moscow was born.

It had about 200 students enrolled in extension and design classes, and another 400 in the distance education courses.

Not all of GIA Italy's students were Italian. Like the Institute's other schools, the Vicenza campus attracted students not only from surrounding countries, but also from Eastern Europe, the Middle East, and even as far away as—ironically— the U.S., South Korea, and Japan. Some were there to build an international career outside their home countries, others to enjoy Italian culture, and still others to study in one of the world's most important jewelry-producing nations.

ONE OF THE MORE INTERESTING GROUPS to visit GIA Italy during the 1990s was from Kristall, the Russian state diamond manufacturing company. In the summer of 1993, Yuri Sorokin, director of the Kristall manufacturing facility in Moscow, and Vladimir Abramov, Sorokin's counterpart in the Ukraine, visited GIA Italy to learn more about the Institute's diamond grading system. They toured the facility and observed the students and instructors. Fred Stocco later said, "They told us all of their graders *must* learn the GIA system, because they are finding that when they have customers in other countries, the GIA system is the most practical one to use." That October, Kristall sent seven employees to Vicenza to learn about diamond grading.

Education of Russian specialists didn't stop in Italy. A delegation of the Committee on Precious Stones and Metals (Komdragmet), which oversaw the diamond trade in Russia, came to GIA's Santa Monica headquarters for an intensive three-week diamond grading course in March 1994. That same month, a 14-member delegation of the General Business Club of Russia, representing diamond cutting and grading operations in Moscow and Yakutsk, came to GIA's New York campus for training. "The Russian Federation is building a new economic infrastructure," commented Dennis Foltz, "and GIA is happy to do what we can to help them develop their diamond industry."

But the Institute also had more in mind, and it began looking into a school in Moscow. The most instrumental Russian official in that endeavor was Dr. Julia Solodova, chief of the gemological faculty at the Moscow National

Gemological Institute (NGI). Dr. Solodova had visited the Santa Monica headquarters on many occasions and showed a keen interest in representing GIA in her country. In 1995, she worked with the education staff to develop a condensed, customized version of GIA programs in Russian. Then in August, she brought 22 NGI students and staff members to the Santa Monica campus. Their goal was to become Graduate Gemologists and return to Russia to set up a G.G. program. Six months later, in January 1996, all 22 earned their diplomas.

In 1997, GIA Moscow was established at the NGI under the sponsorship and management of Dr. Solodova. Within a year, GIA Moscow had taught 60 students, 20 of them through distance education. Training in Moscow, though still modest by comparison to other overseas branches, was ongoing into the 21st century.

WITH TWO CAMPUSES ALREADY PLANTED on European soil, the Institute turned its eyes to the United Kingdom. The British had a rich tradition of gemology dating back to 1913, when the National Association of Goldsmiths (NAG) held its first examinations. GIA's own historical connection with England had begun in 1929, when Robert M. Shipley completed the NAG correspondence course. London, a cosmopolitan city with an educational tradition more than a thousand years old, seemed a logical place for the next GIA campus.

Since its founding in 2001, GIA London has drawn a broad international student body.

The Institute took the first formal steps in late 1999, offering extension classes at the Imperial College of Science, Technology and Medicine in London. The first full-time resident G.G. program followed in 2001, and GIA London was born. The London campus, located near the historic British Museum, attracted an international student body. Under director Edward Johnson, a former GIA Hong Kong instructor, students from 18 different countries received their G.G. diplomas in a March 2003 graduation ceremony.

Celebrating diversity at home: GIA chairman Richard T. Liddicoat enjoys a cultural display presented at the Santa Monica campus by a group of students from India, Pakistan, and Sri Lanka.

WHILE GIA WAS EXPANDING GLOBALLY, it was also becoming more culturally diverse at its U.S. campuses. About half of all students in its on-campus classes were from abroad, and they came from dozens of countries, 43 in 1994 alone, making it a virtual gem-and-jewelry United Nations. According to Dennis Foltz, "One of the benefits of training in residence at GIA's head-quarters is that you get an introduction to the international jewelry trade via your fellow students along with your training. Our diversity is an example of a [global] community working together toward shared goals."

Even with shared goals, international students far from home can feel lonely and isolated. So to help overseas resident students feel comfortable in the U.S., and to help them learn more about American culture, GIA's student services staff initiated a number of programs on their behalf. One such program was "Celebrate Diversity," which offered music, dance, and culinary delights from the students' homelands, provided by the students themselves. Another was holding annual American-style Halloween parties, where students enjoyed dressing up in outrageous costumes.

OF ALL THE BRANCH LOCATIONS OF GIA EDUCATION, the most important was in the heart of New York City. As mentioned in earlier chapters, GIA's New York presence was created in the late 1940s. Originally under the direction of Crowningshield and Krashes, it flourished and became a vital education hub in the U.S.

In the 1970s, full-time on-campus programs were begun under the management of Paul Holt, who was followed by Tom Yonelunas and later Seung-Hae Moon. By 2003, New York Education was under the direction of Dan Campbell, and was teaching a global mix of students who welcomed the school's proximity to the center of the U.S. gem and jewelry trade. To meet the needs of the regional community, New York Education also developed a specialized curriculum of short and evening classes, as well as the highly successful G.G. program and jewelry design course. Over the years, many thousands of graduates hailed from GIA New York, which continued to expand to meet the needs of its cosmopolitan constituency.

In 1997, with the move of the headquarters from Santa Monica to Carlsbad, GIA opened a third U.S. school in Los Angeles, under the direction of veteran instructor Veronica Clark-Hudson. Plans called for expansion in L.A. in the first decade of the new century.

BY 2003, GIA'S COURSES AND PROGRAMS were being taught in 13 schools, in nine countries, on three continents, and in seven different languages. In the U.S., the Institute had trained students from 167 countries. The faculty and student body were ethnically and linguistically diverse, representing the gem and jewelry industry from around the world.

In addition to the Carlsbad headquarters, GIA Education had a major presence in New York, led by director Dan Campbell (left) since 1997. Also in 1997, GIA opened a school in Los Angeles, under the direction of Veronica Clark-Hudson (right).

Director of global education Seung-Hae Moon's primary task was ensuring that GIA's educational standards were maintained consistently worldwide. "Each country is different because of its individual market," she said, "but there is a standard of excellence that GIA has acquired that must be maintained." Students studying in Moscow, Seoul, and New York should all receive the same education in resident, extension, or home study programs. Although it was "an American package," as Moon said, the Institute adjusted its training to suit the needs of different regions without compromising the quality of education.

Brook Ellis set two priorities for continued growth under his watch. First, he wanted to keep GIA's "fingers on the pulse" of the world's large and growing markets. Second, he was committed to providing those markets with the education and skills they needed to prosper. "There is a worldwide need for the level of gemological education that GIA has pioneered," said Ellis in the late 1990s.

The point wasn't expansion for expansion's sake, but controlled growth in concert with GIA's mission to preserve the international standards of its research and education. "It's always a matter of the right time and the right situation," said Boyajian. "We work methodically to develop a relationship and become familiar with a market and culture."

As GIA entered the 21st century, in addition to its many schools, the Institute had presented classes in Australia, Brazil, Canada, China, Colombia, Dubai, Israel, Malaysia, Mexico, New Zealand, the Philippines, Singapore, South Africa, and Switzerland. The internationalization of the Gemological Institute of America had truly been established.

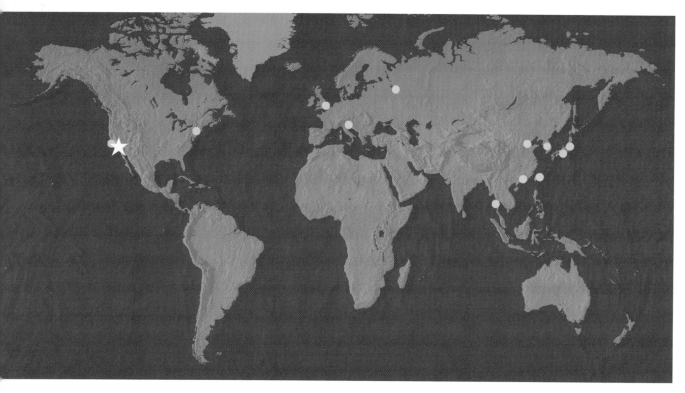

In 2003, GIA Education had 13 schools in nine countries on three continents, and taught in seven different languages. In total, the Institute in the U.S. had trained students from 167 countries.

■EDUCATION INNOVATIONS

Even as it was spanning the globe, GIA continued to revolutionize gemological education. The Institute not only reinforced its existing curriculum, heralded by its respected Graduate Gemologist program, but it also developed unique diploma programs and integrated state-of-the art technology to train a new generation of industry leaders.

PEARLS

By the early '90s, the pearl industry was again changing significantly, and the pearl course that had been updated in 1985 was now in serious need of revision to reflect the current market. The old course had focused primarily on Japanese cultured pearls, with little emphasis on other types. Although Japan's lustrous white and cream Akoyas remained important to the market, a growing number of other cultured pearls—including saltwater from Tahiti and the South Seas, and freshwater from China—began to take larger slices of that market as the supply of Akoyas dropped due to environmental problems. In such a climate, it was imperative for students to draw on updated product knowledge.

Several goals were set for the new course, including standardizing and clarifying pearl nomenclature and giving retailers the necessary tools to build their cultured pearl business. It would cover both freshwater and saltwater—and cultured and natural—pearls, and teach students about production, identification of pearl types, factors of pearl value (such as color or shape), and enhancements. Altogether, it would represent the most thorough and comprehensive pearl course ever produced.

Such a far-reaching revision needed some sizable underwriting, and the pearl industry responded by donating more than $2 million to the project by 1996. Major contributors included Assael International Inc., Mikimoto & Co., the South Sea Pearl Consortium, the government of Tahiti, the Japan Pearl Exporters' Association, G.I.E. Perles de Tahiti, Robert Wan's Tahiti Perles, and Tasaki Shinju Co. Ltd. Many of these same contributors also provided valuable input for the course material.

An important feature devised for the course was a universal standard for pearl grading and terminology called "GIA's Seven Pearl Value Factors" (size, shape, color, luster, surface quality, nacre quality, and matching). The *raison d'être* for these pearl value factors was similar to the logic behind GIA's diamond grading system and nomenclature, introduced in the early 1950s. Both were designed as classroom teaching tools, to provide an organized and consistent way of talking about these gems at a time when their respective industries were beset with a maze of inconsistent terminology. Karin Hurwit, Tom Moses, John King, Cheryl Wentzell, and others at the Gem Trade Laboratory focused on describing nuances of pearl color, while education's Eddie Decsi and her team designed and categorized other variables of the system.

Preparation for this course, as for many modern GIA courses, wasn't all desk and lab work. Education writers and researchers went out into the field to see the processes and products they were writing about, and to secure the gem materials students needed for their studies. Pearl Grading, for example, would require hundreds of cultured pearls of different color, shape, size, and quality for student practice.

So to learn more about the pearl business and buy the hundreds of needed pearls, GIA educators and researchers traveled to major pearl culturing centers in Tahiti, the South Seas, and China. "We felt it was important to learn firsthand what these countries and regions do to produce cultured pearls," said Research director Jim Shigley after his 1997 trip to Tahiti and the South

Terri Weimer/GIA

The revamped pearls course, introduced in 1998, was the most thorough and comprehensive ever produced on the subject.

Chinese freshwater cultured pearls, like those shown here, received extensive coverage in the new pearls course.

Harold & Erica Van Pelt

Seas. "We took photos, shot video, collected literature and, most importantly, listened to the producers' thoughts on the pearl courses we were writing and what they felt was important to teach our students."

In 1998, GIA began the two-part launch of its new pearl education program. First the Institute offered a hands-on pearl grading class, followed by a home study course. The program provided a wealth of information on all the important natural and cultured pearls in the market, imitation pearls, pearl testing, the most popular types of pearl jewelry and effective selling techniques, and post-harvest processing and treatments.

It was, said Fran Mastoloni, vice president of Frank Mastoloni and Sons, quite simply "the definitive pearls course: concise, up-to-date and extraordinarily practical . . . an industry standard."

BUSINESS EDUCATION

A necessary element in GIA's curriculum in the early '90s, its officials believed, was business education. Jewelers needed to learn how to manage an operation profitably and efficiently in an era of computerization and aggressive competition. The Institute was looking into developing a business management program for jewelers when, in 1992, GIA officials learned of an existing one called "Advanced Retail Management Systems" (ARMS). Created by Malcolm Alderton and Don Greig, and tested by New Zealand and Australian jewelers, the ARMS program offered a complete "turnkey" system: computerized inventory and business management software, computer hardware, and technical support and training. Here, it seemed, was just what GIA needed—the logical addition to its gemology and jewelry manufacturing arts courses.

In 1993, ARMS Global Ltd. and GIA signed a multi-year contract for a cooperative venture that made GIA the North American distributor of the ARMS software programs. The plan was for ARMS Global to provide and regularly update its management software, technical training, and support—customized to the operations and needs of U.S. jewelers—while GIA supplied the educational programs and infrastructure to implement and support ARMS. Of course, ARMS wasn't the first inventory control system for retailers; nor was it the first to offer after-sale operational support. What made this system different, said GIA's John Yantzer, was that it was "a complete business management program that represented a synergy between hardware, software, and education." It would teach a jeweler, he said, to "streamline the management of a fine jewelry store, increase profits, avoid liquidity problems, and manage a store with greater ease."

Jewelers who signed on to ARMS generally praised the system, saying it significantly improved their finances and the buying, management, and selling of their inventory. It also enabled them to spot and track what one called "clear inventory winners" and upgrade their operations.

As with any new venture, there were challenges. One was the relatively high cost compared to other systems in the marketplace. Another was the strong opposition the Institute received from jewelry manufacturers. Many claimed the ARMS program disrupted the retailer-supplier relationship, teaching jewelers to focus on computer data to track best-selling merchandise—and aggressively return merchandise that didn't sell. Ultimately, the program didn't catch fire with North American jewelers to the extent anticipated. By 1998, the original developers had several hundred clients in English-speaking countries (including Malaysia, New Zealand, Australia, and the Bahamas). But in North America, after five years of intense promotional activity, GIA ARMS still had just under 200 clients (representing 300 stores) in the U.S., Canada, and the Virgin Islands.

Veteran instructor Carl Chilstrom leads a marketing class in the GIA School of Business, created in 2001.

In late 1998, the Institute decided to end its sale of ARMS software, though it continued to support clients, honoring the duration of their service contracts. Shortly thereafter, a newly formed company called ARMS USA took over all software support and management services for U.S. and Canadian ARMS jewelers. "The feeling was that the program was now stable enough for the ARMS developers to set up their own U.S. office to service clients directly and extend the market," said Boyajian. "We were pleased to have pioneered a concept and product for the independent jeweler that was clearly needed."

GIA, then, finished the 1990s as it began the decade: still looking for a viable way to provide business management training to jewelers.

THE ANSWER CAME IN 2001, when the Institute created the GIA School of Business at its Carlsbad campus. Developed exclusively for the jewelry industry, it offered diploma programs in jewelry business principles, jewelry finance, merchandising, and U.S. and international business law and trade. The courses used interactive teaching methods and emphasized small-group projects, all designed to provide a solid business foundation to retailers, executives, and aspiring leaders working in the jewelry industry.

Top: The jewelry manu-
facturing arts programs
were revamped during
the 1990s to provide
training in all the skills
needed by the bench
jeweler in the 21st cen-
tury. Bottom: One revo-
lutionary class the
Institute began offering
its jewelry design stu-
dents was the state-of-
the-art CAD/CAM pro-
gram, here being taught
by Russ Hyder.

"This is not your traditional business school," said Brook Ellis. "The GIA School of Business is highly focused to prepare individuals for long and successful business careers in the jewelry industry."

The School of Business met with resounding praise from students. A long-awaited business management curriculum had finally begun, one that could be sustained for many years to come.

JEWELRY MANUFACTURING ARTS AND DESIGN

In 1991, on the 13th anniversary of its jewelry manufacturing arts program, the Institute offered two new titles: Graduate Jeweler (for completing the six-month JMA program) and Graduate Jeweler Gemologist (G.J.G., for completing both the G.J. and the G.G.). The introduction of the two new titles was appropriate, said Boyajian, because "proficiency in both gemology and the jewelry manufacturing arts has become important to the jeweler's success."

Shortly afterward, GIA revamped the JMA curriculum. The G.J. program was restructured to emphasize the basic bench skills demanded by employers: working with precious metals, jewelry fabrication and repair, ring sizing, and stone setting. Specialized classes that had been part of the core JMA curriculum, such as jewelry design, mold cutting and casting, and wax carving, became elective courses instead. Building blocks of skill sets, each reinforcing previously learned skills, replaced the one-at-a-time approach. Students continued to practice and improve fundamental manufacturing skills—sizing rings, soldering, filing, setting stones in varying shapes and sizes—while learning new ones.

As much as possible, the revised six-month program was designed to simulate the "real world." Students were each assigned a fully equipped bench and worked with the same tools and materials that professionals used on the job, performing all the routine tasks of the bench jeweler. Almost half of these G.J. projects were done in karat gold, and training in platinum was added in the late 1990s thanks to a $120,000 donation from Platinum Guild International. Students even got to keep their hand tools, so they would be prepared to work immediately after graduation.

The jewelry manufacturing arts makeover included updating the environment in which students learned. GIA spent more than $200,000 refurbishing JMA classrooms (including tools and new teaching materials) and developing state-of-the art training. The Institute received valuable assistance from companies such as Rio Grande, which donated 120 workbenches and a casting machine. In addition, the new JMA program added a vital educational tool—a series of 60 videotapes, produced by GIA, which demonstrated virtually every technique students were asked to learn.

Meanwhile, one of the Institute's most popular courses at the turn of the century was its jewelry design class, offered on campus in Carlsbad, New York, and most of the international locations. In the eight-week class, students learned to draw, illustrate, and present quality jewelry designs. The course also taught aspiring designers how to tap into their creativity to keep design ideas flowing. Indeed, several of these students combined their own talents with what they learned at GIA to win prestigious international awards for their designs.

John Parrish/AGTA

GIA graduate Saho Kinoshita, G.J.G., won first place in the Evening Division of the AGTA 2002 Spectrum Awards with this necklace.

And for students who wished to move from paper rendering to digital imaging, GIA offered courses in the much-heralded computer-aided design and computer-aided manufacturing (CAD/CAM) program. Using this state-of-the-art technology, students could render a piece of jewelry on the computer screen and then translate that design into a precise, three-dimensional wax model.

THE ACCREDITED JEWELRY PROFESSIONAL

In 1998, GIA made a revolutionary addition to its curriculum with the creation of Diamond Essentials, a concise and comprehensive distance education course customized for salespeople who had no formal jewelry or gemology training. It was the first in a new generation of practical courses designed with the help of leading retail jewelers. Colored Stone Essentials followed in 1999, and with the introduction of Jewelry Essentials in 2000, all three courses led to a new GIA diploma: the Accredited Jewelry Professional (A.J.P.).

The A.J.P. program was designed for quick learning—one to two months per course—and combined real-world sales training with the product knowledge essential to selling gems and jewelry effectively. "Not all sales associates need to be able to identify or grade stones," said Brook Ellis. "They need to be conversational in the language of gems and jewelry, and be able to explain concepts such as synthetics and treatment processes. The A.J.P. gives them the vocabulary to sell jewelry effectively and better serve customers."

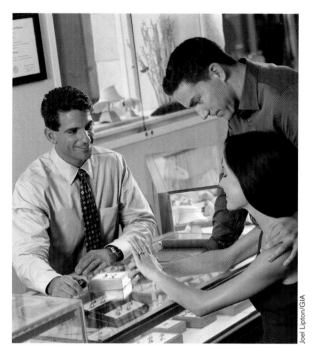

Students learned how to apply the 4 Cs of diamond quality, and how to disclose and sell all gem materials: natural, treated, synthetic, and imitation. They also discovered the key selling points for various precious metals and jewelry designs. And for those who wanted to learn more and go further, two of the Essentials courses—diamonds and colored stones—became part of the requirements leading to a G.G. diploma.

Within three years of its launch, the A.J.P. program had become an unqualified success, with thousands of new students enrolled. "We feel that the program has had a significant impact on the industry. These students have gained a true foundation not only in product knowledge, but also in presenting jewelry to the public in an effective and ethical manner," said education operations director Bill Herberts. "The A.J.P. diploma has opened the door to success for many new to the industry and has inspired confidence from both the trade and the public."

The Accredited Jewelry Professional (A.J.P.) program was designed to provide sales associates with the essential product knowledge needed to sell jewelry effectively. The A.J.P. program was divided into three courses: Diamond Essentials, Colored Stone Essentials, and Jewelry Essentials.

AN ON-CAMPUS EXPERIENCE ONLINE

Even with new GIA campuses being established and extension classes traveling to more cities around the world, most GIA learners still relied on the convenience and flexibility of distance education. Through the mid-1980s, the concept of distance education had changed little since Robert Shipley's original correspondence courses: Students mailed in their lessons and waited for the results to come back by mail. But with the computer networking revolution, a much more efficient alternative became available to anyone with a personal computer and a telephone line. The Institute saw a way to serve its student population like never before.

GIA-Net, the Institute's original online education and information network, developed by Dennis Foltz, was unveiled February 1, 1987. For the first time, the Institute's home study students could dial in to submit their lesson questionnaires, completed on-screen, anytime day or night, and get their scores back within moments. They could also correspond electronically with GIA instructors—or the accounting department when it came to payments—and even post messages on an electronic "bulletin board" divided into special-interest sections. GIA-Net was well received, marking its 200,000th call in 1996.

In 1997, GIA-Net was expanded to the Web, making it even more accessible, and its name was changed to GIA Online. The lessons submitted via GIA Online came from places as remote as Antarctica, the address of one of the Institute's most "distant" students in the late 1990s. Texan Gregory Harrison, stationed as an air traffic controller at McMurdo Station, was surrounded by penguins, icebergs, active volcanoes, and over five million square miles of virtually uninhabited snow and ice—rather forbidding and lonely. But his computer modem and GIA Online enabled Harrison to complete the gemology courses.

GIA Online, Harrison said in 1997, was "the crux to my academic survival and an umbilical cord to the rest of the world." It enabled him to study at a pace that suited his "rather unusual lifestyle." It was one of the most sophisticated educational communication systems of its era, allowing users to interact with GIA and each other.

In early 2001, GIA Online was replaced by the more powerful GIA Virtual Campus. In addition to a new, more user-friendly environment, Virtual Campus enabled distance education students to monitor their progress and connect with the Institute with only a few keystrokes. Now it was faster and more convenient than ever for students to attain their educational goals. By 2003, 85 percent of all lessons submitted came through GIA's Virtual Campus.

Distance education student Gregory Harrison, an air traffic controller at McMurdo Station in Antarctica, completed most of his G.G. requirements via GIA Online. In 2001, GIA Online was replaced by the more powerful GIA Virtual Campus, which made it faster and more convenient than ever for students to attain their educational goals.

SEVEN DECADES AFTER HE MAILED his first typewritten, mimeographed lessons, GIA founder Robert M. Shipley would have been delighted with the Institute's ability to provide a first-class education to students anywhere in the world, at any time. The gemology courses—diamonds, diamond grading, colored stones, colored stone grading, and gem identification—had been completely revamped by the start of the 21st century, providing Graduate Gemologists with an even stronger foundation for a career in the gem and jewelry industry.

The G.G. program was, and always would remain, GIA's cornerstone series of courses. But as it grew internationally, the Institute also expanded beyond the G.G. program to teach jewelry design and manufacturing skills, essential product knowledge for sales professionals, and the management and finance principles needed to succeed in the "business" of jewelry.

At the end of the 21st century, generous financial support helped GIA train a new generation of industry leaders, uphold industry standards through applied research and instrument development, and secure public confidence.

SECURING THE FUTURE

1986–2003

Even though donations are the lifeblood of most educational and research institutions, for most of its history GIA had no ongoing effort to solicit financial support. That changed in 1991, when Bill Boyajian kicked off Vision 2000, the Institute's multi-year capital campaign to raise $23.7 million. It was a bold endeavor, but one that was met with overwhelmingly generous support from the industry and the alumni network. And at the turn of the century, an even more ambitious undertaking would follow: a $75 million endowment campaign to ensure GIA's future as the custodian of standards and integrity for the international gem and jewelry industry.

IN 1991, GIA LAUNCHED one of the most ambitious projects in its history. It didn't involve treated gems or new labs overseas or a radical approach to education. It was "Vision 2000," GIA's first formal fundraising campaign. When Bill Boyajian announced the campaign in June 1991, there was considerable surprise in the industry. Despite its economic problems in the early 1980s, many assumed, as one columnist wrote, that the Institute was "rolling in revenue."

During its first years—when it was a small, private partnership owned by Robert and Beatrice Shipley—GIA managed to get by on the revenues from sales of its lessons, books, and equipment, and on personal gifts or donations by individuals or groups. Then, in the early 1940s, when it seemed the Institute's existence was threatened by the wartime induction of jewelers and their employees into military service—all potential tuition-paying students— the industry formed a nonprofit group that acquired GIA. A key feature of that 1943 acquisition was a $50,000 endowment fund (which grew to $100,000 in the 1950s) to provide a financial cushion for the Institute in hard times. That nest egg seemed unnecessary once the war was over and GI Bill financing enabled thousands of veterans to enroll in GIA correspondence courses, boosting the Institute's revenues significantly.

But the Institute became so dependent on this influx of students that the end of the GI Bill in the early 1950s could have had a devastating effect. Rather than turn to the industry for support, or draw on the endowment, Richard Liddicoat and his staff devised a brilliant diamond grading system that attracted new students and ultimately provided new funding sources for GIA's laboratory. At that time, at least, the Institute appeared to think that asking for money was somewhat unseemly. "GIA officials were always cautious about seeking support," said Boyajian. "They were concerned that it would get in the way of our independence and objectivity."

THE DIAMOND INVESTMENT BOOM OF THE 1970S provided a big boost to the Institute's revenues from grading services, education, and instrument sales. However, the collapse of that boom in the early 1980s not only saw diamond prices plummet, but it also caused GIA revenues to tumble, forcing sharp cutbacks in staffing and a temporary downsizing of services.

Under the strict business regimen of Glenn Nord, who succeeded Liddicoat as president in 1983, and aided by a reviving diamond market, the Institute's revenues began climbing again. Nord also initiated somewhat tentative attempts at fundraising. The first major contributor was Jewelers of America (JA), the largest trade association for U.S. retail jewelers. In addition to 200 annual GIA scholarships for JA members (worth a total of $100,000) that it was already providing, JA chairman Michael Roman presented Nord with a check for $25,000 in 1984. The money was earmarked for the Institute's research activities, "in view of the importance of research in the field of gemology [and] GIA's ongoing commitment to the science of gemstones," said Roman.

Encouraged by that gift, Nord toyed with the idea of hiring a professional fundraiser to create an endowment fund and other money-raising projects, but it was his successor, Boyajian, who picked up on the idea and made fundraising a cornerstone of the 1988 Master Plan. Under Boyajian, GIA's revenues kept growing, to $24.4 million in 1987—a 15 percent gain over 1986—and then $29.4 million by 1989. But he knew GIA couldn't continue its historical rollercoaster pattern of financing. Just as important, the Institute needed to increase its annual revenues if it wanted to expand its educational, research, and laboratory services—and could not risk falling behind.

"If GIA is to continue to provide a broad range of services to the industry and maintain our position of leadership, we must find new, additional sources of funding for our educational and research programs," Boyajian said in a 1991 message to all employees. There was also another practical reason. According to Boyajian, "All nonprofit, tax-exempt organizations raise money to support their mission-driven objectives. It is something that we simply should be doing."

■A NEW "VISION"

In 1989, the Institute hired a national consulting firm to gauge trade reaction to the prospect of a major GIA fundraising campaign. The response was encouraging. Industry leaders wanted the Institute to stay ahead of technological and market changes, not simply keep pace with them, and they certainly didn't want it to fall behind.

With that assurance in hand, Boyajian and his staff outlined several areas in serious need of support. They included:

- Education and professional training

- Research and technical development

- Information systems (automation and computerization)

- International expansion

- Scholarships and financial aid for students

Although not officially introduced until 1991, the new capital campaign got rolling in 1990. "Vision 2000," as it was called, was originally designed to last up to a decade. First, the Institute canvassed its own officials and staff for donations. Chairman Richard Liddicoat led the way with a personal pledge of $700,000. It was a riskier time for jewelers than the 1950s and '60s, when he had opposed such efforts, Liddicoat explained. "In today's world, with all these new developments in synthetics and treatments, we do need this," he said in 1997. Fellow GIA pioneer Bob Crowningshield weighed in with $283,000. Pledges from GIA governors and other members of GIA's family added another $350,000.

Outside the Institute, GIA began contacting companies and organizations. A number of industry leaders were enlisted for the campaign's executive committee, which oversaw the Vision 2000 program, while another 125 joined the campaign's advisory committee. Editors and publishers from the trade press were asked for their support. Milton Gralla, then publisher of *National Jeweler*, was named chairman of the advisory committee.

Over the next few months, into early 1991, the Institute's unofficial solicitations evoked a strong response from the industry. An important gift early on came from Tiffany & Co. Boyajian knew he needed a pledge from a marquee name to motivate others to give, and Tiffany chairman William Chaney committed $250,000. Boyajian recalled leaving Chaney's office in New York that day. "With Tiffany's support, I felt like I was floating down Fifth Avenue," he said.

After that, Cartier and the World Gold Council each pledged $300,000, and Jewelers of America pledged $1 million to set up the Michael J. Roman Scholarship fund. Other firms contributed $75,000 to $150,000. De Beers trumped them all, with a $1.5 million pledge—to be given to GIA in five annual installments of $300,000—the largest single contribution to the capital fund campaign. In all, over $5 million had been pledged before the campaign was officially launched.

Cartier chairman and GIA governor Ralph Destino, here unveiling the plaque designating the Liddicoat Library's Cartier Rare Book Repository and Archives, also chaired the Vision 2000 campaign.

The formal kickoff took place during the second International Gemological Symposium, held in June 1991 to mark GIA's 60th anniversary. The largest gemological event of its kind, it was the perfect forum in which to introduce Vision 2000. Funds from the campaign, Boyajian said at a press conference, would be used to support and enhance GIA's education and research programs. They would equip the Institute to continue to address the critical issues confronting the gem and jewelry industry through research into new materials and treatment methods, as well as the development of new identification techniques and technology. The goal was to raise $23.7 million. The more than $5 million in commitments GIA already had received, he said, demonstrated "unprecedented industry-wide leadership and support."

GIA ASSEMBLED A SMALL DEPARTMENT to oversee fundraising, with a director of institute relations. Industry leaders also volunteered their time and service, including Cartier chairman Ralph Destino, who chaired Vision 2000, and Michael Barlerin, chief executive officer of the World Gold Council, who chaired the leadership gifts committee. Yet by early 1994, Vision 2000 was still only halfway to its mid-decade goal of $12.1 million. GIA's first serious try at fundraising, which had begun so auspiciously, seemed to have run out of steam.

To get it going again, Boyajian decided to start afresh and hire a new head fundraiser. The person he chose was Jim Littman, then director of the Jewish National Fund in Los Angeles (where he had boosted donations tenfold) and a consultant to the United Jewish Appeal. Littman was an innovative and relentless fundraiser with clear ideas on how to revamp and improve GIA's development endeavors. Boyajian hired him in mid-1994 to take over the Institute's fundraising activities and broadened his portfolio to include alumni operations and two Institute publications, *The Loupe: GIA World News* and *In Focus*.

What Littman did first was evaluate GIA's prior efforts in detail, and he was disappointed. The momentum from the impressive 1991 takeoff had been squandered. There was no organized, ongoing fundraising effort; no real outreach to the industry; no clear, easy-to-read materials that made the case for supporting the Institute. Nor was there a formal program to publicly thank major donors. Above all, there was no "spark plug" to get things moving and keep them moving.

Littman would be that spark plug. As director of development (the renamed institute relations department), Littman began making changes immediately and threw himself into learning as much as he could about the industry and introducing himself to its leaders. "My first job was to learn how business is done in this industry," he said later, "to find what is unique about it."

Littman also discovered that the industry didn't know as much about GIA as the Institute thought it did. Most in the diamond trade saw it, as one dealer put it, as "just a take-in window" where diamonds were graded and gems were identified. Others saw it as a supplier of gem instruments. If you were a GIA graduate, you saw it as a school where you had received your diploma. Few people completely understood all that the Institute was and did. Even as late as 1994, many assumed GIA was flush with monies and didn't really need industry support. "Few people even knew we were a nonprofit organization," said Littman, amazed. "They thought it was a high-profit money machine, funded by revenues from Education and the Gem Trade Laboratory."

So Littman's message, which he delivered systematically and repeatedly, was that state-of-the-art gem education, research, grading, and identification services were expensive. For example, it cost hundreds of thousands of dollars just to develop a new distance education course of GIA quality. If the Institute was to maintain its educational excellence without supplemental support—and this was a time of declining state and federal funding for student loans—it would have to keep raising tuition and fees. In addition, the Liddicoat Library and Information Center, the world's greatest gemological reference source, needed industry backing to maintain and expand its collections of books, images, and research materials.

But the sector most in need of ongoing financial support was the research department. It was, said Boyajian in 1994, "at the core of GIA's activities. It is what drives our educational and identification efforts." The data gathered by GIA researchers supported the accuracy and currency of the Institute's training and provided the basis for detection techniques that its laboratory and the industry needed to deal with the synthetic and treated gems flooding the market in the 1990s. "If we didn't have [GIA] to tell us how to detect the

Jim Littman was hired in 1994 to lead the Institute's fundraising activities. Over the next six years, he generated unprecedented support from the gem and jewelry industry.

Gem-quality synthetic diamonds were one of the technological challenges GIA researchers addressed in the 1990s. This photo shows, bottom center and to the right, six De Beers experimental synthetic diamonds. At the top center and to the left are natural diamonds.

synthetic gems," said George Kaplan, "we'd be somewhere between trouble and collapse."

Yet just when GIA's research efforts were most needed by the industry, its scientists were being overwhelmed. By the early 1990s, GIA's 10-person research staff was working on at least two dozen major projects in addition to their daily work with the Gem Trade Laboratory. The flood of new gem materials and enhancements, thanks to advancing technology and deep-pocketed corporate laboratories, was unrelenting and rising. "We have a long list of projects in Research," said Dr. Ilene Reinitz in the early 1990s, "but no matter how many we finish and take off the top of that list, it keeps getting longer because we are always adding more at the bottom."

IT WAS, IN A WAY, DAVID VERSUS GOLIATH. Despite having the most advanced gemological laboratory in the industry, GIA's research budget was miniscule compared to the "billions of dollars"—as Boyajian put it in 1991, with only a little hyperbole—large corporations were putting into research and development of synthetic diamonds, thin films, and filling substances, or creating new colored stone treatments and synthetics.

Already in early 1991, Liddicoat had said, "To retain respect, GIA has to stay one step ahead of a rapidly developing science, [but] we need more research facilities than our income can justify. We just can't afford to spend $500,000 or $1 million for some special project."

GIA was hard pressed to meet all the expenses required to build and maintain a major research program. One cost was hiring and holding skilled researchers, many with advanced degrees. Another was the sophisticated equipment and technology, such as infrared spectroscopy, energy-dispersive X-ray fluorescence, and laser Raman microspectrometry, that GIA needed for serious research. "When we buy a new instrument for $250,000, everyone is happy that we have a new tool. But over five to seven years, it has to be repaired and then, with advances in technology, it's obsolete and we have to replace it," said research director Jim Shigley. "People don't seem to understand that technical equipment has a limited lifespan."

And that's why Littman and other GIA officials and volunteers told the industry, "The Gemological Institute of America needs your support."

In late 1994 and early 1995, Littman began preparing a campaign of trade advertisements, special events, and trade show participation to publicize GIA's dilemma. He also enlisted the help of industry leaders and opinion makers. *The Loupe* and *In Focus* were redesigned to tell the Institute's story in a more informative and entertaining manner. Both expanded their readership, reaching a combined circulation of 87,000 readers in the late 1990s. A promotional video with compelling testimonials from industry leaders was produced to show the Institute's vital research efforts. As GIA governor Ralph Destino explained, "If there were no GIA, we'd have to invent one."

ON THE EVENING OF APRIL 11, 1995, the once-dormant Vision 2000 campaign was relaunched at a cocktail reception attended by almost 150 industry leaders at the New York salon of luxury jeweler and longtime GIA supporter Harry Winston Inc. And in that presentation, a new phrase entered GIA's development language. Through the rest of the decade, it would be used repeatedly as a subtle but unforgettable mantra of what GIA was doing for the industry: "Securing the Future."

Attention was also devoted to soliciting "gifts-in-kind," donations of tax-deductible, non-cash assets. The Institute had received donations of instruments, books, and gemstones from its earliest days. But the Treasured Gifts

"IF WE DIDN'T HAVE [GIA] TO TELL US HOW TO DETECT THE SYNTHETIC GEMS," SAID GEORGE KAPLAN, "WE'D BE SOMEWHERE BETWEEN TROUBLE AND COLLAPSE."

In addition to its significant financial commitment, Tiffany donated $50,000 of gemstones to the Institute, which included an assortment of opals, tanzanites, ametrines, spinels, tourmalines, and chrysoberyls.

The Loupe, GIA's quarterly news publication, reached an audience of 87,000 in the late 1990s, and became an integral part of the Institute's communication efforts.

Council, established in early 1995, was the first coordinated effort to seek non-cash donations from around the world. Many of the in-kind donations were gem materials, including imitations and synthetics, for use in classroom studies, research, and the Institute's collections.

Littman and his staff also created the International Executive Council (IEC), composed of more than 140 leading figures in the gem and jewelry industry. Council members met at least once a year with GIA officials to hear about the Institute's plans and programs, and to offer their own input. The IEC helped build international understanding and support for GIA, and opened the Institute to valued insights from various segments of the global industry.

PUBLIC RECOGNITION OF DONORS also became an important part of the development program. It not only showed the Institute's appreciation for the gift and the giver, but it also put the media spotlight on GIA, strengthening industry and public awareness of its activities. Donors to education programs, for example, had their names placed on classrooms or attached to courses or research projects, while donors of major in-kind gifts received the Treasured Gifts Award.

The most prestigious acknowledgment of all, though, was the GIA League of Honor. The league applauded those in the worldwide gem and jewelry industry who made outstanding personal or corporate contributions ($100,000 or more) to the Institute. The inductees, called "sovereigns," were publicly honored and given a stylish medal (designed by GIA student Somkid Huangthanapan) during the annual League of Honor dinner. Held at New York's famed Plaza Hotel for many years, the dinner became a "must" social event in the industry. It also became a major fundraiser, averaging some $350,000 in donations each year.

To launch the first League of Honor dinner on October 24, 1995, at which nine industry leaders were inducted, GIA also publicly honored two of its most esteemed pioneers. Liddicoat and Crowningshield received lifetime achievement awards for their work on behalf of gemology for over half a century. "These are two men who built GIA's international reputation and brought a moral standing to this industry that will benefit countless generations in gemology," Boyajian told the capacity crowd, which gave Liddicoat and Crowningshield a standing ovation.

Then, turning to the first nine sovereigns to be inducted, he noted that they had "given generously and without hesitation of both their time and financial support to help underwrite the Institute's mission." It was a pattern for all who followed them.

VISION 2000'S MISSION was to secure funding from individual and institutional donors to support GIA's education programs, broaden its research and development projects, provide scholarships and student aid, and expand the Institute's educational outreach in key jewelry centers worldwide. It succeeded admirably.

In education, there was a significant increase in underwriting the core training programs, both existing and new. De Beers' $1.5 million pledge in 1991 underwrote GIA diamond training throughout the world, and the production of instructional and reference tools for jewelers, such as GIA's wall chart and video on fracture-filled diamonds, a chart on separating natural from synthetic diamonds, and numerous research projects. In 1996, De Beers committed another $1.5 million toward diamond research and education, and in 2000 it became sole sponsor of the Diamond Essentials course. Premier Gem, a New York–based manufacturer and diamond importer, pledged $50,000 to GIA's training. Christie's auction house made a major donation to the GIA Diamond Grading course in 1995, while the U.S. firm Suberi Inc. and the Swiss firm Boghossian co-sponsored GIA's updated diamonds course. In 1996, Sotheby's auction house donated $100,000 to support GIA's colored stones program.

Left: League of Honor co-chairs Robert Bridge (standing, far left) and Eli Izhakoff (standing, far right) with the first inaugurated members of the GIA League of Honor, in October 1995. Front row, left to right: James Quinn (accepting for William Chaney), Simon Critchell, Ara Arslanian, Ralph Destino. Back row: Bridge, Michael Roman, Helmut Swarovski, William Goldberg, and Izhakoff. Not shown: Nicholas Oppenheimer and Michael Barlerin. Right: The annual League of Honor dinner in New York became a "must" social event in the industry.

LEAGUE OF HONOR MEMBERS

The GIA Honor Roll of Donors represents a group of supporters committed to helping GIA serve the industry and protect the public trust. The individuals and organizations listed here donated cumulative amounts of $100,000 or more to the Institute through mid-2003.

Rosy Blue president and CEO Dilip Mehta is a three-time inductee into the League of Honor.

$5,000,000 or more
Mouawad Family

$1,000,000 to $4,999,999
Assael International, Inc.
G. Robert Crowningshield*
D. Swarovski & Co.
The De Beers Group
Richard T. Liddicoat*
Rosy Blue, N.V.
Stuller, Inc.
Tahiti Perles
The Steinmetz Group of Companies
Tiffany & Co.

$500,000 to $999,999
Argyle Diamonds
Cartier, Inc.
The JCK Shows and *JCK* Magazine
Jewelers of America
K. Mikimoto & Co., Ltd.
Kwiat, Roisen and Ferman
Mikimoto (America) Co., Ltd.
South Sea Pearl Consortium
Vicenza Trade Fair
World Gold Council

$250,000 to $499,999
ABN AMRO Bank
Christie's
Fortunoff Fine Jewelry
G.I.E. Perles de Tahiti
Graff Diamonds, Ltd.
Japan Pearl Promotion Society
Jewelers Mutual Insurance
Kyocera Corporation
P. Lancon, S.A.
Leo Schachter Diamonds LLC/Schachter & Namdar Group
Michael M. Scott
Tasaki Shinju Co., Ltd.

$100,000 to $249,000
Amira Aya N.V.
John W. Bartlett
BHP Billiton Diamonds Inc.
Boghossian, S.A.
William E. Boyajian*
Chatham Created Gems
Codiam & Rand
Cora Diamond Corporation
Ralph Destino
E. Schreiber Inc.
Eurostar Diamond Traders
Fred Leighton, Ltd.
Galaxy Diamond
Gembel, N.V.
Dr. Edward J. Gübelin
Hearts on Fire
International Jewelers Block & Fine Arts Insurance Services, Inc.
Ishaia Trading Corporation
Julius Klein Diamonds Inc.
The Kazanjian Foundation
Lee Michaels Fine Jewelry
Lorenzo Jewelry Manufacturers (H.K.), Ltd.
Louis Glick Diamond Corporation
M. Fabrikant & Sons
Platinum Guild International
Premier Gem Corporation New York
Premier Gems Trading Co., Ltd.
Rough Diamond Traders, Inc.
Joseph H. Samuel, Jr. and the DeYoung Family
Sierra Gem Diamonds
Sotheby's
Susan Eisen Fine Jewelry & Watches
Tse Sui Luen Jewellery Co., Ltd.
Tycoon, Tycoon Cut Diamonds
VNU Business Media
William Goldberg Diamond Corporation

*Includes a planned gift.

Other donations made it possible to expand the curriculum. Platinum Guild International, for instance, pledged $120,000 to add a class in manufacturing techniques with platinum in the jewelry manufacturing arts programs. And in 1998, GIA debuted its revamped pearl education program, sponsored by several pearl-producing associations.

But support for the Institute's educational programs wasn't limited to its curriculum. In 1996, well-known New York jeweler Helene Fortunoff, an active GIA supporter, donated $125,000 to furnish and fully equip the "Fortunoff Family Design Classroom" on the ground floor of GIA's New York campus on Fifth Avenue. Fortunoff did it, she said, "to serve as a constant reminder to the daily passing trade that GIA is a meritorious establishment . . . supported by the people."

In the late 1990s, Vision 2000 donations enabled the Richard T. Liddicoat Gemological Library and Information Center to expand its offerings in ways it could not have done otherwise. For example, it began a collection of books on jade and jade carving, thanks to the generosity of New York diamond and estate jewelry dealer Andrew Cohen.

Cartier's gift of $300,000 was directed toward maintaining the library's rare book archives. "It's imperative that students wishing to become jewelry retailers or designers have access to the historical ancestry of the trade," said Simon Critchell, president of Cartier, Inc. Equally important, added Cartier chairman Ralph Destino, the sizable donation made Cartier "together with GIA . . . the custodians responsible for preserving our industry's history for generations to come."

Underwriting GIA's research was a major goal of the Vision 2000 capital campaign, and the trade responded impressively. Kyocera Corp. of Japan donated 50 million yen (about $438,000 at the time of the gift in mid-1997) to create an endowment for colored stone research. Other diamantaires followed De Beers' lead in supporting diamond studies. New York diamond manufacturer and importer Codiam Inc., for instance, donated $100,000 to GIA's diamond research, while Rosy Blue, an international diamond manufacturing and import/export firm, contributed a similar amount toward GIA's efforts to identify gem-quality synthetic diamonds.

In 1999, in the midst of the industry storm over General Electric's supposedly undetectable HPHT process for enhancing color in diamonds, Australia's

Left: New York jeweler Helene Fortunoff donated $125,000 to establish the "Fortunoff Family Design Classroom" at GIA's New York campus. Right: Lee Berg, president of Lee Michaels Fine Jewelry in Baton Rouge, Louisiana, was inducted into the League of Honor in 2002.

Development professional Linda Ellis (later Linda Ellis Harmeling) took over the Institute's fundraising efforts in 2000. Under Ellis, GIA began an ambitious $75 million endowment campaign, a permanent fund that would be invested to grow long into the future.

Argyle Diamonds—one of the world's largest diamond producers—donated $500,000 to the Institute's research into the GE process. It did so to "protect the premium attached to natural diamonds," said Gordon Gilchrist, managing director of Argyle Diamonds. Detection of treated diamonds was "the key," and GIA was the one to find it.

Vision 2000 funding also enabled GIA Research to increase its staff to 35 by 2003, and purchase much of the expensive equipment it needed. Although new technologies continued to pose new threats, GIA Research at the beginning of the 21st century was in a better position to meet these threats than ever before.

WHEN VISION 2000 BEGAN IN 1991, its long-term goal was $23.7 million. For a while in the early 1990s, that goal seemed unattainable. But the revitalized Vision 2000 campaign, and its attendant fundraising programs, succeeded magnificently in the second half of the decade.

When the campaign officially ended in October 2000 at the annual League of Honor dinner, it had raised not the $23 million first envisioned—but $30 million in support of GIA's pledge to "secure the future" of the industry. And it did so without compromising the Institute's independence or integrity. With fundraising firmly entrenched as an ongoing GIA activity, Littman left the Institute in late 2000, turning over the reins to development professional Linda Ellis (later Linda Ellis Harmeling).

■THE GIA ENDOWMENT

That same year, before Vision 2000 even ended, work began on an even more ambitious fundraising program: the development of a major endowment campaign. To ensure that GIA could continue its nonprofit education and research mission regardless of future economic cycles, the contributions would be permanently invested to grow, and the interest would be used to fund critical activities. In the early 2000s, these included not only research, the Liddicoat Library, and the core education programs, but also a growing museum collection and the new School of Business.

GIA, which celebrated its 70th anniversary in 2001, had earned its reputation as the "world's foremost authority in gemology." And a strong GIA meant a

Matt Stuller of Stuller, Inc., shows a set of diamonds to Linda Ellis Harmeling and Jane Lynch, director of institute relations. Stuller, a GIA governor, was named chairman of the endowment campaign.

strong gem and jewelry industry. Gifts to the endowment would guarantee that strength in perpetuity. The industry agreed. Almost immediately after the board of governors formed an endowment committee in 1999, efforts on behalf of the campaign were begun, with major support from the Institute itself, the governors, and GIA officials, as well as lead gifts from Tiffany & Co., Rosy Blue, and D. Swarovski & Co. By the time the endowment campaign was formally launched at the November 2002 League of Honor dinner, $33 million had been pledged toward the $75 million goal. In 2003, endowment campaign chair Matt Stuller, himself a $1 million donor, said he was very gratified with the campaign's start.

"We are extremely grateful for the financial support of these and other industry leaders who have demonstrated their commitment to help the Institute launch the endowment campaign," Harmeling said. "They leave a significant legacy, as their names will forever be associated with GIA's efforts."

Fundraising was ratcheted up in other areas under Harmeling. Greater emphasis was placed on planned giving, spearheaded since 2000 by director of institute relations Jane Lynch, with several million dollars committed to GIA in trust.

And in 2002, development associate Patricia Syvrud began a campaign to secure in-kind gifts of gems and jewelry for the GIA Collection, a world-class repository of beauty, creativity, and craftsmanship. By developing various

TREASURED GIFTS CIRCLE OF HONOR

GIA accepts non-cash, gift-in-kind donations of jewelry, gem materials, books, equipment, and other items. These Circle of Honor inductees made cumulative gifts valued at $100,000 or more through mid-2003.

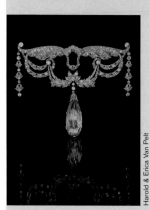

Harold & Erica Van Pelt

This Belle Epoque stomacher (circa 1905) was donated by Stephen and Eileen Silver.

$500,000 to $999,999

Kurt Nassau, Ph.D. • synthetic crystals and gemstones, publications

PierLuigi Dalla Rovere • housing for GIA Italy for five years, GemFest gala dinners

Vicenza Trade Fair • 24 GemFest programs over 10 years

$250,000 to $499,999

The Bell Group Rio Grande • training program in Tucson, jewelry manufacturing equipment

Chatham Created Gems, Inc. • synthetic gem materials

Ramsey Gem Imports • assorted gemstones

D. Swarovski & Co. • assorted glass and synthetic gem materials, and the GIA Tower of Brilliance

Touraine Family Trust • collection of pieces created by Pierre J. Touraine

$100,000 to $249,999

American Pearl Co. • pearls and shells

Aurafin-OroAmerica • assorted gemstones

Banks International Gemology, Inc. • assorted gemstones, sapphire sculpture of Richard T. Liddicoat

Nancy E. Brewer • assorted gemstones

J. O. Crystal Co., Inc. • synthetic rubies and alexandrite

JewelAmerica, Inc. • assorted gemstones to education

KCB Natural Pearls • natural abalone pearls, assorted library materials

William F. & Jeanne H. Larson • assorted gemstones, minerals, carvings, and jewelry

Art Sexauer • "symphony" of gemstone instruments, tourmaline from Maine

Ambaji Shinde • personal collection of jewelry renderings

S. H. Silver Co. • Edwardian pink topaz stomacher, loose gemstones

United States Pearl Co. • pearl and shell collection, gem and mineral collection

Photos by Dwight Gooch/GIA

"Symphony in Gemstones," a 21-piece miniature orchestra created from various gem materials, was donated by Art Sexauer, a longtime benefactor of the Institute. The harp (above) is made from tiger's-eye quartz.

types of collections—such as designer, historical, and international—and making them available in Carlsbad and elsewhere, the Collection was intended to strengthen public interest in the fascinating world of gems and jewelry, and inspire them to learn more. Within months of the campaign's launch, a number of important donations were made, including the "Symphony in Gemstones" display donated by Art Sexauer, a wide range of Ramaura synthetic rubies from manufacturer Judith Osmer, and two intarsia boxes by Nicolai Medvedev that were contributed by Fred and Carol Seeman.

ONE OF THE GIA PROJECTS THAT MOST NEEDED the international gem and jewelry industry's support was not part of either Vision 2000 or the endowment campaign, yet it would impact the Institute, its students, and the industry well into the 21st century: GIA's new world headquarters. The $40 million-plus project was the most expensive and demanding in the history of the Gemological Institute of America. It was also one of the most successful.

Patrick Ball was named director of the GIA Alumni Association in 1997. Under Ball's leadership, the association strengthened its global network of alumni.

A "NEW" ALUMNI ASSOCIATION: THE SECOND DECADE

For much of the 1990s, GIA's Alumni Association was a work in progress. The association began 1992, its 10th anniversary, with several far-reaching changes. It was placed under the year-old institute relations department, and GIA veteran Susan Johnson replaced Gary Roskin as assistant director. That year, the association also announced its annual-giving fund campaign (later called the GIA Annual Fund), to support association and chapter activities and to assist GIA in purchasing equipment and materials for educational and research purposes. The Annual Fund campaign also gave the association the opportunity to reach out to the Institute's entire alumni network (then approximately 100,000 worldwide) and encourage them to be more involved with GIA.

The next step came in June 1993, with formation of the first-ever GIA Alumni Association advisory board, later known as the Alumni executive committee. The purpose of this group, composed of leading alumni, was to help guide the global network of 85 Alumni chapters in setting priorities and future directions. But in actuality, the board members (elected to serve 18 months) were designing, with Alumni officials, what would be a re-energized Alumni Association. The board drafted a definitive mission statement and bylaws aimed at increasing support for local chapters and individual alumni.

That year the association also reactivated five chapters in the U.S., launched a chapter in Moscow, and laid the groundwork for chapters in Japan, Korea, Taiwan, and Italy. And it sought to improve its communications by updating the design and editorial content of its *In Focus* magazine and launching a quarterly newsletter for chapter officers. Nevertheless, total membership remained stubbornly unchanged. At the end of 1994, the membership figure was the same as at the start of the decade: about 4,000.

When Jim Littman took over as development director in mid-1994, Alumni membership was widened to include not only GIA students and graduates, but also *anyone* who wanted access to GIA programs, newsletters, and networking opportunities. The organization, renamed GIA Alumni and Associates, continued its open membership policy until 2001, when it reverted to students and graduates only.

In 1997, Johnson was named GIA's dean of students, and Patrick Ball, who had been director of education at GIA New York, came west to head the Alumni Association. Led by Ball, the association strengthened contact with its global network of alumni and chapters by creating an online, searchable, worldwide member directory to complement the printed version. Consumers anywhere could now search for a GIA-trained jeweler or gemologist in their area. (The Alumni directory went exclusively online in 2003.)

In February 1998, following months of revamping, the "new Alumni Association" was officially unveiled during the annual Tucson gem shows. This time, the primary ingredient that would drive Alumni membership and financial support was professional recognition.

The Carat Point system of recognition encouraged professional development beyond GIA diplomas or certificates by awarding members points for participating in a variety of career-enhancing activities. These included attending chapter seminars and professional events, becoming an Alumni chapter officer, or successfully completing the annual *Gems & Gemology* Challenge quiz. Carat Point achievers were spotlighted at alumni events and through *In Focus*, the member directory, and the Alumni website. Those who earned 25 or more points joined the Alumni Circle of Achievement.

"This is a peer-recognition system that's been long overdue," said Ball. "And with the increase in synthetics and treatments, the public is looking for a higher level of professional development in the trade."

Further enhancing the visibility of its members, the Alumni Association discontinued *In Focus* in 2001 and began featuring an Alumni section in *The Loupe*, the Institute's quarterly news publication. Although *In Focus* had served as the association's official publication since 1982, its circulation was always limited to the few thousand Alumni Association members. With publication in *The Loupe* of chapter news and events, alumni profiles, and Carat Point achievers, GIA Alumni activities now reached an audience of 87,000 in the industry and the public at large.

To help the association grow even stronger, GIA created the Alumni endowment fund in 2002. This permanent fund was established to finance guest speaker tours to all Alumni chapters and to pay for books, slides, equipment, and other resources for the almost 5,000 Alumni Association members.

Altogether, these developments marked what Ball described as a "new era" for the GIA Alumni Association.

Larne Boyles/GIA

Diamond expert and longtime De Beers executive Robin Walker addresses GIA students and alumni in June 2001. Walker's talk was one of many professional development events hosted by the GIA Alumni Association.

An aerial view of the Institute's Carlsbad headquarters, which officially opened May 28, 1997.

A NEW WORLD HEADQUARTERS:
FROM DREAM TO REALITY

1986–2003

During its first five decades, the Gemological Institute of America was frequently on the move. Not just in developing new educational programs and services around the world, but literally on the move. In its first 45 years, GIA had five headquarters. Now, nearing the end of the century, it was time to move again.

When the Institute built its Santa Monica headquarters in 1976, GIA officials confidently assumed it would serve GIA's needs for many years. But the boom in student enrollment and demand for grading services in the late 1970s quickly changed that.

In 1977, just a year after opening the new headquarters, GIA had to rent an additional 50,000 square feet in two nearby buildings. With growing demand in education, the laboratory, and instruments, by 1981 GIA was actively looking for a new campus. However, the early '80s was a time of inflation and high interest rates. In addition, the Institute was just beginning to feel the effects of the collapse of the diamond investment boom. And then came GIA's downsizing, Liddicoat's heart attack, and Nord's efforts to financially rebuild the Institute. So, any serious thoughts of a new headquarters were put away until Bill Boyajian took over as president.

Once the Institute did build a new headquarters in the mid-1990s, the results would far exceed all expectations.

AS EARLY AS 1986, Bill Boyajian was already considering physical expansion. He even began to explore the idea of a new home for the Institute, one with enough room to grow to support its broadening activities. But this was a project that would ultimately require tens of millions of dollars, not to mention tenacity and commitment from those directly involved.

"I needed someone I could trust to shoulder our facilities planning," said Boyajian. The person he turned to almost immediately in December 1986 was Gary Hill, his assistant when he supervised GIA's resident colored stone program in the late 1970s and early '80s. "I knew him. I trusted him. And I knew he could get things done," said Boyajian later.

Hill was a unique individual: an excellent researcher, a consummate planner, and a self-assured project leader and innovator. Though a geologist and gemologist by training, he threw himself into learning facilities management. He joined the International Facilities Management Association, enrolled in

As early as 1986, Institute veteran Gary Hill began planning a new home for GIA's headquarters. Hill visited well over 200 sites before settling on the perfect location.

home study courses of the Building Owners and Management Institute, and immediately applied what he was learning to his new duties. GIA was in a growth pattern once again by 1987 and felt the need to both consolidate West Coast operations (moving the L.A. lab to Santa Monica in 1988) and provide room for expansion, both of which were accomplished with the purchase of a 64,000-square-foot building next door to the Stewart Street location.

All the while, Hill kept an eye on his personal grail—a new headquarters. At the time, few GIA officials really believed the Institute would, or could, move to a new home anytime soon. Even Boyajian had to "sell" himself on the justification for this huge project, since there were good reasons not to do it. Such a venture would be very costly and distracting, in both monetary and human terms. In addition, campus space anywhere near Santa Monica came at a premium.

As one option, Boyajian and Hill commissioned a scenario plan to expand the Santa Monica headquarters. The expense, Boyajian said, was prohibitive, and helped him gain incentive to look for a new home for GIA at a more affordable price.

The tenacity Hill brought to the project surprised everyone, even Boyajian. "I knew Gary was the man for the job. What I didn't anticipate was the total commitment he brought to it."

Nevertheless, Boyajian insisted that the project become a two-man effort: Hill and Vince Manson, by now GIA's director of strategic planning, co-chaired it. "I was the dreamer," said Manson later, "deciding what the facility should encompass, in terms of scale and objectives. But Gary was the project leader, the nuts-and-bolts man.

"We worked together as a team, and when it was time to design the campus, the architect took his directions from both of us, so we had to agree! And if we didn't—and that was rare—we went to Bill to resolve it. So we formed a very good partnership, a balance that was essential to garner maximum success."

"We began looking outward for a site where we could have unimpeded growth for the next 50 years," said Boyajian. It had to be in the West, they agreed, and near a major airport (because of the frequent travel of GIA staff members, and for the convenience of students and visitors).

Hill started to make inquiries. Though Institute officials hoped to remain in the Los Angeles area, Hill cast a wide net in his search. "I looked as far east as Dallas and Fort Worth, Texas. I also looked in Reno and Carson City, Nevada, and in Arizona and northern California," he said later. "I gathered data on 300 sites, and personally visited well over 200 sites in four different states."

After he targeted a potential area, Hill got information about it from the local chamber of commerce, subscribed to the local newspapers, and checked out the crime statistics and local politics. He studied tax bases and attended city council meetings, noting the issues that came up and how they were resolved. He looked at local health care provisions and services, the cost of living, possible housing for GIA employees, and the distance of that housing from potential campus sites.

"We had to predict what those communities would be like 10, 30, 50 years from now. We weren't just moving the Institute and its employees: We were also moving hundreds of families. So it had to be a place that would remain a quality community well into the future."

MEANWHILE, BOYAJIAN, HILL, AND MANSON were also concerned about the impact a project of this magnitude would have on Institute life, including operations, activities, people, and financing. So they set out to better understand the vision for a new campus by documenting every possible aspect of why this venture was both reasonable and feasible. Students, staff, industry representatives, and GIA governors were included in the process. There were numerous interviews, staff and student surveys, memos and reports, and other interactions between 1988 and 1990.

In his search, Hill—sometimes accompanied by Manson—found himself repeatedly coming back to Southern California as the best area for the site. GIA already had its roots there. The area gave the Institute access to what Hill called "a pool of instructors, laboratory graders, and the kinds of people we needed."

"The employees helped us determine the climate and the environment they wanted, and it boiled down to a coastal environment in Southern California," said Hill. That eliminated communities east of L.A., "where the smog piles up," he explained. "So I stayed along the coast, where the air is the cleanest and there is a moderate climate."

WHEN HILL LEARNED ABOUT A CITY CALLED CARLSBAD, a coastal community about 100 miles south of Los Angeles and 30 miles north of San Diego, he

ACCORDING TO HILL, THE INSTITUTE'S FUTURE HOME "HAD TO BE A PLACE THAT WOULD REMAIN A QUALITY COMMUNITY WELL INTO THE FUTURE."

The Southern California coastal community of Carlsbad was chosen for GIA's new world headquarters.

was impressed by its clean air, low traffic and crime, and friendly people. The city also had an excellent growth management plan. It became clear that Carlsbad's pluses outweighed the difficulties GIA would have in relocating to a new home 100 miles from Santa Monica.

There were several possible campus sites in the Carlsbad area, all of which were closely evaluated by Hill. "We looked at their proximity to earthquake faults, checked environmental concerns such as air quality and the climate, and economic factors such as selection of housing, neighborhoods, and services within a short distance."

Finally, Hill found the one. It was on a gently sloping hill with plenty of acreage, overlooking the Pacific Ocean a mile away, on the former Carlsbad Ranch, a flower farm famous for its poinsettias. One could see scenic mountain vistas in the distance to the east, and the beautiful Pacific Ocean to the west. "This site will provide an atmosphere that promotes productivity and creativity," said Boyajian. "It is one of the last great pieces of land between Los Angeles and San Diego—a prestigious address for GIA at the best possible price."

Wanting is not the same as having, though. GIA may have decided to buy land in Carlsbad, but they had to work hard to get it. Indeed, the developer tried to sell the Institute every site on the farm (including one transected by power lines) except the one Hill wanted at the north end. Ultimately, Hill convinced the seller that nothing else was acceptable. (GIA also had the advantage at that moment of being the only serious bidder.)

Then the developer was willing to sell GIA just one seven-acre lot, but Hill bargained hard to buy that lot and others adjoining it. Over several months of negotiating, he managed to widen the Institute's purchase to 30 contiguous acres on the west side of the street dividing the ranch. Under the agreement, GIA would immediately buy 18 acres, with an option to purchase the other 12 between 2001 and 2003.

In fact, the deal was even better than it first seemed, because Hill was able to get the land for $4.4 million, almost $2 million less than the price originally quoted. At the time GIA and the developer reached a tentative price for the property, real estate prices in the Carlsbad area were dropping due to the recession of the early '90s, reaching an all-time low in 1993. With the support of the GIA Board of Governors, the deal was closed on January 14, 1994. Only months later, the toy giant Lego acquired a large parcel near GIA's site to build a theme park—which sent land prices soaring. "Our timing was perfect," said Hill. "If we had waited just a little longer, we wouldn't have stood a chance."

From GIA's new headquarters, employees, students, and visitors could enjoy a panoramic view of the famous Carlsbad flower fields and the Pacific Ocean.

WITH THE NEW HEADQUARTERS SITE APPROVED and secured, part two of the big project began: designing and redesigning the facility, putting together the development team (architects, engineers, a project manager, and a construction firm), building the campus, and transplanting GIA's staff to it. Hill and Manson's collaboration during this four-year period was essential.

"Vince had lots of dreams," said Hill. "We would sit down and talk concepts and bounce ideas off each other. For example, we talked about where the library should go. By the 1990s, it was an important source of knowledge and information for the industry and the public, and we concluded it should go front and center and be the first thing you see when you enter. A lot of people didn't agree. They remembered the way the library was in the 1970s or '80s, when it wasn't as important. Vince developed the concept of why it should go where it did and how to explain it to them."

Again, input from GIA staff and the trade was important. "From the very outset, we shared every aspect of our thinking and planning with the staff and industry leaders," said Boyajian. "Ultimately, this was a great team effort, and I believe that was the key to making the entire project a success."

Hill and Manson polled employees about the Santa Monica headquarters. "We asked them what they needed to work and held brain-storming sessions on what our goals should be," said Manson later. "Then, we discussed all environmental and structural considerations, and boiled that down to a 600-page book that summarized what GIA is and what we want it to become. We gave that to the architect saying, 'This is what we want you to design from.'"

This view of the Assael grand atrium at the Carlsbad campus shows the facility's open, minimalist design.

The Institute went with a medium-sized firm, LPA Inc. of San Diego. The firm's principal architect, Robert Coffee, was also the lead architect on the GIA project. Hill found that one of his biggest challenges during the planning and construction was "getting GIA to hold still long enough to get the campus built! GIA is a very dynamic organization and its needs are always changing," he explained. To design the Gem Trade Laboratory wing, for example, Hill and his team had depended on the lab's initial estimate of the amount of space it would need by 2000. But in the mid-'90s the laboratory had already reached that size, "so we had to stretch the building out" in the final plans and construction.

The final blueprints for the new campus offered what *JCK* called "a 230,000 sq. ft. magnum opus to gemology," twice as large as GIA's old home in Santa Monica. Indeed, all five of the Institute's previous headquarters could have fit comfortably into its new world headquarters, with room to spare.

There were enough classrooms to handle 450 students at a time. There was twice as much space for GIA's marvelous gemological library, for example, with ample room for expansion and additions. The Gem Trade Laboratory area was designed for functionality and comfort, and to accommodate the growing needs of its clientele. There was space for additional staff and improved services and operations.

The research department was twice as large as in Santa Monica, with space for additional personnel, larger and more sophisticated equipment, and areas for the most sensitive technical work. Altogether, it would "strengthen our ability to respond to the ever-changing needs of gemology," said research director Jim Shigley.

GEM Instruments' expanded quarters included a fully appointed showroom, with space to examine, test, and purchase the most modern tools and equipment. There was a larger warehouse, more room to develop new products and programs, and improved customer support systems.

The design of the complex was minimalist with almost no ornamentation and, in Hill's words, "Mediterranean." That meant buildings of glass, steel, and granite created to take advantage of the sunny climate, with open atriums and lots of windows, skylights, and balconies. An abundance of floor-to-ceiling glass "walls" throughout let natural light fill the interior, which was adorned with glittering gem displays. Outside, there were wide piazzas, colonnades, eating areas, and a grassy forum overlooking the Pacific Ocean.

"We designed the complex to be a very livable area" said Hill, "where the outdoors could sneak right in." Indeed, there was as much emphasis on ensuring the comfort, security, and well-being of employees and students as there was on functionality. Hill made sure the plans included such amenities as movable walls, European-style air conditioning systems (which gave individual employees control over their own local temperature), and state-of-the-art "raised floors"—about 18 inches above the foundation slab—to allow easy routing of phone and computer lines, as well as distribution of air conditioning and heat. Diffused lighting was used throughout to "mimic" daylight in darker areas and minimize glare on computer screens. In addition, the overall design took into consideration the unique security needs of the Institute.

AN ABUNDANCE OF FLOOR-TO-CEILING GLASS "WALLS" THROUGHOUT LET NATURAL LIGHT FILL THE INTERIOR, WHICH WAS ADORNED WITH GLITTERING GEM DISPLAYS.

Left to right: Vince Manson, Bill Boyajian, and Gary Hill prepare for the groundbreaking of the Carlsbad headquarters in June 1995.

But to the casual observer, the most impressive aspect of the building was that, as *San Diego Union-Tribune* reporter Kelly Thornton noted, "virtually every classroom and office [had] a stunning view" of the Pacific Ocean, a lagoon, or the famous Carlsbad flower fields, with several commons areas having the best views. "Our feeling is that everyone has a right to a view," Hill said. "We want the views to be remembered by students, friends, and alumni who visit the Institute from around the world."

The end result of all these considerations was what Boyajian referred to as "a great place to live at work."

GROUNDBREAKING FOR WHAT WAS NOW called "The New World Headquarters" of GIA took place on a sunny but breezy Friday afternoon, June 2, 1995. Liddicoat and Boyajian, using shiny shovels, dug the first spadefuls. It was a brief ceremony, but important enough to have the Carlsbad mayor and city council present and to attract the attention of the local newspaper, the *Carlsbad Sun*, which called GIA the "first jewel" in the Carlsbad Ranch development site. "The quality of the organization coming here is incredible," a delighted Dale Condy, owner of Gems of La Costa and a 1972 GIA graduate, told the newspaper.

Core construction on the new site took a year, and included three large buildings, two of which were connected by a grand atrium. One housed classrooms, offices, and the Liddicoat Gemological Library and Information Center. Another housed GIA's non-education operations—the Gem Trade Laboratory, GIA Research, GEM Instruments, GIA ARMS, the print shop, shipping, and a warehouse with a state-of-the-art inventory control system. The third building housed GIA's administrative and corporate offices. The plans provided for future additions on the other 12 acres—possibly including an auditorium, a museum, and a cafeteria—based on the expectation that GIA would eventually grow in the 21st century to more than twice its 1997 size.

During the building phase, Hill was assisted by GIA project manager Tom Costello. Other Institute officials and employees periodically visited the

Carlsbad site to see it for themselves. Jim Shigley, for example, came to inspect the new research facilities as they neared completion. "It's a special feeling to stand on that hill, surrounded by flowers, looking out at the Pacific Ocean, and to realize that this huge campus is devoted to the growth of the jewelry industry," he said later. "I wish everyone could stand on this spot. They would begin to grasp just how much this place means to the future of gemology."

With construction nearing completion, the next part of the plan called for relocating the Institute's staff, equipment, and departments. The biggest concern was that the move would interrupt regular operations and cause the loss of key staff members. To minimize disruption, GIA relocated in two phases over 16 months, from 1996 through the spring of 1997. First to move were the West Coast Gem Trade Laboratory, GIA Research, GIA GEM Instruments, GIA ARMS, and the printing and shipping departments. To reduce delays and keep up with demand, the laboratory functioned for months with both its old computer system and the new Horizon management system, while it integrated Horizon into its operations.

Between January and May 1997, the second half of GIA's contingent moved—education, the bookstore, the library, marketing, development, accounting, *Gems & Gemology*, and the president's office. Much of the coordination for all of these moves was provided by director of materiel services Cynthia Sanders and relocation manager Dan Tilton.

From within the flower fields, GIA headquarters is shown here under construction.

EVEN WITH THE RELOCATION OF ITS HEADQUARTERS to Carlsbad, GIA continued its presence in Los Angeles as an educational center. On August 25, 1997, it opened a new educational facility in the International Jewelry Center building at 550 South Hill Street. It was designed, said Veronica Clark-Hudson, the director of GIA Los Angeles education, for people juggling a busy schedule who want to complete their GIA classes and assignments in one handy place. "We may have moved our headquarters and campus 100 miles south of Los Angeles, but our ties with L.A. remain strong," she said.

Indeed, for GIA staffers, they were very strong. Boyajian had hoped that a large majority of the 391 staff members in Santa Monica would relocate to Carlsbad. In the end, 241—62 percent—of GIA's family trekked south.

THE FINAL COST OF THE CARLSBAD PROJECT, INCLUDING LAND PURCHASE, CONSTRUCTION, AND RELOCATION, WAS $39.4 MILLION.

However, an even higher percentage of key department heads and technical personnel made the move. Most of those who stayed in Los Angeles did so for family reasons. Some who relocated weren't happy doing it, but almost all were soon pleased with the new location, the new headquarters, its amenities, and the environment of North San Diego County. One staff member of the West Coast lab summed up those conflicting feelings when she told Boyajian after GIA had settled into its new home, "I wanted to punch you in the nose when you announced our move to Carlsbad. Now, I could hug you!"

THE FINAL COST OF THE CARLSBAD PROJECT—including land purchase, construction, new furnishings, equipment, landscaping, and relocation—was $39.4 million, a bargain in view of rising costs and property values at the decade's end. To pay for it, the Institute used several sources of financing. It sold its properties in Santa Monica for about $15 million. Of that, $8.8 million (four times GIA's original purchase price) was for the old headquarters itself, which was sold to Santa Monica College on March 4, 1996. "It's gratifying to know," Boyajian said then, that the campus would "continue in the service of higher education."

In addition, as a nonprofit educational institution, GIA in 1995 was able to borrow $30 million at a fixed low-interest rate from the California Statewide Community Development Authority. Under terms governed by GIA's non-profit status, the Institute floated tax-free bonds called "certificates of participation" to accumulate the funding necessary to complete the move and construction of the Carlsbad campus. And it developed a special program called the New World Headquarters Capital Campaign to help raise money for the building activities.

That campaign, launched in November 1996, the same month the new campus was dedicated, was designed to give individuals, organizations, and companies in the international gem and jewelry industry the chance to establish what GIA literature called "an enduring affiliation with the Institute" by donating money to have buildings, sections, or areas of the new campus named in their honor.

The industry's generous response to the project was overwhelming, with many of the initial donations coming from the pearl sector. Mikimoto of Japan, whose founder created the cultured pearl, pledged $500,000 to name the rotunda inside the main building. Salvador J. Assael, chairman of Assael International Inc., a leader in producing, processing and distributing South Sea and Tahitian cultured pearls, contributed $1 million to name the grand

The Mouawad brothers (from left: Pascal, Alain, and Fred) join Bill Boyajian next to a rendering of the entrance to the Robert Mouawad Campus.

atrium. Robert Wan, a pioneer in Tahitian black cultured pearls, donated $1 million to name an education wing in honor of his family's dedication to "excellence and quality in the pearl market." Jewelers Mutual Insurance Co., a trade leader in jewelry insurance, gave $200,000 for the Jewelers Mutual Plaza overlooking the ocean, while the International Jewelers Block & Fine Arts Insurance Services pledged $150,000 for a fully fitted and equipped classroom named in its honor.

But the largest, most important—and staggering—"naming" gift of all came at the start of the campaign and sprang from the filial devotion of three sons.

IN 1996, GIA GRADUATES FRED AND PASCAL MOUAWAD, both G.G.'s, and their brother Alain, donated $6.8 million to name the entire GIA campus for their father, Robert Mouawad. Little known at the time to most U.S. jewelers, the Lebanese-born Mouawad was the head of an international jewelry manufacturing and retailing empire, the Mouawad Group. Though he had been studying medicine, at age 19 Mouawad took over the family firm when his father fell ill, and subsequently built it into a global mega-business.

By the end of the 1990s, when Robert Mouawad was in his 50s, the Mouawad Group employed 1,400 people worldwide and enjoyed annual sales topping $300 million. Headquartered in Jeddah, Saudi Arabia, it had offices and

Third-generation jeweler Robert Mouawad built the family business into an internationally renowned jewelry house.

Gregory Zabilski

jewelry-making operations in Paris, Geneva, and Bangkok; diamond buying and cutting offices in Antwerp; and retail stores in Europe, the Near East, and the Far East. Mouawad jewelry was worn by heads of state and movie stars, as well as by dignitaries as varied as U.S. President George Bush, the Emperor and Empress of Japan, and Britain's adored Princess Diana. By then, Robert Mouawad had also become one of the world's leading collectors of rare diamonds and other gems, spending $300 million between 1976 and 1993 to buy gems at auctions. His three sons, all employed by the Mouawad Group, considered the chance to name GIA's campus for their father the ideal way to honor him.

"His success story had similarities to the success of GIA," said Fred Mouawad, his eldest son, who later became chairman of the new world headquarters fundraising campaign. Like Institute founder Robert M. Shipley, Mouawad was "a self-driven man [who] seized an opportunity and deployed an extraordinary effort to grow his business and extend it around the world, [who] kept his reputation untouched through his fair and ethical conduct, and who took risks at times when others did not have the courage to do so."

His sons told Mouawad of their gift at his home in Geneva, Switzerland, and this demonstration of their love and respect for him literally brought tears to the global businessman's eyes. It was "the most precious gift my children ever gave me," he said later. "This important decision" also demonstrated their ability "to be visionary . . . to give back to society and [showed] that they valued the education they had pursued, especially the one at GIA."

By the end of May 1997, little more than half a year after the capital campaign began, GIA had already received some $10 million in fundraising pledges, demonstrating, more than ever perhaps, the trade's view of GIA's essential mission.

WHILE CONSTRUCTION CREWS put on the finishing touches, a series of events over a 10-month period starting in late 1996 helped introduce the new campus to the local, domestic, and international gem and jewelry communities.

The new world headquarters was officially dedicated on the first weekend of November 1996, with industry dignitaries from around the world participating. On November 1, major donors to the Vision 2000 campaign planted

GEMOLOGICAL INSTITUTE OF AMERICA

THE ROBERT MOUAWAD CAMPUS

The front entrance to
the Robert Mouawad
Campus.

20 trees leading to the main entrance of the campus. On the afternoon of
November 2, guests were given personalized tours of the campus before
being seated with GIA staff near the center of the new complex for a dedication ceremony led by chairman Richard T. Liddicoat.

"It is really a wonderful thing to see the support we've received over the
years and to see it make possible an edifice of this magnitude," said Liddicoat
in an eloquent and emotional speech.

"In recognition of the commitment of the staff, leadership, board of governors, and supporters gathered here," he then declared, "and in recognition
of GIA's goal to serve and grow in strength, vitality, and vision as the world
center for research and education of the gem and jewelry industry, protect-
ing the public trust and training legions of people in the jewelry profession
as we stand on the threshold of the new century, I hereby dedicate the new
world headquarters of the Gemological Institute of America."

At the front of the campus, an artist's rendition of the monument (then under
construction) naming the campus in Robert Mouawad's honor was unveiled
for the guests. Mouawad described the new campus as an environment "of

excellence, dedication, and ambition, an environment that inspires students from all over the world to come and pursue an education in our industry." It was, he said as he looked around at GIA's magnificent new home, "the fruits of a vision, the result of great perseverance."

That was true of the builders, the planners, Boyajian, Manson, and the board of governors. And it was especially true of Gary Hill, whose tenacity and commitment had seen the project to its conclusion, and made the dream a reality, almost a decade after he had been assigned this mission by Boyajian.

On May 28, 1997, a sunny day with gentle breezes wafting over the gleaming new Carlsbad campus on a hill overlooking the Pacific Ocean, a lighthouse for the industry shone brightly as it prepared to enter the 21st century. Nearly 1,000 industry leaders, students, GIA staff members, and media from around the world attended the official grand opening of the new world headquarters of the Gemological Institute of America.

In the atrium, major donors were recognized as each stepped forward to whisk away black drapes from signs bearing their names and that of the campus area their donations sponsored. "The signs will stay there for generations to come in their honor, reminding visitors, students, and GIA staffers of their dedication to GIA and the betterment of the trade," said an Institute spokesperson later. The official opening was not only important for GIA, but it was also "an auspicious occasion for the worldwide gem and jewelry community," Boyajian told guests.

THE NEW CARLSBAD HEADQUARTERS, LIDDICOAT SAID, IS A PLACE "WHERE TODAY'S STUDENTS CAN BUILD THE CAREERS OF TOMORROW."

"As we sit on the threshold of the next century," said chairman Richard Liddicoat to those assembled, "GIA has readied itself as never before to face future challenges." The new Carlsbad headquarters, he said, "bridges the gap between science and business [and is a place] where today's students can build the careers of tomorrow. This confirms GIA as a remarkable educational institute, unique in American industry. I'm sure that our founder, Robert M. Shipley, would be as proud of this achievement as we are."

Even before this official welcome, the first resident students of the new Carlsbad campus—13 members of the jewelry design course—were graduated on April 25. Then on July 24 and 25, GIA graduated 35 students, from a wide network of homelands ranging from the U.S. to Tanzania to Japan, who were the first Graduate Gemologists, Graduate Jewelers, and Graduate Jeweler Gemologists of the new world headquarters and campus.

"As the first gemologists and jewelers graduating from our new campus, you will always be remembered as the pioneers who brought the Carlsbad campus to life," Boyajian told them.

The first students to graduate from the Carlsbad campus are joined in the rotunda by jewelry manufacturing arts manager Sherrie Kysilka and instructor Bob Ahrens (far left) and education vice president Brook Ellis (far right).

MAY 1997 WAS A TIME OF EXHILARATION FOR GIA. The long-dreamed-of campus was a magnificent reality, in a wonderful location with plenty of room to grow and a steady stream of local, national, and international visitors.

But for one man, it was a bittersweet moment. For Richard Liddicoat, the old Santa Monica headquarters had been, he said often, "my second home." Now, it was time to formally say goodbye.

The farewell came on May 30, 1997, two days after the grand opening of the new Carlsbad headquarters, but it was a much smaller and more subdued ceremony. Liddicoat and Hill, with a few close friends, walked the old headquarters' hallways for the last time, occasionally looking in at the empty classrooms and offices. As they did, they reminisced about students and colleagues of days gone by.

And then they left.

Liddicoat was the last person to exit the building. As he turned to lock the front doors of GIA's former Santa Monica headquarters for the very last time, he reflected on the many graduating classes that had passed through

Former GIA president and chairman for life Richard Liddicoat officially locked the door of the Institute's Santa Monica facility on May 30, 1997.

the facility. To him, this was also the Institute's alma mater, the place, he said, "where we added to the foundation [of GIA and gemology] that enabled us to realize our dreams."

But, Liddicoat said later, "any sadness was short-lived, because I know that GIA's future is secure at our new headquarters in Carlsbad." The Institute's crowded halls, frequent moves, and inadequate expansions of past years were over. "Now, we have built a home to service our students and gem and jewelry industry professionals for generations to come," said the Institute's proud chairman.

Though the Carlsbad headquarters was 100 miles away from his home in Los Angeles, Liddicoat was still an active part of the Institute. Indeed, it wouldn't have been GIA without him. In Carlsbad, he had a large corner office filled with bookcases and mementos of a distinguished career. A wall of windows in one corner gave him a magnificent view of the ocean. It was only a few paces from Boyajian's office.

Liddicoat frequently drove down to Carlsbad, spending much of the week there until illness at the end of the 1990s made traveling more difficult. For Boyajian, Liddicoat's counsel was invaluable.

"He's the source, the authority, the father of modern gemology," said Boyajian in 1997 of his mentor. "He is quiet and humble by nature, with a dry, impish sense of humor and a sharp intellect. Yet I've never seen anyone so personally understated who stands out so much among people. He is the embodiment of GIA," said Boyajian.

Richard Liddicoat's insight, experience, and advice—and that of his friend and past president Glenn Nord—were still essential to the affairs of GIA as it prepared to enter the 21st century. Liddicoat remained active as chairman of the board of governors. He reviewed course materials and continued attending AGS Conclaves and other gemological conferences. In the spring of 2002, he celebrated his 50th anniversary as editor-in-chief of *Gems & Gemology*.

Indeed, Liddicoat enjoyed the freedom that being chairman gave him. "I had the opportunity to point out areas of concern and things that I think should occupy our attention. I could support the president or be lukewarm if I wanted to be. But generally, it gave me a chance to push areas that were important to Glenn when he was president or to Bill, and to me."

The Institute gained strength from the involvement of its former presidents, who had secured the future that the new campus embodied.

IN CARLSBAD, GIA QUICKLY BECAME INVOLVED in the daily life and activities of its new community. When Institute staff learned, for example, that La Palma High, a small local high school, had to make do annually with a simple yearbook of photocopied pages, they offered the school their assistance. Course development's graphics team provided technical support and training to La Palma students, and GIA's printing facilities, under the direction of Steve Knoop, produced 175 copies. The result was a professionally printed yearbook—and a delighted student body. In a letter to Boyajian, school principal Lou Pollock thanked GIA for its staffers' "generosity of spirit to help, mentor, and support."

Amy Toosley/GIA

Carlsbad assistant city manager Frank Mannen (center) and GIA community development director Gary Hill (right) review the printing of a booklet for a local high school with GIA print shop manager Tim Wolf in 2002.

Hill also led a program that included many GIA volunteers to build a citywide network of walking trails. Indeed, Hill became such an active figure in the Carlsbad community that the *North County Times* wrote that if the community gave "an award for best community project leader of the year, Gary Hill would head the list." His efforts had helped save the city almost $200,000 in building the trail system. Hill also became very active in the Carlsbad Chamber of Commerce, and served as chairman of its board in 2002.

IN THE EARLY 21ST CENTURY, the Institute added a pair of spectacular touches to its Carlsbad campus. First, a museum gallery was established in April 2000. Open for public viewing, it displayed important gem, jewelry, and photo collections. Development of the museum concept continued in 2001, with a grand reopening in an expanded gallery. Jewelry historian Elise Misiorowski, who had worked for GIA as a research librarian during the 1980s, returned to the Institute as museum director. Under Misiorowski's leadership, the GIA Museum continued to develop its collections and host a variety of exhibits and special presentations. Additional displays of gemological interest throughout the Institute, such as cases dedicated to honor Shipley and Liddicoat, furthered the efforts to turn the campus into a living museum.

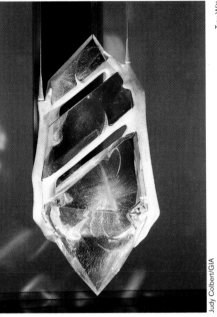

Judy Colbert/GIA

Troy Witt

With the creation of the GIA Museum in April 2000, the Carlsbad campus became a living gallery of the gem and jewelry industry. Left: The rutilated quartz carving Bahia, at over 966,000 carats possibly the world's largest cut gem, holds a place of honor in the grand atrium. Right: GIA governor Eli Haas and his wife Norma view award-winning pieces from the World Facet Award 2002 for jewelry design.

Another touch for the Carlsbad headquarters was completed November 10, 2002, with the unveiling of the GIA Tower of Brilliance. The 55-foot tower housed a one-ton "crystal" octahedron custom-designed and donated by the famed crystal manufacturer D. Swarovski & Co. The crystal octahedron was the largest of its kind in the world. More than 600 guests attended the unveiling ceremony and watched as the octahedron illuminated the evening sky for the first time. Helmut Swarovski, the firm's chief executive officer, said, "A permanent landmark of perpetual light, the GIA Tower of Brilliance signifies our gratitude and admiration for GIA, as well as our commitment to the Institute's future."

JUNE 10, 2000, MARKED A SPECIAL DATE in the history of the Gemological Institute of America and its picturesque new campus.

On that Saturday afternoon, the Institute held an official commencement, the first in history, for any GIA diploma holder. Close to 300 graduates, many of whom had never seen the Carlsbad campus, accepted the invitation and attended Commencement 2000. There were young women who had earned their diplomas doing coursework online, and retirees who

The GIA Tower of Brilliance was unveiled November 10, 2002. Its one-ton "crystal" octahedron was designed and donated by D. Swarovski & Co.

Denis Poroy

remembered waiting weeks for their next lessons to be delivered. There were small-town jewelers and industry leaders, some who had come from as far away as Russia, Japan, New Zealand, and Pakistan for their formal graduation ceremony.

After the keynote address from Dr. Christopher Bramlett, a GIA graduate with a distinguished career in education and the jewelry industry, the graduates crossed the stage as several hundred family members, friends, and colleagues looked on. Former GIA president Glenn Nord, a 1959 graduate, was the first one honored. Each diploma holder received a commemorative medallion bearing the likeness of Institute founder Robert M. Shipley.

The event was held almost exactly 70 years to the day after San Diego jeweler Armand Jessop had convinced Shipley to give a series of evening lectures on gems, the popularity of which led to the founding of GIA in 1931. And Commencement 2000 was proof, with graduates from all over the world meeting on a remarkable campus filled with educational and scientific resources, of how thoroughly the Institute had "professionalized" the global gem and jewelry industry.

Melissa Jacobs/GIA

GIA graduates Sara Gübelin, Daniela Pescher, and Margaret Byworth attended Commencement 2000, the first formal commencement ceremony in the Institute's history.

Corporate executive Peter Ueberroth, *Time* magazine's Man of the Year in 1984, delivers the keynote address at GIA's third International Gemological Symposium.

FACING THE FUTURE:
THE INTERNATIONAL GEMOLOGICAL
SYMPOSIUMS OF THE '90s

1986–2003

Two significant events for GIA and the global gem and jewelry industry book-ended the 1990s: the Institute's International Gemological Symposiums of 1991 and 1999. They were important not only for bringing together the leaders of the world's gemological community, but also for the spotlight they cast on the major issues, controversies, and challenges facing the industry and GIA at the end of the 20th century.

▪FACING THE FUTURE:
THE 1991 INTERNATIONAL GEMOLOGICAL SYMPOSIUM

In February 1987, about the same time GIA's top executives began drafting the Institute's Master Plan for its future, Bill Boyajian and Vince Manson were also recalling its past. Knowing that 1991 would mark GIA's 60th anniversary—its Diamond Jubilee—they began to think about an occasion to celebrate the milestone achievements of GIA and the gem and jewelry industry. But they also wanted a forum in which to address the profound industry changes in the 1980s, as well as the emergence of a global economy in the 1990s.

"Our world was shrinking, and our industry was on the threshold of a surge unequaled in its history, drawing players from around the world into a common market," Boyajian wrote later. "What, then, could we do to honor the industry and this exciting new global era?"

Actually, they already had the answer. Taking their cue from the Institute's groundbreaking 1982 International Gemological Symposium, they decided to create another meeting of the minds that would provide an international gathering unlike any before it. It would also be one of the largest, most demanding projects GIA had ever undertaken.

As he had been for the first Symposium, Manson was tapped to chair the event, which adopted the theme "Facing the Future." It was an appropriate choice. Manson was an idea man, a visionary, and an energetic facilitator who took what in other hands might be routine and turned it into something exceptional. Manson wasn't content to simply repeat the agenda and format of the 1982 Symposium.

Significantly, the focus was no longer on gemology and gemological research alone. The 1991 Symposium's spotlight was wider, covering a

The 1991 Symposium's poster session was a "marketplace of ideas," showcasing the latest research in key areas of gemology. Here, famed diamond cutter Basil Watermeyer prepares his poster presentation on diamond brilliance.

range of practical applications. The theme of "Facing the Future" entailed many other aspects, including globalization, marketing, technology, economics, and jewelry arts.

So a key objective was to turn the Symposium into a sort of industry roundtable for the "global village," bringing retailers, gem dealers, and management into contact with key industry players the world over. The opportunity to mix with these people and share views would be just as important as the program's content.

IN ADDITION TO THE SPEAKERS and panel sessions on key issues, a new feature Manson introduced at the 1991 Symposium was the poster session. In a large conference room, poster presenters were given booth space to exhibit their new research, techniques, software, collections, designs, and other concepts. This "marketplace of ideas," as Manson christened it, would showcase state-of-the-art information using handouts, photos, models, and other visual displays. While not new to academic conferences, the concept of a poster session was certainly new to gemology.

And to ensure that the event would be enjoyable as well as informative, the 1991 Symposium was planned with a variety of distinctly non-academic events—such as a pearl fashion show, an evening gala celebrating Italy's jewels and cultural legacy, and a fabulous night dancing among the dinosaurs at the Los Angeles County Natural History Museum. Manson sought not only the right blend of technical presentations, but also a powerful visual and emotional experience.

IT TOOK NEARLY FOUR YEARS TO PUT TOGETHER the second International Gemological Symposium, but from early on many organizations and firms lent their support. Several important trade associations chose to link their own convocations with the event. GIA's younger sibling, the American Gem Society, held its 57th annual Conclave concurrent with the Symposium, with some 400 AGS members attending. The Gemmological Association of Great Britain, which had a relationship with GIA dating back to GIA founder Robert Shipley, celebrated its 61st anniversary at the Symposium. The Nihon Gem Society and AGT (GIA's Japanese affiliate, which later became GIA Japan) each

Rikio Tanaka (front right) and members of the Nihon Gem Society, which celebrated its 20th anniversary at the 1991 Symposium. The NGS was one of several important associations that linked their own anniversaries with the event.

celebrated its 20th anniversary, and the American Gem Trade Association its 10th. The International Colored Gemstone Association scheduled its 1991 Congress in Hawaii right before the Symposium so that members could travel on to Los Angeles the following week. Delegations also came from the Instituto Gemmologico Mediterraneo in Italy, the Gemological Institute of Korea (later GIA Korea), and the Canadian Jewellers Institute.

The second International Gemological Symposium was held June 20–24, 1991, at the Century Plaza Hotel in Los Angeles (also the site of the first Symposium). More than 1,800 people from 42 countries attended. It was a magnificent way to celebrate the Institute's 60th anniversary. The Symposium's schedule of events offered insights from more than 100 industry experts. Over three days, attendees took part in 73 speaker presentations and 10 panel discussions, with 95 poster session displays.

Diamond-related topics prevailed at the 1991 Symposium. But true to Manson's promise of facing the industry's future in all its aspects, the sessions also covered dozens of other topics—ranging from gem sources in Afghanistan to 19th-century French jewelry, from new synthetics and advances in gem identification to demographics, from Vietnamese rubies to computer databases, and from marketing in the '90s to the impact of global economics on local jewelry retailing. Altogether, the Symposium's program was the most diverse and comprehensive yet offered to members of the gem and jewelry industry.

The 1991 Symposium was the most important global gathering of gemological researchers assembled up to that point. Left: Robert Kane and Jean-Paul Poirot prepare a presentation. Right: Peter Read, Tom Moses, Dr. Henry Hänni, Robert Kammerling, and Dr. Karl Schmetzer share ideas.

ONE MAJOR THEME THAT FLOWED THROUGH the 1991 Symposium was globalization and its effect on the gem and jewelry industry. The keynote speaker at the opening ceremony was John Naisbitt, whose 1985 book *Reinventing the Corporation* had greatly impressed Boyajian during his first year as GIA's president. His 1986 book, *Megatrends*, became a best seller, as it pointed to 10 new directions that would impact the 1990s.

The move to commercial globalization was evident at the end of the 1980s in a variety of ways, Naisbitt told the audience. Increased international trade, telecommunications, and travel had laid the groundwork. Multinational firms such as IKEA, McDonald's, and Benetton were "homogenizing" the global marketplace, while American exports of entertainment and technology had made English an international language, unifying more than one billion English speakers around the world.

As the '90s progressed, he predicted, there would be more free-trade zones and an eventual breakdown in global trade barriers. The bottom line to this increasingly international commercialization, he said, was that "the booming, affluent '90s are coming. The new era has begun."

The 1991 Symposium, the most important gathering of gem and jewelry professionals assembled up to that point, ended with Boyajian identifying key challenges to the gem and jewelry industry in the immediate future.

"Our industry must support the research needed to keep us well ahead of the developing [synthetic and treatment] technologies, and thus preserve the integrity of the market," he said. "It must educate sales and technical personnel so they can deal with those technologies and maintain customer confidence."

Then, peering deeply into his audience, Boyajian closed the second Symposium by telling them, "You saw the future here, and the future is bright. Let us face the future together and make our dreams—for ourselves and for our industry—come true!"

■MEETING THE MILLENNIUM: THE 1999 INTERNATIONAL GEMOLOGICAL SYMPOSIUM

By the late 1990s, the "bright future" Bill Boyajian referred to in his closing speech had become a robust and yet unsettled present for the gem and jewelry trade.

In the years since the second Symposium, there had been enormous changes in the industry. Gem enhancements had become increasingly sophisticated, including new emerald fillers and supposedly "undetectable" diamond treatments. Antwerp diamond dealers had been forced to overhaul their business practices, while Israel's cutters had turned to robots and computers. The once-powerful Asian markets were weakened by economic crisis. De Beers had initiated the concept of branding their diamonds. Diamond profit margins were declining, while defining the best cut had become a controversial issue. The once staid and stable industry now included a multinational manufacturer of appliances and jet engines (General Electric Co.) that treated diamonds, as well as Internet retailers and television shopping networks competing against traditional jewelers.

As the world stood on the threshold of the 21st century, it clearly was time for GIA to convene another International Gemological Symposium to help make sense of the rapid changes and uncertainties. For the third time, Manson was named Symposium chairman and placed in charge of planning the massive global gemological convocation, which this time would be held in San Diego. Because this event would be far more expensive to produce than the previous ones, and to keep costs to attendees down, GIA depended on its base of donors to provide an even greater level of support. Altogether, the Institute raised well over a million dollars to help offset the costs of the third Symposium, from more than two dozen major co-sponsors and contributors.

THE THIRD INTERNATIONAL GEMOLOGICAL SYMPOSIUM OPENED June 21, 1999, on a Monday afternoon at the Hyatt Regency Hotel in San Diego. More than 1,400 people representing 49 countries attended the four-day event. Attendees included a cross section of the industry, from mom-and-pop stores and major chains to jewelry manufacturers and gem dealers.

In his valedictory address, Bill Boyajian urged 1991 Symposium attendees to "face the future" with commitment and resolve.

In June 1999, the gem and jewelry industry gathered at the San Diego Hyatt Regency Hotel (far left) for the Institute's third International Gemological Symposium. The four-day event drew more than 1,400 people from 49 different countries.

Symposium founder Vince Manson, speaking at the 1991 event. Manson was unable to attend the 1999 Symposium and succumbed to cancer just days after it concluded.

"We are making history this week," Boyajian told the opening session. Not only had this Symposium "attracted the best in all classes, from the most brilliant scientists to the most savvy retail jewelers," he continued, but this grand meeting also marked "the gemological finale of the 20th century."

Boyajian's reference to a finale was bittersweet, because the 1990s had seen the passing of a number of GIA leaders who had helped the Institute reach this level of recognition and influence: Eunice Miles, the pioneering female gemologist of GIA's New York lab; Dennis Foltz and John Hummel, who had given GIA's educational portfolio new vitality and relevance; James Lucey, who exemplified GIA's talented and resourceful teachers; and Robert Kammerling, brilliant in so many posts, from teacher to author to gem researcher.

For those attending the third Symposium, though, the most poignant loss was of the Symposium's founder, Dr. Vince Manson. For more than a year before the start of Symposium, while orchestrating its many details, he also waged a courageous battle against cancer. When the 1999 Symposium finally arrived, he was simply too weak to attend his greatest innovation. Manson died shortly after its conclusion.

But Manson did have one final gesture to make to the industry. He sent a message to the Symposium attendees, which his longtime friend and colleague Alice Keller read at the opening ceremony.

"I am known as a dreamer," he wrote. "Thankfully, our industry is full of dreamers—taking dreams, creating visions, and making reality . . . .

"It gives me great pleasure, then, to invite you, the great people of the jewelry industry, to pick up this work in progress, to carry it forward toward the new millennium . . . Ladies and gentlemen, I declare this Symposium . . . open!"

THE INSIGHTS AND OPINIONS that marked the 1999 Symposium were delivered in a variety of informative, provocative formats. The core of the program was a series of concurrent speaker and panelist sessions addressing such topics as sources, production, and marketing of diamonds, colored stones, and pearls. Other presentations included gem identification, synthetics, treatments, antique and estate jewelry, fine jewelry, and retailing. The popular poster session of the second Symposium was back, with 66 booths offering a new selection of intriguing ideas. A stimulating lineup of social events was put together, including the "Meeting the World" opening reception, the "Nature of Diamonds" event at the San Diego Natural History Museum, and pearl and Italian jewelry fashion shows.

New to the 1999 program were four War Room sessions. These freewheeling forums were designed to tackle the industry's most contentious topics—branding, appraisals, diamond cut, and disclosure of treatments—through lively debate and wide-open audience participation. While the moderators fired hard-hitting questions at the panelists, roaming microphones drew spontaneous reactions from the audience. Each of the War Room sessions drew standing-room-only crowds, producing some of the 1999 Symposium's most dynamic moments.

BECAUSE OF THE SWEEPING CHANGES taking place in the gem, jewelry, and retail industries, this GIA Symposium was the most controversial yet. If the second Symposium was designed to "Face the Future" with its evolving globalization and technology, the third event confronted attendees with the realities of those changes.

The "Pearl Fashion Preview" (top) was just one of several elegant events at the third Symposium. The War Room sessions (bottom) featured rapid-fire, lively debate and audience participation. At the Disclosure War Room, moderator Cheryl Kremkow and the panelists listen as synthetic gem producer Tom Chatham voices his opinion.

Joe Duffy/GIA

The Internet made its presence felt at the 1999 Symposium, where attendees were anxious to learn how this new medium would affect the industry in the future. GIA's T. Scott Hemphill and James Marker (foreground) were among the many users of the event's Internet Café.

One was the Internet, a computer technology that few, if any, at the 1991 Symposium had even heard of. By 1999 it had emerged as a mass communication medium, a part of everyday life for much of the world's population. The Internet's presence seemed to be everywhere at the Symposium. While some presentations were devoted entirely to the Internet, it permeated nearly every other session, as attendees scrambled to learn more and more about it as a medium for retail, distribution, and marketing. They also debated—sometimes intensely—its potential impact on the gem and jewelry industry in the coming century.

Another significant characteristic of the third Symposium was its focus on business in the new century. Not the business of gemology or jewelry or diamonds, but the business of business. Indeed, Symposium planners considered business strategy so important that, at the suggestion of Marketing vice president Kathryn Kimmel, they set aside an entire day for it. And the people they chose to address those issues came from outside the gem and jewelry industry. Even the keynote speaker for this world summit wasn't an icon of the trade, but corporate executive Peter Ueberroth, best known as the organizer of the 1984 Summer Olympics in Los Angeles and honored as *Time* magazine's Man of the Year that year. Other business heavyweights included marketing and branding guru Al Ries, digital technology expert Donald Tapscott, ethicist Rushworth Kidder, and economist Arthur Laffer.

But the issues that dominated this Symposium more than any others were diamond related, and they revealed an industry in flux, divided on how to handle new challenges. That was evident right from the Symposium's opening, when De Beers chairman Nicholas Oppenheimer addressed the audience via videotape (as he had in 1991). Oppenheimer pointed out that the end of the '90s was a time of change for De Beers, long an industry symbol of stability and control. He spoke of its separation from Anglo-American Corp., a plan to extend the life of its mines, new marketing projects in the U.S., a joint venture to open a mine in Canada, and a "strategic review" of its operations—which in its vagueness made some attendees uneasy.

In the Branding War Room, the debate quickly narrowed to diamond branding, especially the De Beers Millennium Diamonds. In the Diamond Cut War Room, the relevance of the "ideal cut" in a new age and GIA's research on the effect of cut on diamond appearance were hotly debated. The GIA brilliance paper—the result of a decade of study—came under attack, although supporters and Institute officials said it would ultimately provide cutters with far wider parameters and opportunities to cut quality diamonds.

But the most controversial diamond issue at the Symposium—"the number one topic among attendees," reported *JCK* magazine—was General Electric's supposedly undetectable process for improving the color of natural diamonds and its implications for the industry. Announced in March 1999, the treated diamonds were sold exclusively by Pegasus Overseas Limited (POL, later Bellataire), a division of longtime GIA supporter Lazare Kaplan International (LKI).

Joe Duffy/GIA

With its focus on business in the new century, the 1999 Symposium featured an entire day of distinguished business speakers from outside the gem and jewelry industry. Ethicist Rushworth Kidder posed the question: "Will we self-regulate, or have regulation imposed on us?"

The prospect of an undetectable diamond treatment shocked the industry. In April, after intense talks with GE and POL officials, the Institute established an agreement whereby GE would identify all processed diamonds with a laser inscription ("GE POL") on their girdles and POL would submit them to GIA for grading.

The issue and its possible effects on the jewelry market were so troubling to so many that GIA held a special luncheon session at the Symposium to update the trade on its research into the GE POL diamonds. It was a panel of the Institute's top technical officials—Bill Boyajian, Tom Yonelunas, Tom Moses, and Jim Shigley—who faced a capacity crowd. GE scientists had been invited but declined to attend.

Not surprisingly, LKI was criticized by many in the audience for letting down the industry and GIA. But some also criticized GIA for negotiating with GE and LKI and continuing to grade their diamonds. Boyajian, though, told the audience that the April agreement was in fact a compromise by both sides, "the first step in ongoing discussions."

"It is in the best interests of the industry and the public," he said, "for us to be able to examine these goods and work in cooperation with LKI." POL's agreement not to sell processed rough was "tremendous," he added,

On the next-to-last day of the 1999 Symposium, Bill Boyajian and Tom Yonelunas headed a panel that updated the trade on GE-processed diamonds, the most controversial topic of the four-day event.

because otherwise the diamonds "would be impossible to trace" with the technical information available at that time.

Indeed, discovering the identifying signatures of the treated diamonds was "so critical to the future of the diamond market," Boyajian said, that GIA had pulled researchers off other projects to work on it. "We've focused almost entirely on this since we learned of it," he said.

And they were having some success. Among the hundreds of GE POL diamonds they had inspected, Yonelunas said, GIA researchers had detected "recognizable features" left by the GE process in many of them (later detailed in the Fall 1999 issue of *Gems & Gemology*).

Then Yonelunas casually dropped a bombshell, the very thing some in the industry had feared: Just before Symposium, the Gem Trade Laboratory had received—and immediately identified, thanks to the database of its Horizon computer system—two GE POL diamonds with their identifying laser inscriptions completely or partially polished away. Yonelunas refused to say which clients had submitted them.

The audience was momentarily stunned and then began asking questions, which built to a crescendo in a few minutes. Could other undetectable gems already be in the market without their inscriptions? If GIA needed sophisticated equipment to spot the altered GE POL diamonds, what were jewelers who relied on traditional methods going to do? How would the processed gems affect diamond values, and what was GIA going to do if more showed up?

The answer came quickly. Two weeks after the Symposium's close, Boyajian announced GIA's enforcement policy at the Presidents' Meeting of the World Federation of Diamond Bourses in Moscow. When the Gem Trade Laboratory flagged a GE-processed stone missing all or part of its inscription, he said, GIA would ask the client to let the lab re-inscribe "GE POL" on the gem within 48 hours. If the client refused, GIA would report it to "the appropriate authorities," including the Jewelers Vigilance Committee, and publicize the "potential misrepresentation in the marketplace." For re-inscribed stones, it would issue an updated lab report with the comment that "GE POL" was on the girdle and that a GIA report previously issued for the same stone had said it was "processed to improve its appearance by the General Electric Company."

Still more questions revolved around the issue of disclosure. Industry ethics demanded disclosure of treatments, but how could a jeweler disclose undetectable treatments of which he hadn't been informed? What would happen to public confidence in the jewelry industry? There were no easy answers, but it was apparent to many that with the advent of GE-processed diamonds—and GIA's own diamond color enhancement research—the diamond industry was plagued by the same thorny problem with which the colored stone industry had grappled for decades: when and how to disclose treatments and enhancements.

Some called for more government involvement. A number of others, including some appraisers, said that for their own protection jewelers should warn customers that they could no longer guarantee that their diamonds were untreated. Still others called for statements on every diamond report saying it was possible the gem was treated. But that was too extreme, said Boyajian, who cautioned calm. "Don't overreact," he told the audience. "Consumers need more confidence, not less."

As at the 1991 Symposium, one of the closing speakers was Maurice Tempelsman of Lazare Kaplan International, the firm at the center of the GE POL diamond controversy.

"We must proceed carefully and systematically so we don't do anything to harm the industry," he said, adding that "a new treatment, properly identified and disclosed, doesn't damage the sanctity of the all-natural products."

Still, this was only the beginning of increasingly sophisticated diamond treatments. Russian scientists reportedly had developed a process similar to that of GE, whose own officials were predicting even more technological changes that would revolutionize the diamond industry in the early 21st century.

The debate over diamond enhancements continued even into the Symposium's closing session. The first speaker was none other than Maurice Tempelsman, chief executive officer of LKI, who had also been a closing speaker at the 1991 Symposium along with Gerald Rothschild and Boyajian.

But rather than address the controversy, as many had hoped, Tempelsman touched on it only briefly. Instead, he reviewed the effects of globalization during the decade and—ironically—spoke of increasingly sophisticated technology in the diamond industry.

The influences of technology on the diamond industry were positive and "irreversible," he said. Advances such as satellite imaging and breakthroughs in geochemical and geophysical prospecting had increased diamond

Joe Duffy/GIA

At the "Gemology Greats" session, three of GIA's living legends—Richard T. Liddicoat, G. Robert Crowningshield, and Bert Krashes—joined former president Glenn Nord to offer Symposium attendees colorful insights.

production. Other innovations, such as the GE process to "improve the color of a small portion of diamonds" and automated cutting, had changed the way rough was transformed into polished diamonds. The result of these developments was a broader, more diverse supply of diamonds to the consumer.

"Adjustment to some changes may be painful in the short run," Tempelsman concluded, but "globalization and technology will open new and challenging opportunities for those with the vision to see them and the courage and optimism to grasp them.

"The industry is too robust and too vibrant to do otherwise."

If this was the most unsettled and challenging Symposium for attendees, it was also the most nostalgic. While preparing for the uncertainties and opportunities of the next millennium, it was appropriate to take a few moments to look at the past, said Boyajian, "lest we lose sight of our roots."

So a highlight for Symposium attendees was the "Gemology Greats" session, an opportunity to see and hear four of GIA's most influential pioneers in a panel held on the final day. Sharing more than 200 years of experience among them were GIA chairman Richard T. Liddicoat, Gem Trade Laboratory veterans G. Robert Crowningshield and Bert Krashes, and former GIA president Glenn Nord. Under Boyajian's gentle nudging, they recounted colorful tales of the Institute's early decades, its efforts to spread its training and gemological standards, and the struggle to establish the GIA Gem Trade Laboratory.

A tribute to one of these giants of gemology was unveiled in a touching ceremony on June 25, at an open house for Symposium attendees at GIA's two-year-old campus in Carlsbad.

Richard Liddicoat thought he was simply dedicating a new statue for the GIA headquarters. But when he pulled off the sheet covering it, a gasp went up from the hundreds of people in attendance, and Liddicoat looked in amazement at a life-size clay sculpture of himself—which would soon be cast in bronze. The surprise was four years in the making, according to sculptor Michael Clary, a longtime employee of the West Coast laboratory. The moment overwhelmed Liddicoat. "I've had everything I could possibly hope for—and now this is more than I could have imagined," he said.

Capping off the 1999 Symposium was an open house at GIA's Carlsbad headquarters, where a life-size clay sculpture of Richard Liddicoat was unveiled. A year later, Liddicoat and sculptor Mike Clary, a veteran of the Gem Trade Laboratory, enjoy the dedication of the bronze statue at the main entrance.

Liddicoat, after thanking Clary, waved aside compliments. "What this statue of me needs now," he joked with typical modesty, "is a few pigeons." After being cast in bronze, the 400-pound sculpture was placed at the main entrance to the Institute's world headquarters in June 2000.

Sadly, two years later, on July 23, 2002, Richard T. Liddicoat passed away after a lingering illness. Widely respected as the "Father of Modern Gemology," he left an indelible mark on the jewelry industry, GIA, and the thousands of students he influenced. Over the course of more than six decades, he took Robert Shipley's creation and built it into a world-renowned center for gemological education, research, instruments, and laboratory services.

THE FINAL ADDRESS AT THE 1999 SYMPOSIUM, by GIA president Bill Boyajian, looked to both the future and the past in defining the means to operate successfully in the years ahead. He was greeted with a standing ovation, in part due to his powerful message. Yet, in a very distinct way, it was most certainly also a gesture of support and thanks for what had been a marvelous four days when industry professionals closed the 1990s and met the new millennium.

As the new century opened, Boyajian and other GIA officials had already begun contemplating the next International Gemological Symposium, planned to coincide with the Institute's 75th anniversary in 2006.

"The Graduates" (1991) marked a turning point in GIA's advertising efforts, now led by marketing professional Kathryn Kimmel.

From left to right: José Hess, Designer/Principal, José Hess, Inc.; Helene Fortunoff, Principal, Fortunoff; Henry Dunay, Designer/Principal, Henry Dunay Designs, Inc.; Elsa Martinez-Phillips, President, Roberto Martinez, Inc.; Judith and Jack Rosenberg, Principals, Judith Jack, Inc.; Marcee Fineberg, Marketing Manager, Lazare-Kaplan International, Inc.; Jane Goodman Baum, Vice-President/Co-Chairman, I.B. Goodman Diamond Co.; Jay Mednikow, Vice-President, J.H. Mednikow & Co., Inc.; Howard Sherwood, Vice-President, Sherwood Management; Samuel Getz, President/C.O.O., Mayor's Jewelers; R. Andrew Johnson, President, The Johnson Family Diamond Cellar; Michael Vesely, Vice-President, Kolman Jewelers; Joel Schechter, Vice-President, Honora; Mark C. Ginsberg, Owner, M.C. Ginsberg Jewelers, Inc.; Jay Barrier, Vice-President, Barrier's, Inc.

The Graduates.

This photograph is a "Who's Who" of the jewelry industry. A portrait that represents GIA... a cross-section of the thousands of jewelers across the United States who are graduates of the Gemological Institute of America. That should tell you something. Each one of these jewelers, gemologists, designers and industry professionals knows that to be the best, you have to learn from the best. And in the jewelry industry, that means the Gemological Institute of America.

Whether you're just starting out, or you've been working in the jewelry business for years, GIA has a program designed just for you. Each is created by top professionals... and backed by 60 years of experience. Each is outlined in our complimentary catalog, where you'll also find all the details on how to begin your GIA education by learning at home, on campus or in various cities throughout the world. Make your plans now to be one of the graduates, and to join the "Who's Who" of the jewelry industry.

GEMOLOGICAL INSTITUTE OF AMERICA

For your complimentary catalog or further information, phone toll-free (800) 421-7250, ext. 292. Outside the United States call (213) 829-2991, ext. 292. Circle number 47 on reply card.

COMMUNICATING THE MESSAGE

1986–2003

In 1990, Bill Boyajian finally had to make a decision he had been putting off since his rise from marketing manager to GIA president four years earlier. Though few people outside the Institute were aware of it, Boyajian had not actually left all of his old responsibilities behind. He had continued to oversee GIA's marketing efforts in addition to his new, broader responsibilities. But he was beginning to reach a point of diminishing returns.

"I felt I had taken the marketing element of GIA as far as I could," Boyajian reflected, "and I needed someone to raise it to the next level." He knew it was time to hand over the marketing reins. The question was: Who could best do the job?

The answer was industry veteran Kathryn Kimmel, who would lead the Institute's Marketing and Public Relations department into the 21st century. Kimmel took GIA's brand and visibility to unprecedented heights, while bringing the Institute closer to the trade and public than ever before.

■MARKETING MAGIC

When Bill Boyajian decided to hire a new marketing director in 1990, the decision was far from trivial. Marketing was the "face" of GIA. Advertisements, press releases, events, education catalogs, and the like were usually the first—and sometimes only—impressions the general public received of the Institute. GIA needed a more powerful and consistent image. Why? Increased public awareness would fuel demand for GIA's services within the industry. But more importantly, a distinctive image would allow the Institute to further its nonprofit mission by making the trade and the public more aware of its many activities.

Finding the right person to spearhead the effort—someone with marketing savvy, a wealth of trade experience, and the GIA mindset—was critical. "I needed someone I could trust to take over the job, to uphold the GIA standard and, most importantly, to represent the Institute with the trade and the public."

In 1990, Boyajian met Kathryn Kimmel, then the vice president of marketing at Nova Stylings, a fine-jewelry manufacturer in Los Angeles. Kimmel had a lifelong association with the trade: She had worked in her family's jewelry store as a teenager, and later rose through the ranks to become one of the industry's top marketing executives. A specialist in branding and image-building in the commercial sector, Kimmel was also an active

Kathryn Kimmel, one of the jewelry industry's top marketing executives, joined the Institute in 1990. Under her leadership, the Marketing and Public Relations department strengthened the GIA brand and created a far greater awareness of the Institute worldwide.

participant in industry service organizations. She was a founding member of the Women's Jewelry Association (WJA) and president of its Los Angeles chapter, as well as a board member of the 24 Karat Club of Southern California.

Boyajian was impressed with Kimmel's energy, marketing background, and insider's knowledge of the trade. He knew she was the catalyst GIA needed and soon offered her the job of marketing director. Kimmel joined the Institute in July 1990.

After taking the helm, Kimmel immediately set out to create a strong and consistent image for GIA. She found that the Institute tended to communicate in a multitude of voices—sometimes contradictory ones. A strong brand, clearly articulated, would allow the Institute's single voice to rise above the cacophony of the marketplace.

One of her early steps to that end was to replace the existing public information office with a streamlined public relations (PR) department. The PR department not only communicated GIA's message through the trade press, but it also made a connection with the jewelry-consuming public by more actively distributing Institute news and events to consumer media such as newspapers, television, and radio, and eventually the Internet.

Kimmel and her staff accommodated the media whenever they could, from arranging interviews with Institute officials, to providing gem-buying tips to local newspaper columnists, to working with visiting television crews. In the summer of 1996 alone, the Santa Monica campus buzzed with media activity. A film crew from the A&E cable television network arrived to shoot a segment about the Hope diamond. A *Los Angeles Times* reporter came to do research for a story on GIA and the Gem Trade Laboratory, and *Asia Times* sent a reporter for a piece on the Institute's Asian students. "We're becoming less of a well-kept secret as far as the general public is concerned," said a delighted Kimmel in July 1996.

At the same time, Kimmel launched a major advertising effort. As prevalent as its advertisements were in the trade press, the Institute had only scratched the surface. Besides adding some much-needed design flair to make the pieces more fun and contemporary, Kimmel also developed a new approach that better conveyed the vitality of the Institute. Take, for instance, the earlier ads for GIA's education programs. Even though its graduates were a "who's who" of the jewelry industry, the Institute neglected these success stories, tending to show models in a retail setting or relying on testimonials from graduates who had not yet earned industry recognition. Kimmel saw testimonials from well-known graduates as the key to promoting GIA education, and the marketing team rushed into production on a new ad campaign.

The first ad, 1991's "The Graduates," featured such industry luminaries as Helene Fortunoff and Henry Dunay. Two years later, "We All Speak the Same Language" combined that type of name recognition with a global touch, showing a group of distinguished GIA graduates from Asia, Europe, and the Middle East, as well as North America. The success of this campaign, combined with a series of redesigned, award-winning catalogs under marketing general manager Sue Petrich, made the Institute far more effective in promoting its educational offerings.

We all speak the same language.

"We All Speak the Same Language" showcased distinguished GIA graduates from around the world. Top, from left: Vanessa Swarovski (Austria), Sergio Antonini (Italy), Israel Itzkowitz (Israel); middle: Henry Ho (Thailand); bottom, from left: Yasukazu Suwa (Japan), Tina Segal (U.S.), Pravin Mehta (India).

■GIA GOES LIVE

In 1987, long before the Internet went mainstream, GIA first went online. But GIA-Net, the dial-up bulletin board system that gave distance education learners the power to complete lessons and access library reference materials from their personal computers, marked only the beginning of the Institute's online capability.

With the rise of the Internet in the mid-1990s, Kimmel and her team had a daunting task at hand: to develop a marketing and informational website for the Institute. Their goal of informing the trade about "who GIA was" was achieved in 1995, when the GIA website first went online. But in the late 1990s, as the Internet became more consumer oriented, Kimmel and Boyajian recognized the need for a more interactive website that would better serve the Institute's public-service mission. It marked a dramatic shift in the Institute's online strategy. "We were speaking not only to the trade, but to the consumer as well," noted Kimmel.

In March 2002, GIA launched a redesigned website that offered informative links and new features such as the interactive tutorial "How to Buy a Diamond" (left). The Institute unveiled a new version of its website (right) in October 2002.

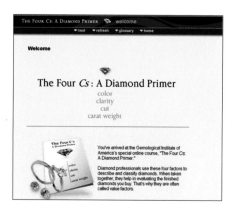

In late 1999 and early 2000, Kimmel's team worked with GIA's information technology department, headed by Don Foster, to build a dynamic website that provided fresh content and interactive features for the trade and the public alike. "From the very beginning, we committed ourselves to a site that was more than just an electronic brochure for the Institute," Kimmel said. "The idea was to offer a constant flow of valuable information."

The redesigned website went live March 8, 2000. Besides sporting a new look, it featured an array of intriguing new options. Users could browse the Education catalog, catch up on Institute news and events, shop at GEM Instruments' online store, search industry job listings, learn about GIA grading and identification reports, and even take an interactive tutorial called "How to Buy a Diamond." From the homepage, links to major GIA activities—Education, the Gem Trade Laboratory, GIA Research, the Liddicoat Library, GEM Instruments & Books, Development, the Alumni Association, Career Services, and *Gems & Gemology*—were just a click away. The GIA website won first place in the *GemKey* Magazine Website Awards 2000 competition, but that was only the beginning.

Marketing director Armando de Peralta spearheaded the next major revision of the website, which was relaunched in October 2002. New features included a redesign of the homepage to make it more user friendly, a media newsroom, a free image gallery, and an interactive GIA history timeline. All of these improvements served to make gemological information more readily available to the public and the trade.

But the website wasn't GIA's only means of leveraging digital media in the 1990s. Boyajian was eager to get information to the Institute's constituencies faster, and a significant milestone for GIA's marketing and public relations took place October 15, 1999, with the first edition of the *GIA Insider*. This biweekly electronic newsletter, available free by subscription, delivered e-mail bulletins from the Institute. Regular contents included breaking news from the gem and jewelry industry, GIA's analysis of the hottest issues, and GIA research discoveries. Subscribers could access gem identification tips from the Gem Trade Laboratory and updates from Education, GEM Instruments, and *Gems & Gemology*. In 2003, under the editorship of senior public relations manager Alex Angelle, the *GIA Insider* boasted 41,000 subscribers.

The *GIA Insider*, a free biweekly electronic newsletter launched in 1999, became the Institute's forum to keep readers rapidly informed.

▪ THE GIA BRAND

In 1998, the marketing department began an ongoing global effort to promote the Institute to consumers and retailers as "the world's foremost authority in gemology." One way was to distribute GIA news reports to the world media, but another was more active participation in international trade shows. Under the guidance of Vivianne Del Signore, trade show and advertising senior manager, these became hubs of GIA activity and publicity in important regional markets. Exhibiting at fairs of all sizes in large, custom-made booths, GIA promoted its education programs, sold its books and instruments, and answered trade and consumer queries about laboratory services. The Institute also held classes and seminars, president's receptions, and leadership dinners in connection with major trade shows.

During the 1990s, trade shows became major hubs of GIA activity. GEM Instruments veteran Gaston Lopez is seen here with fellow staff members at the 2003 JA Show in New York.

Members of the gem and jewelry industry gather at GIA's GemFest Basel 2001: A Gemological Forum. Events such as this helped the Institute establish itself as "the world's foremost authority in gemology."

For evidence of GIA's greater visibility worldwide, one needed to look no farther than the Basel trade fair, the industry's largest watch and jewelry show. "When GIA started exhibiting there in the early '90s, many European retailers weren't very familiar with the Institute," noted Kimmel. "You could walk the show's aisles and see a lot of material referring to other educational organizations and laboratories, but not GIA. By the late 1990s—when the Institute not only had a booth presence, but GemFest and other activities at Basel—you saw GIA everywhere."

Under Kimmel, who became a vice president in 1995, the marketing and public relations departments helped the Institute greatly expand its audience and increase its global stature. Strategic advertising and marketing campaigns helped solidify GIA's extraordinary brand recognition factor of 96 percent among jewelry trade professionals, as determined in a July 16, 1996, Gallup Organization retailer study. In addition, GIA's growth as an institution had tripled from 1990 to 2003, and its stature had risen to heights that even Boyajian could not have imagined.

Web-based marketing, video programs, consumer-oriented articles and tutorials, and effective communication with news media had all extended the Institute's reach to the public. In the year 2002 alone, consumers made contact with GIA's key messages and brand image more than 200 million times.

■ "THE LAST BRIDGE"

Back in early 1991, Kathryn Kimmel faced an altogether different type of challenge, one that went beyond branding or advertising and marketing campaigns. Her industry contacts and extensive retail and jewelry manufacturing experience were in demand throughout the Institute in more ways than she had anticipated. Kimmel recalled, "I had a steady stream of students passing through my office who had completed their education at GIA and were ready to move out into the world, but were looking for guidance on how to do it."

Amanda Luke/GIA

Kimmel was dedicated to helping these students, but at most she could mentor only a few each year. There were hundreds more, many of them starting second careers, who needed assistance. While GIA maintained a listing of job opportunities, it had no formal program to facilitate networking between students and the trade. Something needed to be done.

Kimmel knew from her experience in the trade that there was a huge demand for new talent. Now she could see firsthand that the talent was available—the problem was how to bring demand and supply together. She proposed a solution to Boyajian: a GIA-hosted "career fair" that would bring GIA students together with industry figures, both to teach the students more about searching for a job and to introduce them to the trade. Boyajian backed the idea, and Kimmel got to work.

The first place Kimmel went was the 24 Karat Club of Southern California, where she had been a board member for six years. She pitched the idea to her longtime friend Howard Sherwood. Sherwood immediately agreed to be her co-chair, but others were not as convinced. "Some of them told me it was impossible," Kimmel said. "I responded, 'Just watch!'"

Throughout that summer of 1991, Kimmel worked with a steering committee assembled from members of the 24 Karat Club, among them the club's president, Jack Zemer; Bart Boydston and Earl Lynch of the Diamond Promotion Service; Lynn Diamond of *National Jeweler*; and Matt Runci of the Manufacturing Jewelers & Silversmiths of America. The committee set out to

Another of Kimmel's innovations was the GIA Career Fair, which began in 1991 and became a biannual event that has placed thousands of Institute graduates with firms in the gem and jewelry industry. Left: A recruiter greets a job seeker at the 2000 Career Fair in Carlsbad. Right: Carolyn Jacoby, of the Australian Pearl Centre, meets with a Career Fair attendee for one-on-one guidance at the 2002 Career Fair in New York.

Kathryn Kimmel (center) joins San Diego news anchor Desiree Carvajal (left) for an October 2002 in-studio interview. The interview also featured Heather Shrosbree (right), a Graduate Gemologist who landed a position in the jewelry industry through Career Fair.

build support, financial and otherwise, for a GIA Career Fair. One by one, the doubters were won over, and momentum grew rapidly.

The first Career Fair was held at GIA's Santa Monica campus in October 1991, in conjunction with the 24 Karat Club of Southern California's annual dinner dance. Two hundred and fifty students attended a series of panel discussions on job opportunities in the gem and jewelry industry, the various fields within the trade, and how to move from the classroom to a full-time job. In addition, 23 companies came to recruit.

Industry response was enthusiastic. When the second Career Fair was held in 1992, something new became its most successful feature: one-on-one guidance from industry leaders on how to find openings and prepare resumés, and to hear about trade opportunities firsthand. "We had a lot of smart students who had little experience in preparing a resumé," Kimmel said.

In January 1993, GIA New York inaugurated its own Career Fair. Kimmel believed that Career Fair could do far more than recruit GIA students for industry jobs—it could also attract talented people to the industry. It was a promise that was realized more fully than Kimmel anticipated.

For the Zale Corp., then the largest U.S. jewelry retailer, Career Fair was "our premier recruitment event," said Susan Goodfellow, the company's staffing manager, in 1998. "We [come] looking for regional managers, store managers, and sales associates nationwide. We [hire] jewelry professionals at all levels of expertise, including buyers and store operations personnel."

By 2002, the Career Fair in New York was attracting more than 1,000 people, while Carlsbad drew more than 800. With the success of GIA's Career Fair on both coasts, the trade had come to view it as one of the most important services provided by the Institute, not in the least because it was the largest formal recruiting opportunity in the industry. A modest gathering held before the 24 Karat Club's annual dinner had grown into a major industry event where GIA students and jobseekers from outside the industry were able to rub elbows with executives from major jewelry companies.

"Career Fair has done more than just find jobs and mentors for thousands of students," Kimmel said. "It attracted a lot of new talent to the industry, and it allowed industry figures to give back. When people come up to me and say, 'I went to Career Fair eight years ago, and I didn't know a thing, and now I'm vice president of a major jewelry company,' that's when I know it really paid off. It's truly the last bridge from GIA to the trade, and from the trade to our students."

BOYAJIAN'S CHANCE MEETING WITH KIMMEL IN 1990 was a blessing for the Institute. "When people ask me what Kathryn has done," Boyajian said in 2002, "I tell them to look at GIA before she came. Look at what our campus was. Look at our first Symposium. Look at our old promotions and marketing, our public relations, our educational catalog, our videos, and our events, and then look at what we've achieved since then.

"She's not only enhanced the image of GIA, but she has also boosted awareness of the Institute throughout the industry and the public. She's one of the key people who have really made a difference at the Institute."

ACCORDING TO KIMMEL, CAREER FAIR IS "TRULY THE LAST BRIDGE FROM GIA TO THE TRADE, AND FROM THE TRADE TO OUR STUDENTS."

A composite image of GIA students from a September 1952 merchandising class and from a group photographed 40 years later, in the summer of 1992.

EPILOGUE

BEYOND 2003

By 2003, the Institute had become a recognized powerhouse—the world's leading authority in gemological education, research, instruments and laboratory services.

It had been an astonishing evolution:

- From a small organization that sent mimeographed correspondence lessons by mail, GIA had grown into an internationally respected institution offering dozens of courses (translated into many Asian and European languages) on campus and even online, as well as extension classes and seminars. GIA Education had become a global network of 13 schools in nine countries on three continents.

- From makeshift headquarters in the Shipleys' apartment in the 1930s, it had expanded through a succession of offices and small buildings into an awe-inspiring 18-acre campus overlooking the Pacific Ocean.

- From the single room on West 47th Street where Liddicoat and Crowningshield worked in 1949, the New York lab had grown to 30,000 square feet half a century later. And over 500 people were employed in laboratory operations on both coasts, two-thirds of whom were graders and technical personnel.

- From rudimentary testing done on the Shipleys' kitchen table, GIA had evolved into a sophisticated research facility with nearly 40 researchers and the advanced analytical equipment needed to meet future challenges in synthetics and treatments.

- From a couple of gem instruments converted from geology to gemology applications, GIA had become a major purveyor of optical testing equipment for the gem and jewelry industry.

- From a few reference works in Shipley's bookcase, the Institute had developed the world's finest gemological library and information center, with a growing collection of 30,000 books, 28,000 photographic images, 800 videos, and 300 different periodicals.

- From the confusing terms that plagued the Depression-era diamond trade, GIA had created a diamond grading system that became the industry standard—in effect, a gem language understood throughout the global community.

- From a tiny black-and-white publication with only a handful of subscribers in 1934, *Gems & Gemology* had become an award-winning, landmark scholarly journal with thousands of subscribers in some 98 countries.

- From a single teacher in the beginning and only a few dozen staff members in the early 1960s, the Institute had grown over the decades to become an employer of more than 850, including a global faculty of nearly 100.

- From a couple hundred correspondence pupils in the early 1930s, and a few full-time resident students in the early 1960s, by 2003 GIA had become an educational institution with some 15,000 annual enrollments in the U.S. and abroad.

- From middle-aged men with high school educations to a mix of younger, college-educated male and female professionals, GIA's student profile had changed dramatically by the 21st century. In fact, women became the majority, and people new to the industry saw a GIA education as the springboard to enter a trade that for years had been closed to those outside of tight-knit jewelry families.

- And from 13 graduates in 1931, the Institute's alumni base had grown to more than 200,000. It was impossible to calculate the extent to which they carried GIA's professional influence to their local, national, and international communities.

AND WHAT OF THE FUTURE OF THE GEMOLOGICAL INSTITUTE OF AMERICA? How would GIA continue to build on the foundation it had created, nurtured, and expanded since 1931? The events of tomorrow—let alone next year—are always uncertain. But the Institute's long-range plans called for a continuing commitment to reach out to the trade and to the public in new and innovative ways.

- In Education, GIA planned to follow in the direction set by its Essentials courses, introduced at the end of the 20th century, of using contemporary instructional technology to make the material easier to understand and more practical. And it was already developing a variety of courses for specific segments and needs of the trade. One of the most important developments was its School of Business, tailored to the unique requirements of the jewelry industry.

- The Institute planned to continue building its international network of schools. It seemed likely that GIA would have a presence in India and additional outreach in China in the years ahead. Both countries were considered large consuming nations of the future, with combined populations in excess of one-third of the world. Yet there were also possible new school sites outside of Asia that GIA would consider in the years ahead.

- The continuing flow of new gem treatments and synthetics, some approaching nature's own methods, would mean even greater reliance by jewelers and gem sellers on the expertise of GIA's research and laboratory professionals. Ultimately, keeping up with the rapid pace of technological change, and disseminating results as quickly as possible, would drive GIA Research in the new millennium.

- At the same time, the consumer's desire for more knowledge and information, coupled with the anticipated growth in online jewelry and gem retailing, would further propel the use and importance of GIA grading reports to ensure public confidence. And it was likely that the study of cut—and its impact on the appearance of a diamond—would be broadened beyond round brilliants to fancy-shape diamonds. Also possible in the first decade or two, said Institute officials, was the use of grading systems—or practical quality-description systems—in the laboratory for cultured pearls and colored stones.

- Further expansion at GIA's Carlsbad headquarters was expected. Institute officials planned to acquire the additional land that was optioned when they bought the original site, giving the campus a total of 30 contiguous acres. Plans for the new property called for the building of additional office space and possibly a museum or auditorium in the future. The longer-range expectation was that GIA would continue to grow to more than twice its 2003 size in the coming decades.

Shane McClure/GIA

By 2003, the vast majority of rubies and sapphires were routinely heat treated to improve their color or clarity (or both). The continuing flow of treatments and synthetics would mean a greater reliance on GIA Research in the new millennium.

GIA helped organize a display of extraordinary gem diamonds at the Smithsonian Institution in Washington, D.C., during the summer of 2003. Counterclockwise from center: the 203.04-carat De Beers Millennium Star, the 27.64-carat Heart of Eternity, the 5.54-carat Pumpkin, the 5.51-carat Ocean Dream, the 5.11-carat Moussaieff Red, the 101.29-carat Allnatt, and the 59.60-carat Steinmetz Pink.

- Much of the strengthening of operations in the first years of the new century was the result of a vision to take the Institute to new and exciting heights with excellent leadership. Most important was the creation of two new posts, those of chief operations officer (filled by Wayne Pierce since 2000) and vice president and general counsel (occupied by Donna Baker since 2001), to improve GIA's administrative effectiveness.

- The new century also saw the Institute embark on one of the most important programs in its history: to ensure its continued financial stability and effectiveness—indeed, to secure the Institute's own future. GIA had already benefited from the astute fiscal management of chief financial officer Robert Buscher and controller Sabra Norris. In the new century, however, it also established an endowment, the second in its long history, and an ongoing endowment campaign. In addition to the Institute's own contributions, the endowment was to be funded by industry donations. At $37 million in 2003, it was expected to grow in the next several years to some $75 million, becoming an even more important element of GIA's overall stewardship.

"The endowment is the guarantor of our future," said Boyajian. "It will ensure that 50 years from now and long after many of us are gone, the Institute will still be here to preserve the public trust in gems and jewelry."

- The early years of the 21st century saw the Richard T. Liddicoat Library and Information Center continuing to expand its holdings and reference services. Technology would play a crucial role in the Liddicoat Library, with more people accessing it via the Internet and its entire collection of visual resources scheduled for conversion to digital format by 2005.

- Recent years also saw the Institute enlarge its museum collections and gem exhibitions in support of public education. And if successes like its own museum displays in Carlsbad or the 2003 "Splendor of Diamonds" exhibit it helped organize at the Smithsonian Institution were any example, GIA was destined to grow this area of outreach.

- The Internet would undoubtedly become an even more integral tool of Institute operations in the 21st century. Plans in the laboratory, for example, called for development of Web-based customer services, such as information on diamonds submitted for grading and other digital services. Education would continue to expand its student services, shifting from paper-based to electronic formats. The Internet had already become the preferred communication tool for most distance education students in 2003, and would become even more vital in the future.

- Spurred by the desire to broaden its outreach to a diversified industry and an interested public, the Institute also was committed to raising its public profile with a clear, comprehensive, and unambiguous name and message that would be readily recognized and easily accessed anywhere in the world.

- The instrument division, still a cornerstone of GIA activities, planned the production of a new "must-have" line of gemological instruments under the direction of industry veteran Howard Pomerantz. According to Boyajian, "Instrumentation would become more critical to the gemologist of the 21st century than it had at any time since GIA's meager beginning."

- *Gems & Gemology*, the consummate flagship of GIA, would continue to publish the results of the latest research by authors throughout the gemological community. Viewed by both scientists and jeweler-gemologists alike as the definitive peer-reviewed journal in the field, the Institute's commitment to *G&G*—and gemology's need for it—had never been greater.

The GIA Board of Governors in 2003. First row: Eli Haas (president, ENH International), Helene Fortunoff (president and CEO, Fortunoff), William E. Boyajian (president, GIA), Ralph Destino (chairman emeritus, Cartier, Inc.), Susan M. Jacques (president, Borsheim Jewelry Co.), and Dilip Mehta (president, Rosy Blue, Inc.). Second row: Dr. George Rossman (professor of mineralogy, California Institute of Technology), Michael J. Kazanjian (chairman and CEO, Kazanjian Brothers), Anna Martin (senior vice president, ABN AMRO Bank), Glenn R. Nord (retired president, GIA), Nancy Brewer (president, Nancy B. & Co.), Dr. Gordon E. Brown Jr. (Kirby Professor of Earth Sciences, Stanford University), Roland Naftule (president, Nafco Gems Ltd.), Sheldon Kwiat (co-president, Kwiat, Roisen and Ferman), and Dr. William B. Cottingham (president emeritus, G.M.I. Engineering & Management Institute). Not shown: Lee Berg (president, Lee Michaels Fine Jewelry) and Matthew Stuller (president, Stuller Inc.).

- Still another source of confidence and pride for GIA was its board of governors. From a body largely represented by independent retail jewelers through the mid-1980s, the Institute had broadened the board to include nationally and internationally recognized leaders from many trade and public sectors, backgrounds, and professions. "I couldn't be more proud of our current governors and their positive influence on GIA," Boyajian said in 2003.

■ A FINAL WORD ON "A NOBLE MISSION"

As the Institute entered the 21st century, it could not only look back proudly on a history of distinctive leadership, but it could also look forward with enthusiasm to strengthening its public service—"a noble mission," in the words of Bill Boyajian—in recognition of the unique responsibility GIA had garnered through its decades of innovation and hard work.

The Institute's status as a nonprofit organization would allow it to focus on that mission—to ensure the public trust in gems and jewelry—unencumbered by concerns of member interests or shareholder return. It would also allow GIA to continue to reinvest its assets back into this mission, in service to the public.

The Institute had long recognized that its integrity—its hard-earned reputation for objectivity and independence—was of vital importance to its service and success. The GIA logo on the world's most trusted diamond grading and gem identification reports, on the world's premier gem instruments, on the world's most advanced gemological research, and—most important of all—on the world's most respected and prestigious gemological education, was not there by accident. Nor would it remain there without a pure and focused vision. It had come about through a posture of service. It was a reward not just for *being* the world's leading gemological organization but for the continued *act* of leading.

And GIA's management knew that true leadership was about serving those whom they led, about bringing out the best in people and building shared beliefs and values. While it could look back on its many accomplishments in fostering professionalism, integrity, and honesty in the industry, the Institute could not rest on its laurels. It had to remain above reproach, never allowing bias or self-interest to be placed above its legacy of leadership and service. According to Boyajian, "It was not enough to do things right—GIA had to do the right things."

It was a noble mission indeed, and one GIA would continue to pursue with confidence and pride.

appendixes

APPENDIX A

THE GIA BOARD OF GOVERNORS, 1931–2003

Since the founding of GIA, its board of governors has played a crucial role in overseeing the development and policies of the Institute.

1930s

HENRY G. BIRKS • Henry Birks & Sons Ltd., Montreal

GEORGE C. BROCK • Brock & Co., Los Angeles

JAMES D. DOUGHERTY • J. B. Hudson Inc., Minneapolis

GODFREY EACRET • Shreve, Treat and Eacret, San Francisco

LOUIS ESSER • Louis Esser Co., Milwaukee

MYRON EVERTS • A. A. Everts Co., Dallas

PAUL S. HARDY • Hardy & Hayes Co. Inc., Pittsburgh

FRANK HEITKEMPER • Frank A. Heitkemper Inc., Portland, Oregon

EDWARD F. HERSCHEDE SR. • Frank Herschede Co., Cincinnati

E. W. HODGSON • Hodgson, Kennard & Co. Inc., Boston

OSCAR C. HOMANN • The C. B. Brown Co., Omaha, Nebraska

FRANCIS A. KEATING • Grogan Co. Inc., Pittsburgh

H. A. MAIER • Maier & Berkele Inc., Atlanta

WILLIAM ELDER MARCUS • Marcus and Co., New York

H. B. MCCAGUE • The Cowell and Hubbard Co., Cleveland

FREDERICK B. THURBER • Tilden-Thurber Corp., Providence, Rhode Island

WILLIAM G. THURBER • Tilden-Thurber Corp., Providence, Rhode Island

LEO J. VOGT • Hess & Culbertson Jewelry Co., St. Louis

WILLIAM H. WRIGHT • Galt & Bro. Inc., Washington, D.C.

1940s

MAURICE ADELSHEIM • S. Jacobs & Co., Minneapolis

NOLTE C. AMENT • Geiger & Ament, Louisville, Kentucky

J. LOVELL BAKER • Henry Birks & Sons Ltd., Montreal

HENRY G. BIRKS • Henry Birks & Sons Ltd., Montreal

GEORGE C. BROCK • Brock & Co., Los Angeles

CARLETON G. BROER • Broer-Freeman Co., Toledo, Ohio

CHARLES H. CHURCH • Church & Co., Newark, New Jersey

GLYNN CREMER • Glynn Cremer Jewelers, La Crosse, Wisconsin

JAMES D. DOUGHERTY • J. B. Hudson Inc., Minneapolis

Members of the GIA Board of Governors, 1947: Paul S. Hardy, George Carter Jessop, Clifford I. Josephson Jr., Oscar Homann, Burton Joseph, Leo J. Vogt, Myron Everts, and Jerome B. Wiss.

LOUIS ESSER • Louis Esser Co., Milwaukee

MYRON EVERTS • A. A. Everts Co., Dallas

PAUL S. HARDY • Hardy & Hayes Co. Inc., Pittsburgh

EDWARD F. HERSCHEDE SR. • Frank Herschede Co., Cincinnati

E. W. HODGSON • Hodgson, Kennard & Co. Inc., Boston

OSCAR C. HOMANN • The C. B. Brown Co., Omaha

GEORGE CARTER JESSOP • J. Jessop & Sons, San Diego

EARL E. JONES • Jones Brothers Jewelers, Pekin, Illinois

BURTON JOSEPH • S. Joseph & Sons, Des Moines, Iowa

CLIFFORD I. JOSEPHSON JR. • C. I. Josephson Jewelers, Moline, Illinois

H. PAUL JUERGENS • Juergens & Andersen Co., Chicago

LAZARE KAPLAN • Lazare Kaplan & Sons, New York

JOHN S. KENNARD • Kennard & Co., Boston

EUGENE A. KIGER • C. A. Kiger Co., Kansas City, Missouri

PERCY K. LOUD • Wright, Kay & Co., Detroit

H. A. MAIER • Maier & Berkele Inc., Atlanta

WILLIAM ELDER MARCUS • Marcus and Co., New York

H. B. MCCAGUE • The Cowell and Hubbard Co., Cleveland

ERNEST J. MEYER • Meyer's Jewelers, Grand Island, Nebraska

CHARLES D. PEACOCK III • C. D. Peacock Inc., Chicago

HERBERT E. REID • Henry C. Reid & Son, Bridgeport, Connecticut

WILLIAM H. SCHWANKE • Schwanke-Kasten Co., Milwaukee

FREDERICK B. THURBER • Tilden-Thurber Corp., Providence, Rhode Island

LEO J. VOGT • Hess & Culbertson Jewelry Co., St. Louis

JOHN F. VONDEY • Vondey's, San Bernardino, California

JOHN WESLEY WARE • Ware's, San Diego

JEROME B. WISS • Wiss Sons Inc., Newark, New Jersey

WILLIAM H. WRIGHT • Galt & Bro. Inc., Washington, D.C.

1950s

MAURICE ADELSHEIM • S. Jacobs & Co., Minneapolis

J. LOVELL BAKER • Henry Birks & Sons Ltd., Montreal

ALEX BOCKSTRUCK • H. Bockstruck Co., St. Paul, Minnesota

CARLETON G. BROER • The Broer-Freeman Co., Toledo

ROBERT H. BROMBERG • Bromberg & Co. Inc., Birmingham, Alabama

FRED J. CANNON • Koke-Slaudt & Co., Los Angeles

CHARLES H. CHURCH • Church & Co., Newark, New Jersey

GLYNN CREMER • Glynn Cremer Jewelers, La Crosse, Wisconsin

F. FOREST DAVIDSON • Thomas Long Co., Boston

JAMES G. DONAVAN • Donavan & Seamans Co., Los Angeles

MYRON EVERTS • A. A. Everts Co., Dallas

PAUL S. HARDY • Hardy & Hayes Co. Inc., Pittsburgh

EDWARD F. HERSCHEDE SR. • Frank Herschede Co., Cincinnati

FREDERICK O. HERZ • R. Herz & Bros. Inc., Reno, Nevada

OSCAR C. HOMANN • The C. B. Brown Co., Omaha, Nebraska

GEORGE CARTER JESSOP • J. Jessop & Sons, San Diego

EARL E. JONES • Jones Brothers Jewelers, Pekin, Illinois

BURTON JOSEPH • S. Joseph & Sons, Des Moines, Iowa

CLIFFORD I. JOSEPHSON JR. • C. I. Josephson Jewelers, Moline, Illinois

H. PAUL JUERGENS • Juergens & Andersen Co., Chicago

GEORGE R. KAPLAN • Lazare Kaplan & Sons, New York

LAZARE KAPLAN • Lazare Kaplan & Sons, New York

WILLIAM P. KENDRICK • William Kendrick Jewelers, Louisville, Kentucky

JOHN S. KENNARD • Kennard & Co. Inc., Boston

EUGENE A. KIGER • C. A. Kiger Co., Kansas City, Missouri

PERCY K. LOUD • Wright, Kay & Co., Detroit

Longtime GIA chairman
James G. Donavan.

KENNETH G. MAPPIN • Mappin's Ltd., Montreal

ERNEST J. MEYER • Meyer's Jewelers, Grand Island, Nebraska

CHARLES D. PEACOCK III • C. D. Peacock Inc., Chicago

WILLIAM S. PRESTON • F. J. Preston & Son, Burlington, Vermont

WILLIAM H. SCHWANKE • Schwanke-Kasten Co., Milwaukee

STANLEY S. SMITH • J. B. Hudson Co., Minneapolis

WILLIAM G. THURBER • Tilden-Thurber Co., Providence, Rhode Island

LEO J. VOGT • Hess & Culbertson Jewelry Co., St. Louis

JEROME B. WISS • Wiss Sons Inc., Newark, New Jersey

1960s

J. LOVELL BAKER • Henry Birks & Sons Ltd., Montreal

ALEX H. BOCKSTRUCK • H. Bockstruck Co., St. Paul, Minnesota

CARLETON G. BROER • Broer-Freeman Co., Toledo, Ohio

FRED J. CANNON • Koke-Slaudt & Co., Los Angeles

STANLEY E. CHURCH • Church & Co., Newark, New Jersey

F. FOREST DAVIDSON • Thomas Long Co., Boston

JAMES O. DAVIS • Samuel Kirk & Son, Baltimore

JAMES G. DONAVAN • Donavan & Seamans Co., Los Angeles

ROBERT L. EBERT • S. T. Little Jewelry Co., Cumberland, Maryland

JOHN PENN FIX JR. • George R. Dodson Inc., Spokane, Washington

ARTHUR F. GLEIM • Gleim Jewelers, Palo Alto, California

FREDERICK O. HERZ • R. Herz & Bros., Reno, Nevada

BURTON JOSEPH • S. Joseph & Sons, Des Moines, Iowa

CLIFFORD I. JOSEPHSON JR. • C. I. Josephson, Moline, Illinois

H. PAUL JUERGENS • Juergens & Andersen, Chicago

GEORGE R. KAPLAN • Lazare Kaplan & Sons, New York

WILLIAM P. KENDRICK • William Kendrick Jewelers, Louisville, Kentucky

JOSEPH LINZ • Linz Brothers, Dallas

WILLIAM T. LUSK • Tiffany & Co., New York

KENNETH G. MAPPIN • Mappin's Ltd., Montreal

CHARLES D. PEACOCK III • C. D. Peacock Inc., Chicago

HENRY B. PLATT • Tiffany & Co., New York

WILLIAM S. PRESTON • F. J. Preston & Son, Burlington, Vermont

JOSEPH L. ROBERTS JR. • John M. Roberts & Son Co., Pittsburgh

WILLIAM H. SCHWANKE • Schwanke-Kasten Co., Milwaukee

RICHARD SHREVE • Shreve, Crump & Low Co., Boston

LEO J. SIMARD • Leo J. Simard Jeweler, Holyoke, Massachusetts

GEORGE J. SLOAN • Sloan's Jewelers, Tulsa, Oklahoma

STANLEY S. SMITH • J. B. Hudson Co., Minneapolis

ROBERT E. SPRATFORD • C. A. Kiger Co., Kansas City, Missouri

GEORGE H. STAHL • Pilcher Jewelry Co., Mexico, Missouri

WILLIAM G. THURBER • Tilden-Thurber Co., Providence, Rhode Island

EDWARD B. TIFFANY • Henry Birks & Sons Ltd., Toronto

1970s

ARNOLD A. BOCKSTRUCK • Bockstruck Co., St. Paul, Minnesota

CARLETON G. BROER • Broer-Freeman Co., Toledo, Ohio

CARLETON G. BROER JR. • Broer-Freeman Co., Toledo, Ohio

STANLEY E. CHURCH • Church & Co., Newark, New Jersey

JAMES G. DONAVAN • Donavan & Seamans Co., Los Angeles

ROBERT L. EBERT • S. T. Little Jewelry Co., Cumberland, Maryland

JOHN PENN FIX JR. • George R. Dodson Inc., Spokane, Washington

ARTHUR F. GLEIM • Gleim Jewelers, Palo Alto, California

GEORGE R. KAPLAN • Lazare Kaplan & Sons, New York

KURT NASSAU, PH.D. • AT&T Bell Laboratories, Murray Hill, New Jersey

CHARLES D. PEACOCK III • C. D. Peacock Inc., Chicago

HENRY B. PLATT • Tiffany & Co., New York

JOSEPH L. ROBERTS JR. • John M. Roberts & Son Co., Pittsburgh

JAMES M. RUDDER • Claude S. Bennett Inc., Atlanta

HAROLD SEBURN • Churchwell's Inc., Wilson, North Carolina

LEO J. SIMARD • Leo J. Simard Jeweler, Holyoke, Massachusetts

GEORGE J. SLOAN • Sloan's Jewelers, Tulsa, Oklahoma

STANLEY S. SMITH • J. B. Hudson Co., Minneapolis

ROBERT E. SPRATFORD • C. A. Kiger Co., Kansas City, Missouri

GEORGE H. STAHL • Pilcher Jewelry Co., Mexico, Missouri

EDWARD B. TIFFANY • Henry Birks & Sons Ltd., Toronto

1980s

PAUL G. BAILEY • Midlantic National Bank, New Jersey; Citibank, Scottsdale, Arizona

WILLIAM F. BENDER • Gemological Institute of America

WILLIAM E. BOYAJIAN • Gemological Institute of America

ARNOLD A. BOCKSTRUCK • H. Bockstruck Co., St. Paul, Minnesota

CARLETON G. BROER JR. • Broer's Fine Jewelers, Toledo, Ohio

The board of governors in 1989, shown pictured at the Santa Monica headquarters. Front row from left: James C. Clark, Robert E. Spratford, Dr. Kurt Nassau, Dr. Hester Turner, Brook Ellis, Glenn R. Nord, Dr. Gordon Brown. Stairs row on the left, from top: Arthur F. Gleim, Bert Krashes, Paul Campbell, Paul G. Bailey, George R. Kaplan. Stairs row on the right, from top: Arnold A. Bockstruck, Richard T. Liddicoat, Carleton G. Broer Jr., Eli Haas, Frank Maier Jr.

GORDON E. BROWN JR., PH.D. • Stanford University, Palo Alto, California

PAUL CAMPBELL • American Jewelry Company, Bakersfield, California

STANLEY E. CHURCH • Church & Co., Bloomfield, New Jersey

JAMES C. CLARK • B. C. Clark Jewelers, Oklahoma City

BROOK ELLIS • Henry Birks and Sons Ltd., Montreal

ARTHUR F. GLEIM • Gleim Jewelers, Palo Alto, California

ELI HAAS • ENH International, New York

RICHARD JAHNS, PH.D. • Stanford University, Palo Alto, California

GEORGE R. KAPLAN • Lazare Kaplan & Sons, New York

BERT KRASHES • Gemological Institute of America

LEWIS KUHN • William L. Kuhn Co., New York

RICHARD T. LIDDICOAT JR. • Gemological Institute of America

FRANK H. MAIER JR. • Maier & Berkele, Atlanta

KURT NASSAU, PH.D. • AT&T Bell Laboratories, Murray Hill, New Jersey

GLENN R. NORD • Gemological Institute of America

HENRY B. PLATT • Tiffany & Co., New York

JAMES M. RUDDER • Claude S. Bennett Inc., Atlanta

JOSEPH H. SAMUEL JR. • J. & S. S. DeYoung Inc., Boston

ROBERT E. SPRATFORD • C. A. Kiger Co., Kansas City, Missouri

EDWARD B. TIFFANY • Henry Birks & Sons, Toronto

HESTER TURNER, PH.D. • DETC Accrediting Commission, Washington, D.C.

1990s

PAUL G. BAILEY • Citibank, Scottsdale, Arizona; Bank of America, Reno, Nevada

LEE MICHAEL BERG • Lee Michaels Fine Jewelry, Baton Rouge, Louisiana

ARNOLD A. BOCKSTRUCK • H. Bockstruck Co., St. Paul, Minnesota

WILLIAM E. BOYAJIAN • Gemological Institute of America

NANCY BREWER • Nancy B. & Co., Culver City, California

CARLETON G. BROER JR. • Broer's Fine Jewelers, Toledo, Ohio

GORDON E. BROWN JR., PH.D. • Stanford University, Palo Alto, California

PAUL CAMPBELL • American Jewelry Co., Bakersfield, California

JAMES C. CLARK • B. C. Clark Jewelers, Oklahoma City

RALPH DESTINO • Cartier, Inc., New York

BROOK ELLIS • Henry Birks and Sons Ltd., Montreal

HELENE FORTUNOFF • Fortunoff, Uniondale, New York

ELI HAAS • ENH International, New York

SUSAN M. JACQUES • Borsheim Jewelry Co. Inc., Omaha, Nebraska

GEORGE R. KAPLAN • Lazare Kaplan & Sons, New York

BERT KRASHES • Gemological Institute of America

SHELDON KWIAT • Kwiat, Roisen and Ferman, New York

RICHARD T. LIDDICOAT • Gemological Institute of America

FRANK H. MAIER JR. • Maier & Berkele, Atlanta

ANNA MARTIN • ABN AMRO Bank, New York

KURT NASSAU, PH.D. • Lucent Technologies, Murray Hill, New Jersey

GLENN R. NORD • Gemological Institute of America

GEORGE ROSSMAN, PH.D. • California Institute of Technology, Pasadena, California

JOSEPH H. SAMUEL JR. • J. & S. S. DeYoung Inc., Boston

ROBERT E. SPRATFORD • C. A. Kiger Co., Kansas City, Missouri

MATTHEW G. STULLER • Stuller Inc., Lafayette, Louisiana

HESTER TURNER, PH.D. • DETC Accrediting Commission, Washington, D.C.

2000s

PAUL G. BAILEY • Bank of America, Reno, Nevada

LEE MICHAEL BERG • Lee Michaels Fine Jewelry, Baton Rouge, Louisiana

WILLIAM E. BOYAJIAN • Gemological Institute of America

NANCY BREWER • Nancy B. & Co., Culver City, California

GORDON E. BROWN JR., PH.D. • Stanford University, Palo Alto, California

JAMES C. CLARK • B. C. Clark Jewelers, Oklahoma City

WILLIAM B. COTTINGHAM, PH.D. • G.M.I. Engineering & Management Institute, Flint, Michigan

RALPH DESTINO • Cartier, Inc., New York

HELENE FORTUNOFF • Fortunoff, Uniondale, New York

ELI HAAS • ENH International, New York

SUSAN M. JACQUES • Borsheim Jewelry Co. Inc., Omaha, Nebraska

MICHAEL J. KAZANJIAN • Kazanjian Brothers Inc., Beverly Hills, California

SHELDON KWIAT • Kwiat, Roisen and Ferman, New York

RICHARD T. LIDDICOAT • Gemological Institute of America

FRANK H. MAIER JR. • Maier & Berkele, Atlanta

ANNA MARTIN • ABN AMRO Bank, New York

DILIP MEHTA • Rosy Blue Inc., Antwerp

ROLAND NAFTULE • Nafco Gems Ltd., Scottsdale, Arizona

GLENN R. NORD • Gemological Institute of America

GEORGE ROSSMAN, PH.D. • California Institute of Technology, Pasadena, California

JOSEPH H. SAMUEL JR. • J. & S. S. DeYoung Inc., Boston

MATTHEW G. STULLER • Stuller Inc., Lafayette, Louisiana

APPENDIX B

25-YEAR EMPLOYEES OF GIA*

RICHARD ABELLA (1977–present) Quality Assurance Gemologist, Gem Trade Laboratory

SUSAN E. ADAMS (1969–1977, 1978–2002) Manager, Extension Education

IRENE ARMENDARIZ (1978–present) Senior Mail Processor

T. J. BARROWS (1956–1984) Education Administrator

WILLIAM E. BOYAJIAN (1975–present) President

MICHAEL P. BURKE (1978–present) Grading Development Coordinator, Gem Trade Laboratory

SHERYL S. CASHMORE (1976–present) Gemological Services and Accounts Manager, Gem Trade Laboratory

JOSEPH W. CHIARAVALLE (1978–present) Inventory Processing Supervisor, Gem Trade Laboratory

CARL S. CHILSTROM (1978–present) Education Project Specialist

MICHAEL R. CLARY (1977–1978, 1979–present) Client Relations Manager, Gem Trade Laboratory

G. ROBERT CROWNINGSHIELD (1947–present) Vice President, Gem Trade Laboratory

IVY R. CUTLER (1977–present) Records Query Gemologist, Gem Trade Laboratory

*With last or most recent title.

25-year employees in Carlsbad, in 2002. Seated from left: Mike Clary, Bruce Lanzl, Bill Boyajian, Sheryl Cashmore, and Ray Page. Standing: John Koivula, Gaston Lopez, Sue Johnson, Ruth Patchick, Betsy Winans, Karin Hurwit, and Jan Lombardi.

MARIE D'AURIA (1975–present) Accounting Supervisor

ALAN P. DEGHIONNO (1978–present) Laboratory Support Services Manager, Gem Trade Laboratory

DINO G. DEGHIONNO (1978–present) West Coast Identification Services Manager, Gem Trade Laboratory

ROBERT EARNEST (1963–1988) Director, Alumni Association

SALLY E. EHMKE (1976–present) Director of Operations, Gem Trade Laboratory

WILLIAM S. FARLEY (1978–present) Facilities Manager

DAVID L. FOWLER (1973–1980, 1983–present) Gemological Services Representative, Gem Trade Laboratory

CHARLES W. FRYER (1966–1993) Director of Gem Identification, Gem Trade Laboratory

JESSE GALLEGOS (1975–present) Control and Manufacturing Manager, GEM Instruments

GARY S. HILL (1978–present) Director of Community Development

KARIN HURWIT (1972–present) Senior Research Gemologist, Gem Trade Laboratory

GALE JOHNSON (1959–1984) Vice President of Manufacturing, GEM Instruments

SUSAN B. JOHNSON (1974–1977, 1979–present) Director of Education Administration

DEANNA KAPLAN (1972–present) Executive Assistant, Gem Trade Laboratory

CHRISTOPHER B. KEENAN (1978–present) Director, GIA Thailand

JOHN M. KING (1978–present) Laboratory Projects Officer, Gem Trade Laboratory

JOHN I. KOIVULA (1976–present) Chief Research Gemologist

BERT KRASHES (1949–1987) Vice President, Gem Trade Laboratory

BRUCE F. LANZL (1977–present) Director of West Coast Laboratory Operations, Gem Trade Laboratory

RICHARD T. LIDDICOAT (1940–1942, 1946–2002) Chairman of the Board

JAN L. LOMBARDI (1976–2003) Senior Instructor, Distance Education

GASTON A. LOPEZ (1975–present) General Manager, GEM Instruments

SHANE F. MCCLURE (1978–present) Director of West Coast Identification Services, Gem Trade Laboratory

KENNETH MOORE (1948–1982) Vice President of Sales, GEM Instruments

MARGARET G. OROZCO (1949–1953, 1957–1995) Manager of GIA Bookstore

RAYMOND PAGE (1971–present) Accreditation Officer

HELEN RUTH PATCHICK (1977–present) Research Librarian

25-year employees in New York, in 2002: Dave Fowler, Ivy Cutler, Deanna Kaplan, Richard Abella, Marie D'Auria, Lola Sweet, and Tom Yonelunas.

DOROTHY JASPER SMITH (1932–1963) Executive Assistant

LOLA SWEET (1972–present) Senior Customer Service Representative, Gem Trade Laboratory

GWENDOLYN L. TRAVIS (1978–present) Client Services Supervisor, Gem Trade Laboratory

LAURA L. ULATOWSKI (1978–present) Staff Accountant

BOB VANDENHEUVEL (1966–1999) Research and Development Engineer, GEM Instruments

CLARE VERDERA (1939–1964) Manager of Print Shop, Shipping and Receiving, and Purchasing

BETSY WINANS (1975–present) Production Supervisor, Course Development

THOMAS C. YONELUNAS (1976–present) Chief Executive Officer, Gem Trade Laboratory

APPENDIX C: STAFF RECOGNITION AWARDS

RICHARD T. LIDDICOAT DISTINGUISHED ACHIEVEMENT AWARD WINNERS

1994	Dennis Foltz
1995	Robert C. Kammerling
1996	Gary Hill
1997	Thomas C. Yonelunas
1998	Bert Krashes
1999	D. Vincent Manson, Ph.D.
2001	Glenn R. Nord
2002	Thomas M. Moses

STAFF OF THE YEAR

1985	Susan B. Johnson
1986	James R. Lucey
1987	Alan P. DeGhionno, Janet Fryer, Robert Kammerling
1988	Allen Blaugh, Janet Lyon, Robert Meeks, Phillip G. York
1989	Vincent Cracco, Dona Mary Dirlam, Shane F. McClure
1990	Robert Effler, Heather Fretes, Jesse Gallegos, Lisa Hebenstreit, Shari Raicos-Odelson
1991	Michael Burke, John Hummel, Alice Keller, Seung-Hae Moon, Phillip M. Yantzer
1992	Michael R. Clary, Daniel B. Gillen, Susan Gulliver, Richard Lua, Elizabeth Winans
1993	Veronica Clark-Hudson, Angelica S. Giaimo, John M. King, Gaston A. Lopez
1994	Christopher B. Keenan, Bruce F. Lanzl, Lainie Mann, Ilene Reinitz, Darnell Travis
1995	Scott Guhin, Halina Kaban, Judith Shechter-Lankford, Charlotte Williams, Timothy Wolf
1996	Kim Cino, Eddie Decsi, Sally E. Ehmke, Deborah Hiss, Beverly Zimmerman
1997	Sheryl S. Cashmore, Sundari Handaja, Dak Lam Lee, Jan L. Lombardi, Andrew O'Boyle
1998	Robert Ahrens, Jennifer Lin Hwang, Chin L. Kuo, James Marker, Toni Smith
1999	Reina Auza, Carl Chilstrom, Cherie Goon, Jesus Karlton Kapalungan, Marlene Rosenfeld, Kha Binh Thai
2000	Susan E. Adams, Vivianne Del Signore, Maria Frances, James Gonzales, Cathleen Jonathan, Kelly Yantzer
2001	Patrick Ball, Susan Elliott, Matt Hall, Gary Hamada, Mary Johnson, Duncan Pay
2002	Steven Dendy, Andrew Lucas, Luis Luciano, Cynthia Sanders, Andy Wu

selected bibliography

Chapter 1: Before the Beginning (1887–1929)

Gilbert, Mitchell. "Robert Shipley, Mr. Gemology." *Jewelers' Circular-Keystone*, March 1977, pp. 99–104, 106–107.

"In Memoriam: Robert M. Shipley." *Gems & Gemology*, Spring 1978, Vol. 16, No. 1, pp. 2–6.

Kraus, Edward H. "Gemology in North America." *Gems & Gemology*, Vol. 5, No. 9, Spring 1947, pp. 407–408.

Shipley, Robert M. "A National Force." *Jewelers' Circular-Keystone*, March 1959, pp. 92–93, 95–96, 98, 100–101.

Shuster, William George. "Introducing Robert Shipley, Visionary." *Jewelers' Circular-Keystone*, September 1981, pp. 102–104, 106.

Smith, A. "London School Awards Wichitan Gemmology Degree." *Wichita Eagle*, July 28, 1929, p. 8.

Chapter 2: Hard Times (1929–1932)

Cannon, Fred J. "Your Society, Its History." *Guilds*, January 1959, pp. 3–6.

"Famed Expert on Gems in Wichita." *Wichita Eagle*, December 25, 1929.

"Gemmological Education in U.S.A." *The Gemmologist*, September 1931, p. 58.

"The Gemmological Institute of America." *The Gemmologist*, August 1931, Vol. 1, No. 1, p. 13.

Howard, J. H. "The Gemological Institute." *Rocks & Minerals*, December 1932, p. 135.

Shipley, Robert M. "Why the Guild Movement and the Gemological Movement." *Guilds*, February 1935, p. 4.

Shuster, William G. "Hard Sell for a Daring Idea." *Jewelers' Circular-Keystone*, September 1981, pp. 116–122.

Shuster, William G. "The Jeweler Must Know Gems." *Jewelers' Circular-Keystone*, September 1981, pp. 108–110, 112, 114.

Smith, Dorothy J. "Robert M. Shipley." *Gems & Gemology*, Vol. 16, No. 2, Summer 1978, p. 42.

Tiffany, Edward B. "Some Memories of the Early Days and Robert Shipley." *Gems & Gemology*, Vol. 16, No. 2, Summer 1978, pp. 37–38.

Chapter 3: Laying the Foundation (1932–1939)

Broer, Carleton G. "Its Usefulness Grows." *Jewelers' Circular-Keystone*, March 1959, pp. 102–104, 106, 108–109.

"An Evaluation of the Society through Membership and Titles of the Society's First Four C.G.s." *Guilds*, September 1952, p. 4.

Jasper, Dorothy M. "The Story of the GIA Laboratories." *Gems & Gemology*, Vol. 6, No. 2, Summer 1948, pp. 54–55, 58.

"Robert M. Shipley, Jr. Made Honorary Research Member of G.I.A." *Gems & Gemology*, Vol. 6, No. 11, Fall 1950, p. 350.

Thompson, Sharon E. "GIA Gem Instruments: In the Boomtown Tradition." *In Focus*, Spring 1989, pp. 10–13.

Willson, T. Edgar. "The Jeweler Must Know Gems." *Jewelers' Circular*, August 7, 1930, p. 23.

Woodill, Alfred L. "Some Memories of Robert M. Shipley." *Gems & Gemology*, Vol. 16, No. 2, Summer 1978, p. 36.

Chapter 4: The War Years (1940–1945)

"Endowment Members of the Gemological Institute of America." *Gems & Gemology*, Vol. 7, No. 2, Summer 1951, pp. 68–75.

"Eunice Miles: The Grande Dame of Gemology." *In Focus*, Summer 1994, pp. 9–11.

Federman, David. "Lifetime Achievement Award: Richard T. Liddicoat Jr." *Modern Jeweler*, December 1985, pp. 34–42.

"$50,000 GIA Fund Raised." *National Jeweler*, February 1943, p. 134.

"In Memoriam: Beatrice W. Shipley." *Gems & Gemology*, Vol. 14, No. 6, Summer 1973, p. 191.

Jarman, Rufus. "They Spot the Fake Jewels." *The Saturday Evening Post*, June 27, 1953, p. 139.

Jasper, Dorothy M. "The Story of the GIA Laboratories." *Gems & Gemology*, Vol. 6, No. 2, Summer 1948, p. 55.

"Liddicoat Resumes Work at Headquarters." *Guilds*, March 1946, p. 5.

"Membership Acquires G.I.A." *Guilds*, October 1943, p. 1.

"More Jewelry Stores Close as Merchandise, Employees Are Increasingly Scarce." *Jewelers' Circular-Keystone*, September 1943, p. 144.

Morrow, David. "Liddicoat on GIA: Yesterday, Today & Tomorrow." *Jewelers' Circular-Keystone*, September 1981, pp. 17–21.

"Mrs. Hinton: America's 'First Lady' of Gemology." *Jewelers' Circular-Keystone*, August 1943, p. 125.

"1940 Jewelry Business Tops $400 Million." *National Jeweler*, August 1941, p. 172.

"Shipley, Jr. Resumes Instrument Development." *The Loupe*, October 1948, p. 2.

Shipley, Robert M., and R. T. Liddicoat. "A Solution to Diamond Grading Problems." *Gems & Gemology*, Fall 1941, Vol. 3, No. 4, pp. 162–168.

Swindler, Kay. "Celebrating Our 20th Anniversary." *Gems & Gemology*, Vol. 7, No. 2, Summer 1951, pp. 35–48.

"We Give You the GIA Staff." *The Loupe*, July 1947, p. 4.

"Women in Gemology." *The Loupe*, January–February 1954, p. 4.

"Women Jewelers." *National Jeweler*, June 1944, p. 160.

Woodill, Alfred L. "Reflections on the Early Years." *Guilds*, October 1983, pp. 1–2.

Chapter 5: Years of Change (1946–1951)

Christie, Andrew. "An East Coast Education: GIA in New York." *In Focus*, Summer 1994, pp. 24–27, 36.

Christie, Andrew. "Forever Young: Margaret Orozco." *In Focus*, Fall/Winter 1994, p. 9.

"Commemorating Our Silver Anniversary." *Gems & Gemology*, Vol. 8, No. 9, Spring 1956, pp. 259–261.

Federman, David. "Lifetime Achievement Award: Robert Crowningshield." *Modern Jeweler*, December 1995, pp. 25–32.

"In Memoriam: Lawrence L. Copeland." *Gems & Gemology*, Vol. 15, No. 12, Winter 1977–1978, p. 373.

Liddicoat Jr., Richard T. *Handbook of Gem Identification*. Gemological Institute of America, Los Angeles, 1946.

"Richard T. Liddicoat, Jr. Appointed Director of G.I.A." *Gems & Gemology*, Vol. 7, No. 5, Spring 1952, p. 162.

Shipley, Robert M. "A National Force." *Jewelers' Circular-Keystone*, March 1959, pp. 92–93, 95–96, 98, 100–101.

Shuster, William George. "G.I. Gemologists." *Jewelers' Circular-Keystone*, September 1981, pp. 124–126, 128, 130, 132.

"Those Who Lead GIA." *Jewelers' Circular-Keystone*, February 1965, p. 157.

Chapter 6: Facets of a Revolution (1952–1960)

Burke, Carol. "G. Robert Crowningshield, G.G.: 50 Years of Living the Lab Life." *In Focus*, Winter/Spring 1998, pp. 13–17.

Christie, Andrew. "Focus On: Bert Krashes." *In Focus*, Fall 1988, pp. 6–7.

"Commemorating Our Silver Anniversary." *Gems & Gemology*, Vol. 8, No. 9, Spring 1956, pp. 259–261.

Crowningshield, G. Robert. "Spectroscopic Recognition of Yellow Bombarded Diamonds and Bibliography of Diamond Treatment." *Gems & Gemology*, Vol. 9, No. 4, Winter 1957–58, pp. 99–104.

Crowningshield, G. Robert. "Through the Lens at the Gem Trade Lab." *The Loupe*, January–February 1954, p. 2.

Federman, David. "Lifetime Achievement Award: Richard T. Liddicoat Jr." *Modern Jeweler*, December 1985, pp. 34–42.

"GIA to Conduct First Class in Diamond Grading." *The Loupe*, January–February 1953, p. 1.

"Gift from Diamond Corporation." *The Loupe*, July–August 1955, p. 1.

Liddicoat, Richard T. "Development of GIA's Diamond Grading System." *In Focus*, Summer 1991, pp. 13–15.

Liddicoat Jr., Richard T. "How End of G.I. Bill Legislation Gave Birth to GIA Grading System." *Diamond World Review*, May–June 1991, pp. 20–27.

McNeil, Donald S. "Diamond Grading: The Search for Standards." *Jewelers' Circular-Keystone*, September 1981, pp. 188–192, 194, 196, 198.

"New Merchandising Course Set." *The Loupe*, September–October 1952, p. 1.

"Q & A's about GIA." *Jewelers' Circular-Keystone*, February 1961, p. 164.

"Tour of GIA's New Headquarters." *Gems & Gemology*, Vol. 8, No. 9, Spring 1956, pp. 265–281.

"What's Done at the Labs." *Jewelers' Circular-Keystone*, February 1961, p. 149.

"Women in Gemology: Mrs. Eunice Robinson Miles." *The Loupe*, November–December 1953, p. 4.

Young, Barbara A. "Richard T. Liddicoat: The Man Behind the Image." *The Goldsmith*, October 1980, p. 42.

Chapter 7: Bearing Fruit (1960–1969)

Byrnes, Tom. "East Coast Origins." *In Focus*, Spring/Summer 1993, pp. 14–15.

Christie, Andrew. "An East Coast Education: GIA in New York." *In Focus*, Summer 1994, pp. 24–27, 36.

"Gem Talk: GIA Grads Swap Stories on Gemology Past and Present." *Jewelers' Circular-Keystone*, September 1981, pp. 38–40, 42.

"GIA Team Told the Colored Stone Story." *Jewelers' Circular-Keystone*, September 1969, p. 156.

"The Human Side of GIA." *Jewelers' Circular-Keystone*, February 1961, p. 152.

Kadish, Laurel. "Bob Earnest: A Long Overdue Dream." *In Focus*, Winter/Spring 1996, pp. 24–25.

Kosa, Frank. "On the Road with Glenn Nord." *In Focus*, Fall/Winter 1993, pp. 14–15.

Liddicoat Jr., Richard T. "Diamond-Proportion Grading and the New ProportionScope." *Gems & Gemology*, Vol. 12, No. 5, Spring 1967, pp. 130–136.

Liddicoat Jr., Richard T. "A Memorial Tribute to Lester B. Benson, Jr." *Gems & Gemology*, Vol. 10, No. 7, Fall 1961, pp. 206–209.

Liddicoat Jr., Richard T. "Rapid Sight Estimates of Diamond Cutting Quality." *Gems & Gemology*, Vol. 10, Nos. 11 and 12, Fall 1962, pp. 323–335 and 365–375.

Miles, Eunice R. "Diamond-Coating Techniques and Methods of Detection." *Gems & Gemology*, Vol. 10, No. 12, Winter 1962–63, pp. 355–364.

Miles, Eunice R. "First Close-Up Shots of Coated Diamond." *Jewelers' Circular-Keystone*, October 1964, p. 72.

"The New Eastern Headquarters and Gem Trade Lab of the GIA." *Gems & Gemology*, Vol. 10, No. 2, Summer 1960, pp. 35–44.

Pough, Frederick H. "The GIA ProportionScope: A Fast New Measure of Diamond Make." *Jewelers' Circular-Keystone*, November 1962, p. 92.

"Saving Sales on Main Street." *Jewelers' Circular-Keystone*, February 1965, pp. 142, 144.

"Those Who Lead GIA and Teach Jewelers to Be Pros." *Jewelers' Circular-Keystone*, February 1965, p. 157.

"Those Incredible Years, with a Focus on People." *Jewelers' Circular-Keystone*, September 1989, pp. 202–220.

Chapter 8: Boom Times (1970–1980)

Allbritton, Mike, and Janice Mack. "The Penlight Technique of 'Light Identification.'" *Pacific Goldsmith*, July 1977, pp. 116–122.

Boyajian, William E. "An Economic Review of the Past Decade in Diamonds." *Gems & Gemology*, Vol. 24, No. 3, Fall 1988, pp. 139–153.

Byrnes, Tom. "Japan's First Lady of Gemology." *In Focus*, Spring/Summer 1993, pp. 28–31.

"Crowningshield Warns Colorado Jewelers on Considering Gems as Investment." *Modern Jeweler*, June 1977, Vol. 76, No. 6, p. SC-70F.

Federman, David. "GIA's Research Lab: Scientific Answers to Trade Questions." *Jewelers' Circular-Keystone*, April 1978, p. 114.

Federman, David. "Grading Pearls at Home the GIA Way." *Modern Jeweler*, May 1987, pp. 34–40.

"Focus on: Kenzo Yamomoto." *In Focus*, July 1984, p. 9.

"Gem Investment Firms Carp at GIA but GIA Doesn't Seem to Mind." *Jewelers' Circular-Keystone*, March 1979, p. 81.

"GIA Won't Assist Diamond Futures' Plan." *Jewelers' Circular-Keystone*, February 1972, p. 175.

"GIA's Diamond Course Gets Major Overhaul." *Jewelers' Circular-Keystone*, October 1979, p. 92.

"GIA's New Plant to Cost $1.3 Million." *Jewelers' Circular-Keystone*, January 1974, p. 134.

Gilbert, Mitchell. "Gemology: A Fast Changing World." *Jewelers' Circular-Keystone*, April 1978, pp. 104–109.

"In Memoriam: Beatrice W. Shipley." *Gems & Gemology*, Vol. 14, No. 6, Summer 1973, p. 191.

Liddicoat Jr., Richard T. "*Gems & Gemology*: Sixty Years of History and History Making." *Gems & Gemology*, Vol. 30, No. 4, Winter 1994, p. 219.

Liddicoat, Richard T. "The Mid-'70s GIA Explosion." *Guilds*, May-June 1976, pp. 20–21.

Manson, D. Vincent. "Recent Activities in GIA's Research Department." *Gems & Gemology*, Vol. 16, No. 7, Fall 1979, pp. 217–219.

McNeil, Donald S. "Diamond Grading: The Search for Standards." *Jewelers' Circular-Keystone*, September 1981, pp. 188–192, 194, 196, 198.

Montgomery, Lee. "GIA Traveling Classes and One- and Two- Day Seminars." *In Focus*, Winter 1990, pp. 14–15.

Page, Ray. "Jim Lucey Remembered." *In Focus*, Fall/Winter 1994, pp. 14–15.

"Richard T. Liddicoat: The Man Behind the Image." *The Goldsmith*, October 1980, p. 46.

"The Roots of the Traveling Classes." *In Focus*, Winter 1990, p. 15.

Shor, Russell. "GIA Symposium Probes Future." *Jewelers' Circular-Keystone*, December 1990, pp. 72–74.

Shuster, William George. "Into the '70s: The Boom Years." *Jewelers' Circular-Keystone*, September 1981, pp. 134, 136.

Tonelli, Bill. "Gem Investment: The Big Showdown Is Near." *Jewelers' Circular-Keystone*, July 1976, p. 86.

Chapter 9: Celebrating an Era (1980–1982)

Alperstein, Ellen. "A Portrait of Precision: Erica and Harold Van Pelt." *In Focus*. Winter/Spring 1996, pp. 34–38.

"ColorMaster a Collaborative Product." *The Goldsmith*, October 1980, p. 71.

Farrell, Eileen, and Marie E. Thomas. "The Search for a Perfect Language." *The Goldsmith*, October 1983, p. 30.

Federman, David. "GIA's New ColorMaster Will Reproduce Lifelike Image of Any Colored Stone." *Jewelers' Circular-Keystone*, April 1980, pp. 161–162.

"Holy Holograph! GIA Does It Again." *Jewelers' Circular-Keystone*, April 1979, p. 110.

Liddicoat Jr., Richard T. "An Introduction to the New *Gems & Gemology*." *Gems & Gemology*, Vol. 17, No. 1, Spring 1981, p. 1.

Liddicoat Jr., Richard T. "The New *Gems & Gemology* Is One Year Old." *Gems & Gemology*, Vol. 17, No. 4, Winter 1981, p. 183.

"Symposium Attracts Those Interested in Gemology." *Modern Jeweler*, April 1982, p. 10.

Thomas, Marie E. "The Fine Points of Color Theory and a Look at Colored Stone Certification." *The Goldsmith*, May 1982, p. 31.

Chapter 10: Transitions (1983–1986)

"Demise of ColorMaster: End of an Era." *Jewelers' Circular-Keystone*, March 1996, pp. 36–38.

Dirlam, Dona, and Robert C. Kammerling. "GIA Milestones." *Jewelers' Circular-Keystone*, June 1991, pp. 116–123.

"Experts Call American Diamond Market Unsettled." *Modern Jeweler*, April 1982, p. 77.

Federman, David. "Glenn Nord Resigns Top Post at GIA." *Modern Jeweler*, September 1986, p. 28.

Federman, David. "Richard T. Liddicoat Jr.: An Appreciation." *Modern Jeweler*, December 1985, pp. 47–48.

Foltz, Dennis. "Changing Face of Education." *In Focus*, Spring/Summer 1993, p. 23.

"GIA's Glenn Nord." *Modern Jeweler*, September 1983, p. 10.

"Glenn Nord Appointed President of GIA." *Modern Jeweler*, September 1983, p. 10.

"Q & A: The New GIA Diamonds Program." *In Focus*, Fall 1986, p. 22.

Shor, Russell. "GIA Adds Sales to the 4 C's." *Jewelers' Circular-Keystone*, November 1986, p. 148.

Shor, Russell. "The 1980s: Boom, Bust and Bubble." In *Connections: A Profile of Diamond People and Their History*, World Federation of Diamond Bourses, 1993, pp. 137–148.

Shuster, William George. "GIA's Sun Rises in the Far East." *Jewelers' Circular-Keystone*, December 1996, p. 65.

"There's Nothing We Cannot Teach." *Jewelers' Circular-Keystone*, June 1991, p. 93.

Thompson, Joe. "The Joy of Gemology." *Modern Jeweler*, October 1984, p. 11.

Vollmer, Joyce. "Is It True What They Say About Glenn Nord?" *The Goldsmith*, February 1985, p. 46.

Chapter 11: Changing of the Guard (1986–2003)

"Boyajian Named GIA President in Swift Ascent." *National Jeweler*, November 1, 1986, p. 8.

Buchanan, Norma. "Bill Boyajian: 10 Years at the Top." *Modern Jeweler*, August 1996, p. 52.

Diamond, S. Lynn. "GIA Leader with a Mission Vows Industry Leadership." *National Jeweler*, October 1, 1986, pp. 21–22.

"In Honor of Robert C. Kammerling." *Gems & Gemology*, Vol. 32, No. 4, Winter 1996, p. 231.

Chapter 12: The Hallmark of Integrity (1986–2003)

Boyajian, William. "Ethics & GIA Grading." *Jewelers' Circular-Keystone*, February 1987, p. 92.

Buchanan, Norma. "Boyajian's Eight Days in Hell." *Modern Jeweler*, August 1996, p. 53.

Diamond, S. Lynn, and Rob Bates. "GIA to Go Global with Antwerp Lab." *National Jeweler*, May 16, 1994, p. 1.

"GIA and GTL Plan World's Largest Gemological Database." *Through the Loupe*, Fall 1987, p. 22.

Hemphill, T. Scott, Ilene M. Reinitz, Mary L. Johnson, and James E. Shigley. "Modeling the Appearance of the Round Brilliant Cut Diamond: An Analysis of Brilliance." *Gems & Gemology*, Vol. 34, No. 3, Fall 1998, pp. 158–183.

"Inside the GIA Gem Trade Laboratory, Parts I and II." *The Loupe*, Spring 1997, p. 18, Summer 1997, p. 18.

King, John M., Thomas M. Moses, James E. Shigley, and Yan Liu. "Color Grading of Colored Diamonds in the GIA Gem Trade Laboratory." *Gems & Gemology*, Vol. 30, No. 4, Winter 1994, pp. 220–242.

Nestlebaum, Karen. "Director of Gem Trade Lab Seeks to Serve All Publics." *New York Diamonds*, September 1988, pp. 70, 72.

Nestlebaum, Karen Beman. "GTL: Fine Tuning the Engine." *New York Diamonds*, Summer 1989, pp. 42, 44.

Nestlebaum, Karen. "Labs Keep Running to Stay Ahead." *Rapaport Diamond Report*, February 5, 1999, p. 77.

Roskin, Gary. "GIA Gem Trade Lab Reports Go Contemporary." *Jewelers Circular Keystone*, February 2000, p. 68.

Shigley, James E., Robert C. Kammerling, and Thomas M. Moses. "GIA R&D Update: The Computer Simulation of a Faceted Diamond." *The Loupe*, Winter 1993, p. 10.

Shor, Russell. "GIA Cancels Antwerp Lab After Trade Protests." *Jewelers' Circular-Keystone*, July 1994, pp. 28–29.

"Smaller Diamonds Now Accepted for Grading." *Through the Loupe*, September 1987, p. 19.

Chapter 13: Creating a Unique Information Resource (1986–2003)

Alperstein, Ellen. "John Sinkankas: A Collector's Edition." *In Focus*, Spring 1991, pp. 16, 18–21.

"Bringing Students a Little Closer to Home." *The Loupe*, Spring 1999, p. 1.

Dirlam, Dona. "GIA Acquires the Sinkankas Collection." *In Focus*, Spring 1988, pp. 24–26.

Dirlam, Dona M., Elise B. Misiorowski, Juli L. Cook, and Robert Weldon. "The Sinkankas Library." *Gems & Gemology*, Vol. 25, No. 1, Spring 1989, pp. 2–15.

Jones, Bob. "The Sinkankas Collection." *Rock & Gem*, February 1990, Vol. 20, No. 2, p. 86.

"New Computer Service Gives Access at GIA." *Jewelers' Circular-Keystone*, February 1987, p. 230.

Chapter 14: The Industry's Automatic Alarm System (1986–2003)

Fritsch, Emmanuel, and George R. Rossman. "New Technologies of the 1980s: Their Impact in Gemology." *Gems & Gemology*, Vol. 26, No. 1, Spring 1990, pp. 64–75.

Johnson, Mary L. "Technological Developments in the 1990s: Their Impact on Gemology." *Gems & Gemology*, Vol. 36, No. 4, Winter 2000, pp. 380–396.

Kammerling, Robert C., John I. Koivula, and Robert E. Kane. "Gemstone Enhancement and Its Detection in the 1980s." *Gems & Gemology*, Vol. 26, No. 1, Spring 1990, pp. 32–49.

Kammerling, Robert C., John I. Koivula, Robert E. Kane, Patricia Maddison, James E. Shigley, and Emmanuel Fritsch. "Fracture Filling of Emeralds: Opticon and Traditional 'Oils.'" *Gems & Gemology*, Vol. 27, No. 2, Summer 1991, pp. 70–85.

Koivula, John I., Maha Tannous, and Karl Schmetzer. "Synthetic Gem Materials and Simulants in the 1990s." *Gems & Gemology*, Vol. 36, No. 4, Winter 2000, pp. 360–379.

Liddicoat, Richard T., and William E. Boyajian. "The 1980s in Review: New Realities of the Gem and Jewelry Industry." *Gems & Gemology*, Vol. 26, No. 1, Spring 1990, pp. 1–2.

McClure, Shane F., and Christopher P. Smith. "Gemstone Enhancement and Detection in the 1990s." *Gems & Gemology*, Vol. 36, No. 4, Winter 2000, pp. 336–359.

McClure, Shane F., Thomas M. Moses, Maha Tannous, and John I. Koivula. "Classifying Emerald Clarity Enhancement at the GIA Gem Trade Laboratory." *Gems & Gemology*, Vol. 35, No. 4, Winter 1999, pp. 176–185.

Nassau, Kurt. "Synthetic Gem Materials in the 1980s." *Gems & Gemology*, Vol. 26, No. 1, Spring 1990, pp. 50–63.

"On the Research Front—Look Out for Those New Synthetics." *Jewelers' Circular-Keystone*, June 1991, p. 106.

Pawlyna, Andrea. "Critical Need for Gem Research." *Jewellery News Asia*, February 1993, pp. 86–88.

Shigley, James E., Dona M. Dirlam, Karl Schmetzer, and E. Alan Jobbins. "Gem Localities of the 1980s." *Gems & Gemology*, Vol. 26, No. 1, Spring 1990, pp. 4–31.

Chapter 15: Learning from the Foremost Authority (1986–2003)

Alperstein, Ellen. "The Vision of Korea's Kim." *In Focus*, Winter/Spring 1996, pp. 30–33.

Federman, David. "Call to ARMS." *Modern Jeweler*, June 1998, p. 70.

"GIA Expands in Asia." *Jewellery News Asia*, September 1991, No. 109, p. 38.

"GIA Goes 'On-Line.'" *Modern Jeweler*, March 1987, p. 67.

"GIA to Open Italian Facility." *Jewelers' Circular-Keystone*, November 1991, p. 116.

"GIA Italy Hosts GemFest Europa; Accelerated Diamond Programs at GIA Hong Kong." *The Loupe*, Summer 1998, p. 9.

"GIA and the Speed of Learning." *Through the Loupe*, Fall 1987, p. 1.

"GIA Trains Russian Gemologists to Offer Institute Courses in Moscow." *The Loupe*, Spring 1997, p. 11.

"GIA's Revamped JMA Program Helps Students Change Careers." *In Focus*, Winter 1992, p. 30.

"Introducing: GIA-Net." *Through the Loupe*, Spring 1987, p. 12.

"Moon Appointed as GIA's Director of International Education." *The Loupe*, Fall 1997, p. 19.

Roskin, Gary. "A Review of GIA's New Pearl Course." *Jewelers Circular Keystone*, October 1999, pp. 105–108.

"South Seas Trip Beneficial to Development of New GIA Pearl Courses." *The Loupe*, Fall 1997, p. 13.

Yochim, Dayana. "GIA: Not Just Gemology Anymore." *Modern Jeweler*, May 1993, p. 25.

Chapter 16: Securing the Future (1986–2003)

Boehm, Edward. "Gem Ensemble Is Music to Philanthropist's Ears." *The Loupe*, Spring 2003, p. 29.

Federman, David. "GIA Goes for the Gold." *Modern Jeweler*, May 1991, p. 57.

"The GIA Annual Alumni Fund: A New Tradition." *In Focus*, Spring 1992, p. 19.

Roskin, Gary. "The GIA Alumni Association: Goals for 1992 and Beyond." *In Focus*, Winter 1991, p. 12.

Yochim, Dayana. "GIA's Capital Ideas." *Modern Jeweler*, June 1995, p. 74.

Chapter 17: A New World Headquarters: From Dream to Reality (1986–2003)

Donahue, Peggy Jo. "The Man Behind GIA's New Campus Name." *Jewelers' Circular-Keystone*, June 1997, p. 96.

Hauben, Howard. "Carlsbad Case Study: Making Your Executive Vision a Reality." *Mazal U'Bracha*, February 1997, p. 84.

Shuster, William George. "The '80s: Decade of Great Change." *Jewelers' Circular-Keystone*, September 1981, pp. 240–241.

Weldon, Robert. "GIA's Monumental New Home." *Jewelers' Circular-Keystone*, June 1997, p. 91.

Weldon, Robert. "A New Home for GIA?" *Jewelers' Circular-Keystone*, March 1993, p. 126.

Chapter 18: Facing the Future: The International Symposiums of the '90s (1986–2003)

"Facing the Future." *Jewelers' Circular-Keystone*, September 1991, p. 99.

Frederick, Larry. "Mystery Diamond Treatment Dominates GIA Symposium." *Jewelers Circular Keystone*, September 1999, p. 92.

Keller, Alice, Ed. *Proceedings of the International Gemological Symposium 1991*. Gemological Institute of America, Santa Monica, CA, 1992, 192 pp.

Keller, Alice, and Kathryn Kimmel. "The 1999 International Gemological Symposium: What A Ride!" *Gems & Gemology*, Vol. 35, No. 3, Fall 1999, p. 1.

"Oppenheimer and Ueberroth: Embrace Change and Competition." *The Loupe*, June 24, 1999, p. 1.

Tempelsman, Maurice. "Globalization and Technology: Dynamic Forces for the 21st Century." *Gems & Gemology*, Vol. 35, No. 3, Fall 1999, pp. 2–7.

Chapter 19: Communicating the Message (1986–2003)

"GIA Develops Dynamic Web Site to Serve Trade, Consumers." *The Loupe*, Spring 2000, p. 11.

Minotta, Mauricio. "Career Fair Draws Record Numbers, Industry's Top Names." *The Loupe*, Fall 2002, pp. 8–9.

index

Note: Page numbers in italics refer to illustrations. Page numbers followed by "n" refer to footnotes.

CREDITS

Publisher	William E. Boyajian
Editorial Director	Alice S. Keller
Senior Editor	Stuart D. Overlin
Associate Editor	Thomas W. Overton
Designer	Faizah Bhatti
Photo Editor	Teresa M. Weimer
Production Supervisor	Richard Canedo
Production Artist	Karen Myers